*The Complete*

# CELEBRATION HYMNAL
## *with*
## NEW SONGS OF CELEBRATION

McCRIMMONS
Great Wakering, Essex, England.

'Complete Celebration Hymnal' First published in Great Britain in 1984 by Mayhew McCrimmon Ltd.

Compilation and all editorial content ©1977, 1984 Mayhew McCrimmon Ltd.

'New Songs of Celebration' first published in Great Britain in 1989 by McCrimmon Publishing Co. Ltd.

Compilation and all editorial content ©1988 McCrimmon Publishing Co. Ltd. 10–12 High Street, Great Wakering, Essex, SS30EQ (0702 218956).

Revised edition 1990

ISBN 0 85597 434 6 (Plastic)
ISBN 0 85597 427 3 (Softback)
ISBN 0 85597 468 0 (Hardback)

Cover design: Jim Bowler and Paul Shuttleworth
Lithographic artwork: Sheila Mullen
Typesetting: Phoenix Typesetting Ltd, Southend-on-Sea.
Printed in Great Britain by BPCC Wheatons Ltd, Exeter

# MUSIC FOR THE EUCHARIST

**Rite of Blessing of Water**                     Stephen Dean

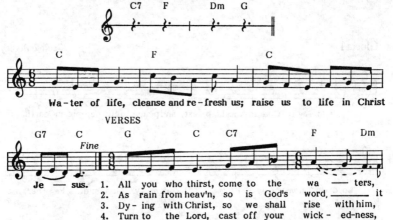

Wa-ter of life, cleanse and re-fresh us; raise us to life in Christ

**VERSES**

Je — sus.
1. All you who thirst, come to the wa — ters,
2. As rain from heav'n, so is God's word, it
3. Dy-ing with Christ, so we shall rise with him,
4. Turn to the Lord, cast off your wick-ed-ness,

and you will nev-er be thirst-y a-gain.
wa-ters the earth and brings forth life.
death shall no long-er have pow'r o-ver us;
you will find peace in his in-fi-nite love.

**Penitential Rite I**                     David Saint

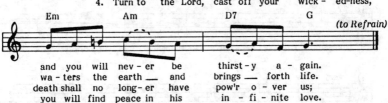

Lord, have mer-cy. Christ, have

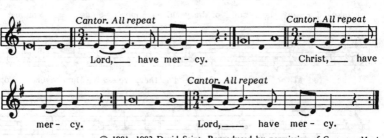

mer-cy. Lord, have mer-cy.

## Penitential Rite II

Seoirse Bodley

Lord, have mer-cy. Christ, have mer-cy. Lord, have mer-cy. A — men.

## Gloria I

Seoirse Bodley

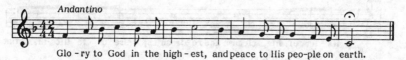

Glo-ry to God in the high-est, and peace to His peo-ple on earth.

Lord God, hea-ven-ly King,— Al-migh-ty— God and— Fa-ther, we

wor-ship— you,— we give you— thanks,— we praise you for your— glo-ry.

Lord Je-sus— Christ, on-ly Son of the Fa-ther, Lord God Lamb of God, you

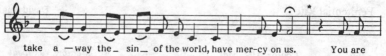

take a —way the— sin— of the world, have mer-cy on us. You are

sea-ted at the right hand of the Fa-ther, re-ceive our prayer. For

You a-lone are the Ho-ly One. You a-lone are the Lord,—

2

You a — lone are the Most High, Je - sus — Christ, with the

Ho - ly — Spir-it in the glo - ry of God the — Fa-ther. A - men.

R. Glory...

## Gloria II

Stephen Dean

*Cantor then ALL*

R. Glo-ry to God in the high-est. And peace to his peo-ple on earth!

1. Lord God, hea-ven-ly King, al - migh-ty God and Fa-ther, we
wor-ship you, we give you thanks, we praise you for your glo - ry.

R. Glory...

2. Lord Je-sus Christ, on-ly Son of the Fa-ther, Lord God, lamb of God, you take a-
-way the sin of the world, have mer - cy on us. (A) Have mer - cy on us. You are
(C)
sea-ted at the right hand of the Fa-ther, re-ceive our prayer. Receive our prayer.
(A)

R. Glory...

3

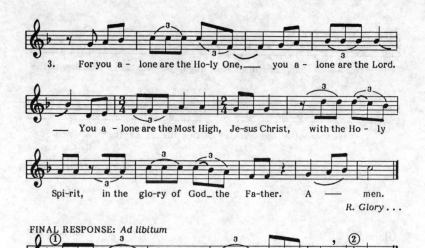

3. For you a - lone are the Ho-ly One,___ you a - lone are the Lord.

___ You a - lone are the Most High, Je-sus Christ, with the Ho - ly

Spi-rit, in the glo-ry of God_ the Fa-ther. A ___ men.

R. Glory . . .

FINAL RESPONSE: *Ad libitum*

Glo-ry to God in the high-est. And peace to his people on earth. A - men.

*Alternate between two groups. Group 2 starts in final bar as marked.*
*End in a unison Amen.*

© From Mass of St Andrew 1987 Stephen Dean

## Gloria III

Mike Anderson

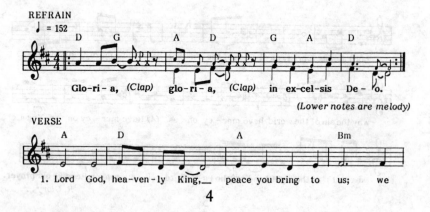

REFRAIN
♩ = 152

| D | G | A | D | G | A | D |

Glo-ri - a, *(Clap)* glo-ri - a, *(Clap)* in ex-cel-sis De - o.

*(Lower notes are melody)*

VERSE

| A | D | A | Bm |

1. Lord God, hea-ven-ly King,___ peace you bring to us; we

4

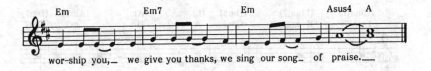

wor-ship you,__ we give you thanks, we sing our song__ of praise.__

2. Jesus, Saviour of all, Lord God, Lamb of God
   you take away our sins, Oh Lord, have mercy on us all.

3. At the Father's right hand, Lord receive our prayer,
   for you alone are the Holy One, and you alone are Lord.

4. Glory Father and Son, Glory Holy Spirit,
   to you we raise our hands up high, we glorify your name.

## Gloria IV

CANON

Glo - ri - a,    glo - ri - a,    in ex - cel - sis De — o!

Glo - ri - a,    glo - ri - a,    al - le - lu - ia,    al - le - lu - ia!

## Eucharistic Liturgy I

Bernadette Farrell

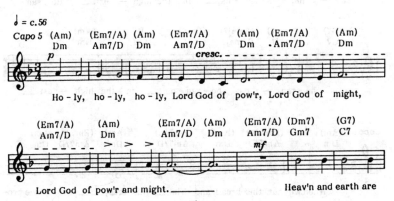

♩ = c.56

Capo 5

Ho - ly,  ho - ly,  ho - ly, Lord God of pow'r, Lord God of might,

Lord God of pow'r and might. _____    Heav'n and earth are

5

full of your glo-ry, Ho-san-na in the high — est. Ho-san-

-na, ho-san — na, ho-san-na in the high — est.

Bless-ed, bless-ed, bless-ed, bless-ed is he who comes in the name, who

comes in the Lord's own name._____ Ho-san — na, ho-

san — na, ho-san-na,__ in the high — est._ Ho-san-

-na, ho-san — na, ho-san-na,__ in the high — est._

When we eat this bread and drink_ this cup,_ we pro-

6

7

# Eucharistic Liturgy II (A Celtic Liturgy)

Christopher Walker

*Repeat with Descant*

8

... all glo-ry and hon-our are yours, al-might-y

*All*

Fa-ther, for e - ver and e - ver. A —— men,

a —— men, a — men,___ a — men.

© 1982 Christopher Walker

## Eucharistic Liturgy III

Seoirse Bodley

*Andante*

Ho - ly Ho - ly, Ho - ly Lord, God of pow'r and might. Hea-ven and

earth are full of your glo-ry. Ho - san-na in the high-est. Bless - ed is

he who comes in the name of the Lord. Ho - san - na in the high - est.

**I**

*Andante*

Christ has died,___ Christ is ris'n, Christ will come a - gain.

A —— men, a —— men, a —————— men.

**II**

*Andante*

Dy - ing you de - stroyed our death, ris —— ing___

you re — stored our life, Lord_ Je - sus, come in glo - ry.

From Mass of Peace © 1981 S Bodley

9

# Eucharistic Liturgy IV

Paul Inwood

All

Ho - ly, ho — ly, ho - ly Lord, God of power and God of might, heav'n and earth are full heav'n and earth are full heav'n and earth are full — of your glo - ry. Ho - san - na, ho - san - na, ho - san - na — in the high - est: ho - san - na, ho - san - na, ho - san - na — in the high - est.

Blest is he who comes, blest is he who comes in the name of the Lord. Ho -

*(Repeat Hosannas as above)*

Christ has died, al - le - lu - ia! Christ is ris'n, al - le - lu - ia! Christ will come a - gain — in — glo - ry! Ho -

*(Repeat Hosannas as in Holy, Holy)*

10

A ——— men, a ——— men, a ——— men!

**Eucharistic Liturgy V** — John Lillis

**ALL REPEAT phrases after Cantor as directed.**

Ho - ly ho - ly ho - ly, God of power and might,

*might.* Your glo - ry fills all heav-en and earth,

Ho —— san - na in the high - est, *Ho - high - est.*

Bless - ed is he who comes in the name of the Lord.

Ho —— san - na in the high - est. *Ho - high - est.*

CODA

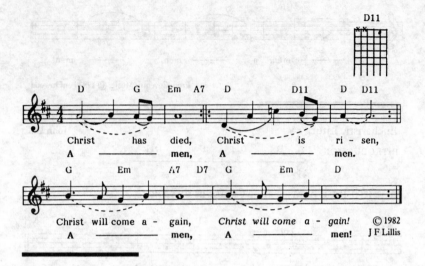

Christ has died, Christ is ri - sen,
A ——— men, A ——— men.

Christ will come a - gain, *Christ will come a - gain!*    © 1982
A ——— men, A ——— men!    J F Lillis

## Eucharistic Liturgy VI

Stephen Dean

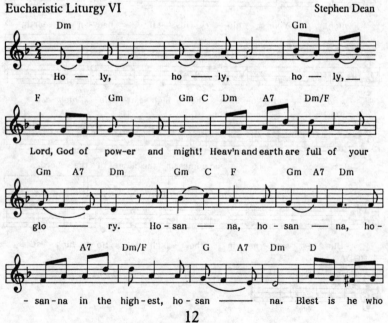

Ho — ly, ho — ly, ho — ly, —

Lord, God of pow-er and might! Heav'n and earth are full of your

glo ——— ry. Ho-san —— na, ho - san —— na, ho-

- san-na in the high-est, ho-san ——— na. Blest is he who

12

comes in the name of the Lord. Blest is he who comes in the name of the Lord. Ho - san —— na, ho - san — - na, ho-san-na in the high-est, ho-san —— na.

*1st time: cantor/choir; all repeat*

Christ has died, Christ is — ri-sen, Christ will come a-gain!

*1st time: cantor/choir; all repeat*

Christ has died, al-le-lu — ia, Christ is ris-en, al-le-lu - ia, Christ will come a —— gain, al-le-lu - ia, al-le-lu - ia.

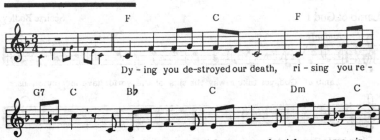

Dy - ing you de-stroyed our death, ri - sing you re--stored our life. Lord Je-sus come, Lord Jesus come, Lord Jesus come — in —

13

Lord Je-sus, Lord Je-sus,— come — in glo-ry!

glo-ry. Lord Jesus come, Lord Jesus come, Lord Jesus come in— glo-ry!

When we eat this bread, when we drink this cup, we pro-

-claim your death, Lord Je-sus, un-til you come in glo-ry!

Through him, with him, in him, in the unity of the Holy Spirit,

all glory and honour is yours, al-migh-ty Fa-ther, for ever and ever:

ALL:

A — men, a — men, a — men!

© 1982 Stephen Dean

## Lamb of God I

Seoirse Bodley

Andante

Lamb of God, you take a-way the sins of the world: have mer-cy on us.

rall.

Lamb of God you take a - way the sins of the world: grant us— peace.

**14**      From Mass of Peace © 1981 S Bodley

## Lamb of God II

David Clark Isele

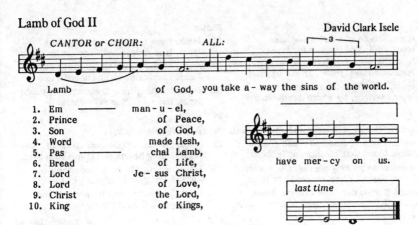

*CANTOR or CHOIR:*      *ALL:*

Lamb     of God, you take a - way the sins of the world.

1. Em ——— man - u - el,
2. Prince of Peace,
3. Son of God,
4. Word made flesh,
5. Pas ——— chal Lamb,
6. Bread of Life,
7. Lord Je - sus Christ,
8. Lord of Love,
9. Christ the Lord,
10. King of Kings,

have mer - cy on us.

*last time*

*For the final invocation, the cantor once again sings*
*"Lamb of God" to which all conclude "grant us peace."*   grant us peace.

## Lamb of God III

Paul Inwood

G      Am7 Dsus4 D Em      Bm7 Am7 Dsus4 D

C(Am)     G(Em7)     Am(F)     Em(C)     C(Am6)     G(Emaj)

Hear our prayer, have mer–cy; hear our prayer, have mercy; give us your peace.

*Capo 5 Chords in brackets are for last time only.*

**General**

1. Jesus, Lamb of God and source of life:
   Jesus, loving bearer of our sins:
2. Jesus, Son of God and Son of Man:
   Jesus, true redeemer of the world:

*3. Jesus Christ, our Way, our Truth,
   our Life:
   Jesus Christ, our living Cornerstone:
4. Jesus, Lord of life and Lord of light:
   Jesus, here in form of bread and wine:

**Advent**

5 = 1

6. Jesus, coming near to bring us joy:
   Jesus, Son of God, Emmanuel:
7. Jesus, bringing hope to all who fear:
   Jesus, bringing strength to all who
   mourne:

*8. Jesus, Saviour heralded by John:
   Jesus, son of David's house and line:

*9 = 4

**Christmas**

10. Jesus, Lamb of God, the Word made flesh:
    Jesus, Son of God come down on earth:
11. Jesus, King of glory, Prince of Peace:
    Jesus, shining in our darkened world:
12. Jesus, King of angels, Lord of joy:
    Jesus, born to save the world from sin:

13 = 4

15

## Lent

14. Jesus, source of everlasting life:
    Jesus, source of reconciling love:

15. Jesus, by whose suffering we are healed:
    Jesus, man of sorrows, friend of grief:

16. Jesus, crucified, transcending time:
    Jesus, Saviour, by whose death we live:

## Eucharistic *(Maundy Thursday, Corpus Christi)*

17. Jesus, Lamb of God and bread of life:
    Jesus, blood that cleanses us from sin:

18. Jesus, showing how we ought to serve:
    Jesus, teaching how we ought to love:

*19. Jesus Christ, our true, eternal priest:
    Jesus, food and drink that makes us one:

20 = 4

## Easter

21. Jesus, risen Lord, triumphant King:
    Jesus, true redeemer of the world:

22. Jesus, Morning Star which never sets:
    Jesus, Paschal Lamb and sacrifice:

23. Jesus, bursting from the shattered tomb:
    Jesus, mighty Victor over death:

24 = 4

## Pentecost *(Spirit, healing . . .)*

25. Jesus, glorious brightness, flame of love:
    Jesus, filling hearts and minds with life:

26. Jesus, healing strength, redeeming power:
    Jesus, burning out the mark of sin:

27. Jesus, by whose truth we are inspired:
    Jesus, present here among us now:

28 = 4

© 1982 Paul Inwood

## Lamb of God IV

Marty Haugen

CANTOR/CHOIR: Je-sus, Lamb of __ God: ALL:
Je-sus, Bread of __ Life: __ you take a-way the sins of the
Je-sus, Prince of __ Peace: __

world, __ have mer-cy on __ us.

FINAL TIME

CANTOR/CHOIR: Je-sus, Lamb of God; __ you take a-way the sin of the world:

grant us your __ peace.     rit.     Fine

16

Jesus, Word of God . . .      Jesus, King of Kings . . .
Jesus, Tree of Life . . .      Jesus, Cup of Life . . .
Jesus, Ancient Cup . . .      Jesus, Fire of Love . . .
Jesus, Lord of Lords . . .      Jesus, Bread of Peace . . .
Jesus, Hope for all . . .

## A New People's Mass

by Dom Gregory Murray

Penitential Rite

Lord, ____ have mer-cy. Lord, ____ have mer-cy. Christ, ____ have mer-

- cy. Christ, ____ have mer-cy. Lord, ____ have mer-cy. Lord, ____ have mer-cy.

Gloria

Glo-ry to God in the high-est, ____ and peace to his peo-ple on earth. ____ Lord

God, hea-ven-ly King, ____ al-migh-ty God and ____ Fa-ther, ____ we wor-ship

you, we give you thanks, we praise you ____ for your glo-ry. Lord Je-sus Christ,

on-ly Son of the Fa — ther, Lord God, Lamb of ____ God, you take a-way the

sin of the world, ____ have mer-cy on us; ____ you are sea-ted at the right hand

of the ____ Fa — ther, re-ceive our ____ pray'r. ____ For you a-

- lone are the Ho-ly One, you a-lone are the Lord, you a-lone are the

Most High, Jesus Christ, with the Holy Spirit

in the glory of God the Father. A — men.

**Eucharistic Acclamations**

Holy, holy, holy Lord, God of power and might, heaven and earth are full of your glory. Hosanna in the highest. Blessed is he who comes in the name of the Lord. Hosanna in the highest.

Christ has died. Christ is risen. Christ will come again.

A — men.

For the kingdom, the power and the glory are yours, now and for ever.

**Lamb of God**

Lamb of God, you take away the sins of the world, have mercy on us.

Lamb of God, you take away the sins of the world, grant us peace.

© 1975 McCrimmon Publishing Company Ltd.

18

## 1

1. Abide with me,
   fast falls the eventide;
   the darkness deepens,
      Lord, with me abide!
   When other helpers fail,
      and comforts flee,
   help of the helpless,
      O abide with me.

2. Swift to its close
      ebbs out life's little day;
   earth's joys grow dim,
      its glories pass away;
   change and decay
      in all around I see;
   O thou who changest not,
      abide with me.

3. I need thy presence
      every passing hour;
   what but thy grace
      can foil the tempter's power?
   Who like thyself
      my guide and stay can be?
   Through cloud and sunshine,
      O abide with me.

4. I fear no foe with thee
      at hand to bless;
   ills have no weight,
      and tears no bitterness.
   Where is death's sting?
      Where, grave, thy victory?
   I triumph still,
      if thou abide with me.

5. Hold thou thy Cross before
      my closing eyes;
   shine through the gloom,
      and point me to the skies;
   heaven's morning breaks,
      and earth's vain shadows flee:
   in life, in death, O Lord,
      abide with me!

   *H. F. Lyte (1793-1847)*

## 2

1. Accept, O Father, in thy love,
   these humble gifts of bread and
                            wine,
   that with ourselves we offer thee,
   returning gifts already thine.

2. Behold this host and chalice, Lord,
   to thee in heaven the gifts we raise;
   through them may we our homage
                            pay,
   our adoration and our praise.

3. No earthly claim to grace is ours,
   save what thy sacrifice has won;
   grant then thy grace, fulfil our
                            needs,
   and may thy will in ours be done.

   *J. Clifford Evers*

## 3

1. All creation, bless the Lord.
   Earth and heaven, bless the Lord.
   Spirits, powers, bless the Lord.
   Praise him for ever.
   Sun and moon, bless the Lord.
   Stars and planets, bless the Lord.
   Dews and showers, bless the Lord.
   Praise him for ever.

2. Winds and breezes, bless the Lord.
   Spring and Autumn, bless the Lord.
   Winter, Summer, bless the Lord.
   Praise him for ever.
   Fire and heat, bless the Lord.
   Frost and cold, bless the Lord.
   Ice and snow, bless the Lord.
   Praise him for ever.

3. Night and daytime, bless the Lord.
   Light and darkness, bless the Lord.
   Clouds and lightning, bless the Lord.
   Praise him for ever.
   All the earth, bless the Lord.
   Hills and mountains, bless the Lord.
   Trees and flowers, bless the Lord.
   Praise him for ever.

4. Springs and rivers, bless the Lord.
Seas and oceans, bless the Lord.
Whales and fishes, bless the Lord.
Praise him for ever.
Birds and insects, bless the Lord.
Beasts and cattle, bless the Lord.
Let all creatures bless the Lord.
Praise him for ever.

5. Let God's people bless the Lord.
Men and women, bless the Lord.
All creation, bless the Lord.
Praise him for ever.
Let God's people bless the Lord.
Men and women, bless the Lord.
All creation, bless the Lord.
Praise him for ever.

*Hayward Osborne*

# 4

1. All creatures of our God and King,
lift up your voice and with us sing
alleluia, alleluia!
Thou burning sun with golden
beam,
thou silver moon with softer gleam:

*O praise him, O praise him,*
*alleluia, alleluia, alleluia.*

2. Thou rushing wind that art so
strong,
ye clouds that sail in heaven along,
O praise him, alleluia!
Thou rising morn, in praise rejoice,
ye lights of evening, find a voice:

3. Thou flowing water, pure and clear,
make music for thy Lord to hear,
alleluia, alleluia!
Thou fire so masterful and bright,
that givest man both warmth and
light:

4. Dear mother earth, who day by day
unfoldest blessings on our way,
O praise him, alleluia!
The flowers and fruits that in thee
grow
let them his glory also show.

5. And all ye men of tender heart,
forgiving others, take your part,
O sing ye, alleluia!
Ye who long pain and sorrow bear,
praise God and on him cast your
care:

6. And thou, most kind and gentle
death,
waiting to hush our latest breath,
O praise him, alleluia!
Thou leadest home the child of
God,
and Christ our Lord the way hath
trod:

7. Let all things their Creator bless,
and worship him in humbleness,
O praise him, alleluia!
Praise, praise the Father, praise the
Son,
and praise the Spirit, Three in One.

*W. H. Draper (1855-1933)*
*Based on the Cantico di Frate Sole of*
*St. Francis of Assisi (1182-1226)*

# 5

1. Alleluia, alleluia,
alleluia, alleluia,
alleluia, alleluia,
alleluia, alleluia.

2. Jesus is Lord, . . .

3. And I love him, . . .

4. Christ is risen, . . .

*Traditional*

# 6

*Alleluia, alleluia!*
*I will praise the Father*
*for all of my life,*
*I will sing to my God*
*as long as I live,*
*alleluia, alleluia, alleluia!*

1. Do not place all your trust
      in the power of man:
   he cannot save.
   His schemes will all perish
      when he yields up his breath
   at the end of his day.

2. But so happy the man
      who will trust in his God:
   he will find help.
   For he is the maker
      of the heavens and earth
   and of all that these hold.

3. All the searchers for justice,
      for freedom, for love,
   he will fulfil.
   The widow, the orphan,
      and the blind and the lame
   in his love are restored.

   *Based on Psalm 146*
   *by Michael Cockett*

# 7

1. Alleluia, sing to Jesus,
   his the sceptre, his the throne,
   alleluia, his the triumph,
   his the victory alone:
   hark the songs of peaceful Sion
   thunder like a mighty flood:
   Jesus, out of every nation,
   hath redeemed us by his blood.

2. Alleluia, not as orphans
   are we left in sorrow now;
   alleluia, he is near us,
   faith believes, nor questions how;
   though the cloud from sight received
                             him
   when the forty days were o'er,
   shall our hearts forget his promise,
   'I am with you evermore'?

3. Alleluia, Bread of Angels,
   thou on earth our food, our stay;
   alleluia, here the sinful
   flee to thee from day to day;
   intercessor, friend of sinners,
   earth's Redeemer, plead for me,
   where the songs of all the sinless
   sweep across the crystal sea.

4. Alleluia, King eternal
   thee the Lord of lords we own;
   alleluia, born of Mary,
   earth thy footstool, heaven thy
                             throne;
   thou within the veil hast entered,
   robed in flesh, our great High Priest;
   thou on earth both priest and
                             victim
   in the Eucharistic Feast.

   *W. Chatterton Dix (1837-98)*

# 8

*All glory, laud and honour,*
*to thee, Redeemer King,*
*to whom the lips of children*
*made sweet hosannas ring.*

1. Thou art the King of Israel,
   thou David's royal Son,
   who in the Lord's name comest,
   the King and blessed one.

2. The company of angels
   are praising thee on high,
   and mortal men and all things
   created make reply.

3. The people of the Hebrews
   with palms before thee went:
   our praise and prayer and anthems
   before thee we present.

4. To thee before thy passion
   they sang their hymns of praise;
   to thee now high exalted
   our melody we raise.

5. Thou didst accept their praises,
   accept the prayers we bring,
   who in all good delightest,
   thou good and gracious king.

   *St Theodulph of Orleans (821),*
   *tr. J. M. Neale*

# 9

1. All hail the power of Jesus' name;
   let angels prostrate fall;
   bring forth the royal diadem
   *To crown him, crown him,*
   *crown him,*
   *crown him Lord of all.*

2. Crown him, ye martyrs of your
   God,
   who from his altar call;
   praise him whose way of pain ye
   trod,
   *and crown him Lord of all.*

3. Ye prophets who our freedom won,
   ye searchers, great and small,
   by whom the work of truth is done,
   *now crown him Lord of all.*

4. Sinners, whose love can ne'er forget
   the wormwood and the gall,
   go spread your trophies at his feet,
   *and crown him Lord of all.*

5. Bless him, each poor oppressèd race
   that Christ did upward call;
   his hand in each achievement trace,
   *and crown him Lord of all.*

6. Let every tribe and every tongue
   to him their hearts enthral:
   lift high the universal song,
   *and crown him Lord of all.*

   *E. Perronet (1762-92), and others*

# 10

1. All people that on earth do dwell,
   sing to the Lord with cheerful voice;
   him serve with fear, his praise forth
   tell,
   come ye before him and rejoice.

2. The Lord, ye know, is God indeed,
   without our aid he did us make;
   we are his folk, he doth us feed
   and for his sheep he doth us take.

3. O enter then his gates with praise,
   approach with joy his courts unto;
   praise, laud, and bless his name
   always,
   for it is seemly so to do.

4. For why? the Lord our God is good:
   his mercy is for ever sure;
   his truth at all times firmly stood,
   and shall from age to age endure.

5. To Father, Son and Holy Ghost,
   the God whom heaven and earth
   adore,
   from men and from the angel-host
   be praise and glory evermore.

   *William Kethe, Day's Psalter (1560)*

# 11

1. All that I am, all that I do,
   all that I'll ever have,
   I offer now to you.
   Take and sanctify these gifts
   for your honour, Lord.
   Knowing that I love and serve you
   is enough reward.
   All that I am, all that I do,
   all that I'll ever have
   I offer now to you.

2. All that I dream, all that I pray,
   all that I'll ever make,
   I give to you today.
   Take and sanctify these gifts
   for your honour, Lord.
   Knowing that I love and serve you
   is enough reward.
   All that I am, all that I do,
   all that I'll ever have
   I offer now to you.

   *Sebastian Temple*

# 12

*All the nations of the earth,*
*praise the Lord who brings to birth*
*the greatest star, the smallest flower.*
*Alleluia.*

1. Let the heavens praise the Lord.
   Alleluia.
   Moon and stars, praise the Lord.
   Alleluia.

2. Snow capped mountains,
       praise the Lord.
   Alleluia.
   Rolling hills, praise the Lord.
   Alleluia.

3. Deep sea water, praise the Lord.
   Alleluia.
   Gentle rain, praise the Lord.
   Alleluia.

4. Roaring lion, praise the Lord.
   Alleluia.
   Singing birds, praise the Lord.
   Alleluia.

5. Kings and princes, praise the Lord.
   Alleluia.
   Young and old, praise the Lord.
   Alleluia.

*Michael Cockett*

# 13

*All things bright and beautiful,*
*all creatures great and small,*
*all things wise and wonderful,*
*the Lord God made them all.*

1. Each little flower that opens,
   each little bird that sings,
   he made their glowing colours,
   he made their tiny wings.

2. The purple-headed mountain,
   the river running by,
   the sunset and the morning,
   that brightens up the sky.

3. The cold wind in the winter,
   the pleasant summer sun,
   the ripe fruits in the garden,
   he made them every one.

4. The tall trees in the greenwood,
   the meadows for our play,
   the rushes by the water,
   to gather every day.

5. He gave us eyes to see them,
   and lips that we may tell
   how great is God Almighty,
   who has made all things well.

*C. F. Alexander (1818-95)*

# 14

1. All this world belongs to Jesus,
   ev'rything is his by right;
   all on the land, all in the sea;
   ev'rything is his by right.

2. Shining stars in all their beauty
   are outnumbered by his gifts.
   Sand on the shore, stars in the sky,
   are outnumbered by his gifts.

3. Ev'ry foot that starts a-dancing
   taps a rhythm full of hope;
   full of his joy, full of his hope,
   taps a rhythm full of hope.

4. All that's good reflects his goodness;
   may it lead us back to him.
   All that is good, all that is true,
   may it lead us back to him.

5. So give thanks for what he's given;
   touch and taste, and feet to dance;
   eyes for the lights, ears for the sound,
   for the wonders of our Lord.

*Willard F. Jabusch*

## 15

1. All ye who seek a comfort sure
   in trouble and distress,
   whatever sorrow vex the mind,
   or guilt the soul oppress:

2. Jesus, who gave himself for you
   upon the cross to die,
   opens to you his sacred heart;
   oh, to that heart draw nigh.

3. Ye hear how kindly he invites;
   ye hear his words so blest:
   'All ye that labour come to me,
   and I will give you rest.'

4. Jesus, thou joy of saints on high,
   thou hope of sinners here,
   attracted by those loving words
   to thee I lift my prayer.

5. Wash thou my wounds in that dear
                                    blood,
   which forth from thee doth flow;
   new grace, new hope inspire, a new
   and better heart bestow.

*18th c., tr. Edward Caswall*

## 16

1. A voice cries in the wilderness
   'Prepare the way of the Lord,
   make straight the road for him,
   he is our God.'
   He will level mountains
   and make the valleys plains.
   He will come into your hearts
   like a light in the dark.

**Jesus, you are the Lord of light,
Son of God, you are the Holy One.
Prince of peace who died for us:
Lord of light you are risen.**

2. And high up on a mountain
   a messenger will shout,
   we see His victory
   He is our God.
   He is like a shepherd
   who cares for his flock,
   He is called the Lamb of God,
   for He died for our sins.

3. The Lord came and dwelt with us,
   the Lord of light and truth;
   the world could not recognise
   He is our God,
   for we know He died for us
   that we may be redeemed:
   now we see He lives again,
   for He rose to set us free.

*Anthony Sharpe*

## 17

1. Almighty Father, Lord most high,
   who madest all, who fillest all,
   thy name we praise and magnify,
   for all our needs on thee we call.

2. We offer to thee of thine own,
   ourselves and all that we can bring,
   in bread and cup before thee shown,
   our universal offering.

3. All that we have we bring to thee,
   yet all is naught when all is done,
   save that in it thy love can see
   the sacrifice of thy dear Son.

4. By this command in bread and cup,
   his body and his blood we plead;
   what on the cross he offer'd up
   is here our sacrifice indeed.

5. For all thy gifts of life and grace,
   here we thy servants humbly pray
   that thou would'st look upon the
                                    face
   of thine anointed Son today.

*Vincent Stuckley Stratton Coles
(1845-1929)*

# 18

1. Almighty Father, take this bread
   thy people offer thee;
   where sins divide us, take instead
   one fold and family.

2. The wine we offer soon will be
   Christ's blood, redemption's price;
   receive it, Holy Trinity,
   this holy sacrifice.

3. O God, by angels' choirs adored,
   thy name be praised on earth;
   on all men be that peace outpoured
   once promised at his birth.

*Anonymous*

# 19

1. Amazing grace! How sweet the
   sound
   that saved a wretch like me.
   I once was lost but now I'm found,
   was blind, but now I see.

2. 'Twas grace that taught my heart to
   fear,
   and grace my fears relieved.
   How precious did that grace appear
   the hour I first believed.

3. Through many dangers, toils and
   snares
   I have already come.
   'Tis grace hath brought me safe thus
   far,
   and grace will lead me home.

4. The Lord has promised good to me;
   his word my hope secures.
   He will my shield and portion be
   as long as life endures.

*John Newton (1725–1807)*

# 20

1. And did those feet in ancient time
   walk upon England's mountains
   green?
   And was the holy Lamb of God
   on England's pleasant pastures
   seen?
   And did the countenance divine
   shine forth upon our clouded hills?
   And was Jerusalem buildéd here
   among those dark Satanic mills?

2. Bring me my bow of burning gold!
   Bring me my arrows of desire!
   Bring me my spear! O clouds,
   unfold!
   Bring me my chariot of fire!
   I will not cease from mental fight,
   nor shall my sword sleep in my
   hand,
   till we have built Jerusalem
   in England's green and pleasant
   land.

*William Blake (1757-1827)*

# 21

1. Angels we have heard in heaven
   sweetly singing o'er our plains,
   and the mountain-tops in answer
   echoing their joyous strains.

   *Gloria in excelsis Deo.*

2. Shepherds, why this exultation?
   Why your rapturous strain prolong?
   Tell us of the gladsome tidings,
   which inspire your joyous song.

3. Come to Bethlehem, and see him
   o'er whose birth the angels sing,
   come, adore, devoutly kneeling,
   Christ the Lord, the new-born king.

4. See him in a manger lying
   whom the choir of angels praise!
   Mary, Joseph, come to aid us
   while our hearts in love we raise.

*James Chadwick (1813-82)*

# 22

1. Angels we have heard on high
sweetly singing o'er our plains,
and the mountains in reply
echo still their joyous strains.

   *Gloria in excelsis Deo.*

2. Shepherds, why this jubilee?
Why your rapturous strain prolong?
Say, what may your tidings be,
which inspire your heavenly song.

3. Come to Bethlehem and see
him whose birth the angels sing:
come, adore on bended knee
the infant Christ, the new-born
King.

4. See within a manger laid,
Jesus, Lord of heaven and earth!
Mary, Joseph, lend your aid
to celebrate our Saviour's birth.

   *James Chadwick (1813-82)*

# 23

*Ask, and you will receive.*
*Seek, and you will find.*
*Knock, and the door will be opened*
*for the love of the Lord has no end.*

1. Is there any man here,
   when his son asks for bread,
would turn him away
   with a stone instead?
Is there any man here,
   when his son asks for meat,
would then give him
   a poisonous snake to eat?

2. So then how could your Father
   in heaven above,
who knows so much more
   of the ways of love,
so then how could your Father
   refuse what is good,
when you ask in the name
   of the Son he loves?

3. So whatever you ask
   you will always receive,
whatever you seek
   you will always find.
For my Father will give
   to all those who believe
in the Spirit of love
   that will never end.

   *Michael Cockett*

# 24

1. As with gladness men of old,
did the guiding star behold,
as with joy they hailed its light,
leading onward, beaming bright,
so, most gracious God, may we
evermore be led to thee.

2. As with joyful steps they sped,
to that lowly manger-bed,
there to bend the knee before
him whom heaven and earth adore,
so may we with willing feet
ever seek thy mercy-seat.

3. As they offered gifts most rare,
at that manger rude and bare,
so may we with holy joy,
pure, and free from sin's alloy,
all our costliest treasures bring,
Christ, to thee our heavenly King.

4. Holy Jesu, every day
keep us in the narrow way;
and, when earthly things are past,
bring our ransomed souls at last
where they need no star to guide,
where no clouds thy glory hide.

5. In the heavenly country bright
need they no created light,
thou its Light, its Joy, its Crown,
thou its Sun which goes not down;
there for ever may we sing
alleluias to our King.

   *William Chatterton Dix (1837-98)*

# 25

1. Attend and keep this happy fast
   I preach to you this day.
   Is this the fast that pleases me
   that takes your joy away?
   Do I delight in sorrow's dress,
   says God, who reigns above,
   the hanging head, the dismal look,
   will they attract my love?

2. But is this not the fast I choose,
   that shares the heavy load;
   that seeks to bring the poor man in
   who's weary of the road;
   that gives the hungry bread to eat,
   to strangers gives a home;
   that does not let you hide your face
   from your own flesh and bone?

3. Then like the dawn your light will
   break,
   to life you will be raised.
   And men will praise the Lord for
   you;
   be happy in your days.
   The glory of the Lord will shine,
   and in your steps his grace.
   And when you call he'll answer you;
   he will not hide his face.

   *Roger Ruston, after Isaiah 58: 5-9*

# 26

1. At the cross her station keeping,
   stood the mournful mother
   weeping,
   close to Jesus to the last;

2. Through her heart, his sorrow
   sharing,
   all his bitter anguish bearing,
   now at length the sword has pass'd.

3. Oh, how sad and sore distress'd
   was that mother highly blest,
   of the sole-begotten One.

4. Christ above in torment hangs;
   she beneath beholds the pangs
   of her dying glorious Son.

5. Is there one who would not weep,
   whelm'd in miseries so deep,
   Christ's dear mother to behold?

6. Can the human heart refrain
   from partaking in her pain,
   in that mother's pain untold?

7. Bruised, derided, cursed, defiled,
   she beheld her tender child,
   all with bloody scourges rent;

8. For the sins of his own nation,
   saw him hang in desolation,
   till his spirit forth he sent.

9. O thou mother! fount of love!
   Touch my spirit from above,
   make my heart with thine accord:

10. Make me feel as thou hast felt;
    make my soul to glow and melt
    with the love of Christ my Lord.

11. Holy Mother, pierce me through,
    in my heart each wound renew
    of my Saviour crucified.

12. Let me share with thee his pain
    who for all my sins was slain,
    who for me in torments died.

13. Let me mingle tears with thee,
    mourning him who mourn'd for me,
    all the days that I may live:

14. By the cross with thee to stay,
    there with thee to weep and pray,
    is all I ask of thee to give.

15. Virgin of all virgins best,
    listen to my fond request:
    let me share thy grief divine;

16. Let me, to my latest breath,
    in my body bear the death
    of that dying son of thine.

17. Wounded with his every wound,
    steep my soul till it hath swoon'd
    in his very blood away.

18. Be to me, O Virgin, nigh,
    lest in flames I burn and die,
    in his awful judgement day.

19. Christ, when thou shalt call me
hence,
be thy mother my defence,
be thy cross my victory.

20. While my body here decays,
may my soul thy goodness praise,
safe in paradise with thee.

*Ascribed to Jacopone da Todi (d. 1306),*
*tr. E. Caswall*

# 27

1. At the Lamb's high feast we sing
praise to our victorious king,
who hath washed us in the tide
flowing from his piercéd side.
Praise we him whose love divine
gives the guests his blood for wine,
gives his body for the feast,
love the victim, love the priest.

2. Where the paschal blood is poured,
Death's dark angel sheathes his
sword;
Israel's hosts triumphant go
through the wave that drowns the
foe.
Christ the Lamb, whose blood was
shed.
Paschal victim, paschal bread;
with sincerity and love
eat we manna from above.

3. Mighty victim from the sky,
powers of hell beneath thee lie;
death is conquered in the fight;
thou hast brought us life and light,
now thy banner thou dost wave;
vanquished Satan and the grave;
angels join his praise to tell –
see o'erthrown the prince of hell.

4. Paschal triumph, paschal joy,
only sin can this destroy;
from the death of sin set free
souls re-born, dear Lord, in thee.
Hymns of glory, songs of praise,
Father, unto thee we raise.
Risen Lord, all praise to thee,
ever with the Spirit be.

*7th c., tr. Robert Campbell*

# 28

1. At the name of Jesus
every knee shall bow,
every tongue confess him
King of glory now;
'tis the Father's pleasure
we should call him Lord,
who from the beginning,
was the mighty Word.

2. At his voice creation
sprang at once to sight,
all the Angel faces,
all the hosts of light,
thrones and dominations,
stars upon their way,
all the heavenly orders,
in their great array.

3. Humbled for a season,
to receive a name
from the lips of sinners
unto whom he came,
faithfully he bore it
spotless to the last,
brought it back victorious
when from death he passed:

4. Bore it up triumphant
with its human light
through all ranks of creatures,
to the central height,
to the throne of Godhead,
to the Father's breast,
filled it with the glory
of that perfect rest.

5. Name him, brothers, name him,
with love as strong as death;
but with awe and wonder,
and with bated breath.
He is God the Saviour,
he is Christ the Lord,
ever to be worshipped,
trusted, and adored.

6. In your hearts enthrone him;
   there let him subdue
   all that is not holy,
   all that is not true;
   crown him as your captain,
   in temptation's hour
   let his will enfold you
   in its light and power.

7. Brothers, this Lord Jesus
   shall return again,
   with his Father's glory,
   with his angel train,
   for all wreaths of empire
   meet upon his brow,
   and our hearts confess him
   King of glory now.

   *Caroline Maria Noel (1817-77)*

# 29

1. Ave Maria, O Maiden, O Mother,
      fondly thy children are calling on
                                    thee;
   thine are the graces unclaimed by
                                    another,
   sinless and beautiful Star of the sea.

   *Mater amabilis, ora pro nobis,*
   *pray for thy children who call upon*
                                    *thee;*
   *Ave sanctissima, Ave purissima*
   *sinless and beautiful Star of the sea.*

2. Ave Maria, the night shades are
                                    falling,
      softly, our voices arise unto thee;
   earth's lonely exiles for succour are
                                    calling,
   sinless and beautiful Star of the sea.

3. Ave Maria, thy children are
                                    kneeling,
      words of endearment are murmured
                                    to thee;
   softly thy spirit upon us is stealing,
   sinless and beautiful Star of the sea.

   *'Sister M.'*

# 30

1. Away in a manger,
      no crib for a bed,
   the little Lord Jesus
      laid down his sweet head,
   the stars in the bright sky
      looked down where he lay,
   the little Lord Jesus
      asleep on the hay.

2. The cattle are lowing,
      the baby awakes,
   but little Lord Jesus
      no crying he makes.
   I love thee, Lord Jesus!
      Look down from the sky,
   and stay by my side
      until morning is nigh.

3. Be near me, Lord Jesus;
      I ask thee to stay
   close by me for ever,
      and love me, I pray.
   Bless all the dear children
      in thy tender care,
   and fit us for heaven,
      to live with thee there.

   *J. Kirkpatrick*

# 31

1. Battle is o'er,
      hell's armies flee:
   raise we the cry of victory
   with abounding joy resounding,
   alleluia.

2. Christ who endured
      the shameful tree,
   o'er death triumphant welcome we,
   our adoring praise outpouring,
   alleluia.

3. On the third morn
      from death rose he,
   clothed with what light in heaven
                                    shall be,
   our unswerving faith deserving,
   alleluia.

4. Hell's gloomy gates
   yield up their key,
   paradise door thrown wide we see;
   never-tiring be our choiring,
   alleluia.

5. Lord, by the stripes
   men laid on thee,
   grant us to live from death set free,
   this our greeting still repeating,
   alleluia.

*Simphonia Sirenum (1695)*
*tr. R.A. Knox*

# 32

1. Be still, and know I am with you,
   be still, I am the Lord.
   I will not leave you orphans.
   I leave with you my world.
   Be one.

2. You fear the light may be fading,
   you fear to lose your way.
   Be still, and know I am near you.
   I'll lead you to the day
   and the sun.

3. Be glad the day you have sorrow,
   be glad, for then you live.
   The stars shine only in darkness,
   and in your need I give
   my peace.

*Anne Conway*

# 33

1. Be still and know that I am God,
   be still and know that I am God,
   be still and know that I am God.

2. I am the Lord that healeth thee,
   I am the Lord that healeth thee,
   I am the Lord that healeth thee.

3. In thee, O Lord, I put my trust,
   in thee, O Lord, I put my trust,
   in thee, O Lord, I put my trust.

*Anonymous*

# 34

1. Bethlehem! of noblest cities
   none can once with thee compare;
   thou alone the Lord from heaven
   didst for us incarnate bear.

2. Fairer than the sun at morning
   was the star that told his birth,
   to the lands their God announcing,
   hid beneath a form of earth.

3. By its lambent beauty guided,
   see the eastern kings appear;
   see them bend, their gifts to offer —
   gifts of incense, gold and myrrh.

4. Solemn things of mystic meaning!
   Incense doth the God disclose;
   gold a royal child proclaimeth;
   Myrrh a future tomb foreshows.

5. Holy Jesu, in thy brightness
   to the gentile world display'd,
   with the Father and the Spirit,
   endless praise to thee be paid.

*Aurelius Prudentius (348-413),*
*tr. E. Caswall*

# 35

1. Be thou my vision,
      O Lord of my heart,
   naught be all else to me
      save that thou art;
   thou my best thought
      in the day and night,
   waking or sleeping,
      thy presence my light.

2. Be thou my wisdom,
      be thou my true word,
   I ever with thee and
      thou with me, Lord;
   thou my great Father,
      and I thy true son;
   thou in me dwelling,
      and I with thee one.

3. Be thou my breast-plate,
   my sword for the fight,
   be thou my armour,
   and be thou my might,
   thou my soul's shelter,
   and thou my high tower,
   raise thou me heavenward,
   O Power of my power.

4. Riches I heed not,
   nor man's empty praise,
   thou mine inheritance
   through all my days;
   thou, and thou only,
   the first in my heart,
   high King of heaven,
   my treasure thou art!

5. High King of heaven
   when battle is done,
   grant heaven's joy to me,
   O bright heaven's sun;
   Christ of my own heart,
   whatever befall,
   still be my vision,
   O Ruler of all.

*Irish (8th C.), tr. Mary Byrne,*
*versified by Eleanor Hull*

# 36

1. Blest are the pure in heart,
   for they shall see our God;
   the secret of the Lord is theirs,
   their soul is Christ's abode.

2. The Lord who left the heavens
   our life and peace to bring,
   to dwell in lowliness with men,
   their pattern and their king.

3. Still to the lowly soul
   he doth himself impart
   and for his dwelling and his throne
   chooseth the pure in heart.

4. Lord, we thy presence seek;
   may ours this blessing be:
   give us a pure and lowly heart,
   a temple meet for thee.

*Verses 1 and 3 by John Keble*
*(1792-1866) verses 2 and 4 from*
*W. J. Hall's Psalms and Hymns (1836)*

# 37

1. Breathe on me, Breath of God,
   fill me with life anew,
   that I may love what thou dost love,
   and do what thou wouldst do.

2. Breathe on me, Breath of God,
   until my heart is pure:
   until with thee I have one will
   to do and to endure.

3. Breathe on me, Breath of God,
   till I am wholly thine,
   until this earthly part of me
   glows with thy fire divine.

4. Breathe on me, Breath of God,
   so shall I never die,
   but live with thee the perfect life
   of thine Eternity.

*Edwin Hatch (1835-89)*

# 38

1. Bring, all ye dear-bought nations,
   bring,
   your richest praises to your king,
   *alleluia, alleluia,*
   that spotless Lamb, who more than
   due,
   paid for his sheep, and those sheep
   you,
   *Alleluia.*

2. That guiltless Son, who bought
   your peace,
   and made his Father's anger cease,
   then, life and death together fought,
   each to a strange extreme were
   brought.

3. Life died, but soon revived again,
   and even death by it was slain.
   Say, happy Magdalen, oh, say,
   what didst thou see there by the
   way?

4. "I saw the tomb of my dear Lord,
I saw himself, and him adored,
I saw the napkin and the sheet,
that bound his head and wrapt his
feet."

5. "I heard the angels witness bear,
Jesus is ris'n; he is not here;
go, tell his followers they shall see,
thine and their hope in Galilee."

6. We, Lord, with faithful hearts and
voice,
on this thy rising day rejoice.
O thou, whose power o'ercame the
grave,
by grace and love us sinners save.

*Wipo (11th C.),
tr. Walter Kirkham Blount*

# 39

1. Bring flowers of the rarest,
bring blossoms the fairest,
from garden and woodland
and hillside and dale;
our full hearts are swelling,
our glad voices telling
the praise of the loveliest
flower of the vale.

*O Mary we crown thee
with blossoms today.
Queen of the Angels
and Queen of the May.
O Mary we crown thee
with blossoms today,
Queen of the Angels
and Queen of the May.*

2. Their lady they name thee,
their mistress proclaim thee.
Oh, grant that thy children
on earth be as true,
as long as the bowers
are radiant with flowers
as long as the azure shall
keep its bright hue.

3. Sing gaily in chorus,
the bright angels o'er us
re-echo the strains we
begin upon earth;
their harps are repeating
the notes of our greeting,
for Mary herself is the
cause of our mirth.

*Anonymous*

# 40

1. By the blood that flow'd from thee
in thy grievous agony;
by the traitor's guileful kiss,
filling up thy bitterness;

*Jesus, saviour, hear our cry;
thou wert suff'ring once as we:
now enthron'd in majesty
countless angels sing to thee.*

2. By the cords that, round thee cast,
bound thee to the pillar fast,
by the scourge so meekly borne,
by the purple robe of scorn.

3. By the thorns that crown'd thy
head,
by the sceptre of a reed;
by thy foes on bending knee,
mocking at thy royalty.

4. By the people's cruel jeers;
by the holy women's tears;
by thy footsteps, faint and slow,
weigh'd beneath thy cross of woe;

5. By thy weeping mother's woe;
by the sword that pierced her
through,
when in anguish standing by,
on the cross she saw thee die.

*Frederick William Faber (1814-63)*

## 41

1. Christ be beside me,
   Christ be before me,
   Christ be behind me,
   King of my heart.
   Christ be within me,
   Christ be below me,
   Christ be above me,
   never to part.

2. Christ on my right hand,
   Christ on my left hand,
   Christ all around me,
   shield in the strife.
   Christ in my sleeping,
   Christ in my sitting,
   Christ in my rising,
   light of my life.

3. Christ be in all hearts
   thinking about me,
   Christ be in all tongues
   telling of me.
   Christ be the vision
   in eyes that see me,
   in ears that hear me,
   Christ ever be.

*Adapted from 'St. Patrick's Breastplate'*
*by James Quinn, SJ.*

## 42

1. Christ is King of earth and heaven!
   Let his subjects all proclaim
   in the splendour of his temple
   honour to his holy name.

2. Christ is King! No soul created
   can refuse to bend the knee
   to the God made man who reigneth
   as 'twas promised, from the tree.

3. Christ is King! Let humble sorrow
   for our past neglect atone,
   for the lack of faithful service
   to the Master whom we own.

4. Christ is King! Let joy and gladness
   greet him; let his courts resound
   with the praise of faithful subjects
   to his love in honour bound.

5. Christ is King! In health and
                     sickness,
   till we breathe our latest breath,
   till we greet in highest heaven,
   Christ the victor over death.

*Ivor J. E. Daniel (1883-1967)*

## 43

*Christ is our king,*
   *let the whole world rejoice!*
*May all the nations*
   *sing out with one voice!*
*Light of the world,*
   *you have helped us to see*
*that all men are brothers*
   *and all men one day will be free.*

1. He came to open
      the eyes of the blind,
   letting the sunlight pour
      into their minds.
   Vision is waiting for
      those who have hope.
   He is the light of the world.

2. He came to speak
      tender words to the poor,
   he is the gateway and
      he is the door.
   Riches are waiting for all
      those who hope.
   He is the light of the world.

3. He came to open
      the doors of the gaol,
   he came to help the
      downtrodden and frail.
   Freedom is waiting for
      all those who hope.
   He is the light of the world.

4. He came to open
      the lips of the mute,
   letting them speak out
      with courage and truth.
   His words are uttered by
      all those who hope.
   He is the light of the world.

5. He came to heal all
      the crippled and lame,
   sickness took flight at the
      sound of his name.
   Vigour is waiting for
      all those who hope.
   He is the light of the world.

6. He came to love
      every man on this earth
   and through his Spirit he
      promised rebirth.
   New life is waiting for
      all those who hope.
   He is the light of the world.

*Estelle White*

# 44

1. Christ the Lord is risen today!
   Christians, haste your vows to pay,
   offer ye your praises meet
   at the paschal victim's feet;
   for the sheep the Lamb hath bled,
   sinless in the sinner's stead.
   Christ the Lord is ris'n on high;
   now he lives, no more to die.

2. Christ, the victim undefiled,
   man to God hath reconciled
   when in strange and awful strife
   met together death and life;
   Christians, on this happy day
   haste with joy your vows to pay.
   Christ the Lord is ris'n on high;
   Now he lives, no more to die.

3. Say, O wond'ring Mary, say,
   what thou sawest on thy way.
   "I beheld, where Christ had lain,
   empty tomb and angels twain,
   I beheld the glory bright
   of the rising Lord of light;
   Christ my hope is ris'n again;
   now he lives, and lives to reign."

4. Christ, who once for sinners bled,
   now the first-born from the dead,
   throned in endless might and
                             power,
   lives and reigns for evermore.
   Hail, eternal hope on high!
   Hail, thou king of victory!
   Hail, thou Prince of life adored!
   Help and save us, gracious Lord.

*Wipo 11th c., tr. Jane Elizabeth Leeson*

# 45

1. Colours of day
      dawn into the mind,
   the sun has come up,
      the night is behind.
   Go down in the city,
      into the street,
   and let's give the message
      to the people we meet.

   *So light up the fire*
      *and let the flame burn,*
   *open the door, let Jesus return.*
   *Take seeds of his Spirit,*
      *let the fruit grow,*
   *tell the people of Jesus,*
      *let his love show.*

2. Go through the park,
      on into the town;
   the sun still shines on
      it never goes down.
   The light of the world
      is risen again;
   the people of darkness
      are needing our friend.

3. Open your eyes,
      look into the sky,
   the darkness has come,
      the sun came to die.
   The evening draws on,
      the sun disappears,
   but Jesus is living,
      and his Spirit is near.

*Sue McClellan, John Pac*
*and Keith Ryecroft*

# 46

1. Come, adore this wondrous presence,
   bow to Christ, the source of grace.
   Here is kept the ancient promise
   of God's earthly dwelling-place.
   Sight is blind before God's glory,
   faith alone may see his face.

2. Glory be to God the Father,
   praise to his co-equal Son,
   adoration to the Spirit,
   bond of love, in Godhead one.
   Blest be God by all creation
   joyously while ages run.

*St. Thomas Aquinas (1227–74)*
*Translated by James Quinn, SJ.*
*See also no.375*

# 47

1. Come, Christian people,
   take heed what I say:
   Here, in this stable,
   your King was born today.

   *Star of wisdom, child of gladness,*
   *tell him all your troubles.*
   *Mary's boy has banished sadness,*
   *why be sorrowful now?*

2. Not much to look at
   – simply straw and hay –
   yet on that carpet
   your King was laid today.

3. Man, are you listening?
   Take heed what I say:
   Here on this planet
   your King still lives today.

*John Glynn*

# 48

*Come, come, come to the manger,*
*children, come*
*to the children's King;*
*sing, sing, chorus of Angels,*
*stars of morning o'er Bethlehem sing.*

1. He lies 'mid the beasts of the stall,
   who is Maker and Lord of us all;
   the wintry wind blows cold and
                                    dreary,
   see, he weeps, the world is weary;
   Lord, have pity and mercy on me!

2. He leaves all his glory behind,
   to be born and to die for mankind,
   with grateful beasts his cradle
                                    chooses,
   thankless man his love refuses;
   Lord, have pity and mercy on me!

3. To the manger of Bethlehem come,
   to the Saviour Emmanuel's home;
   the heav'nly hosts above are singing,
   set the Christmas bells a-ringing;
   Lord, have pity and mercy on me.

*Anonymous*

# 49

1. Come down, O love divine,
   seek thou this soul of mine,
   and visit it with thine own
        ardour glowing;
   O comforter, draw near,
   within my heart appear,
   and kindle it, thy holy
        flame bestowing.

2. O let it freely burn,
   till earthly passions turn
   to dust and ashes in its
        heat consuming;
   and let thy glorious light
   shine ever on my sight,
   and clothe me round, the while my
        path illuming.

3. Let holy charity
   mine outward vesture be,
   and lowliness become mine
        inner clothing;
   true lowliness of heart,
   which takes the humbler part,
   and o'er its own shortcomings
        weeps with loathing.

4. And so the yearning strong,
with which the soul will long,
shall far outpass the power of
human telling;
for none can guess its grace,
till he become the place
wherein the Holy Spirit
makes his dwelling.

*Bianco da Siena d.1434,*
*tr. Richard Frederick Littledale*

# 50

1. Come, Holy Ghost, Creator, come
from thy bright heavenly throne,
come, take possession of our souls,
and make them all thine own.

2. Thou who art called the Paraclete,
best gift of God above,
the living spring, the living fire,
sweet unction and true love.

3. Thou who art sev'nfold in thy grace,
finger of God's right hand;
his promise, teaching little ones
to speak and understand.

4. O guide our minds with thy blest
light,
with love our hearts inflame;
and with thy strength, which ne'er
decays,
confirm our mortal frame.

5. Far from us drive our deadly foe;
true peace unto us bring;
and through all perils lead us safe
beneath thy sacred wing.

6. Through thee may we the Father
know,
through thee th'eternal Son,
and thee the Spirit of them both,
thrice-blessed Three in One.

7. All glory to the Father be,
with his co-equal Son:
the same to thee, great Paraclete,
while endless ages run.

*Ascribed to Rabanus Maurus (776-856)*
*tr. Anonymous*

# 51

1. Come, Lord Jesus, come.
Come, take my hands,
take them for your work.
Take them for your service Lord.
Take them for your glory, Lord,
Come, Lord Jesus, come.
Come, Lord Jesus, take my hands.

2. Come, Lord Jesus, come.
Come, take my eyes,
may they shine with joy.
Take them for your service, Lord.
Take them for your glory, Lord.
Come, Lord Jesus, come.
Come, Lord Jesus, take my eyes.

3. Come, Lord Jesus, come.
Come, take my lips,
may they speak your truth.
Take them for your service, Lord.
Take them for your glory, Lord.
Come, Lord Jesus, come.
Come, Lord Jesus, take my lips.

4. Come, Lord Jesus, come.
Come take my feet,
may they walk your path.
Take them for your service, Lord.
Take them for your glory, Lord.
Come, Lord Jesus, come.
Come, Lord Jesus, take my feet.

5. Come, Lord Jesus, come.
Come, take my heart,
fill it with your love.
Take it for your service, Lord.
Take it for your glory, Lord.
Come, Lord Jesus, come.
Come, Lord Jesus, take my heart.

6. Come, Lord Jesus, come.
Come, take my life,
take it for your own.
Take it for your service, Lord.
Take it for your glory, Lord.
Come, Lord Jesus, come.
Come, Lord Jesus, take my life.

*Kevin Mayhew*

# 52

1. Come, my brothers, praise the Lord,
   alleluia.
   He's our God and we are his,
   alleluia.

2. Come to him with songs of praise,
   alleluia.
   Songs of praise, rejoice in him,
   alleluia.

3. For the Lord is a mighty God,
   alleluia.
   He is king of all the world,
   alleluia.

4. In his hands are valleys deep,
   alleluia.
   In his hands are mountain peaks,
   alleluia.

5. In his hands are all the seas,
   alleluia.
   And the lands which he has made,
   alleluia.

6. Praise the Father, praise the Son,
   alleluia.
   Praise the Spirit, the Holy One,
   alleluia.

*Traditional*

# 53

1. Come, praise the Lord, the almighty,
   the King of all nations!
   Tell forth his fame, O ye peoples,
   with loud acclamations!
   His love is sure;
   faithful his word shall endure,
   steadfast through all generations!

2. Praise to the Father most gracious,
   the Lord of creation!
   Praise to his Son, the Redeemer
   who wrought our salvation!
   O heav'nly Dove,
   praise to thee, fruit of their
   love.
   Giver of all consolation!

*Psalm 116,
versified by James Quinn, SJ.*

# 54

1. Come to the Lord
   and gather round his table.
   Gather round his table
   and come to the Lord.

2. Speak to the Lord
   and gather round his table.
   Gather round his table
   and speak to the Lord.

3. Sing to the Lord
   and gather round his table.
   Gather round his table
   and sing to the Lord.

4. Clap to the Lord
   and gather round his table.
   Gather round his table
   and clap to the Lord.

5. Dance to the Lord
   and gather round his table.
   Gather round his table
   and dance to the Lord.

*Estelle White*

# 55

1. Come, ye thankful people, come,
   raise the song of harvest-home!
   All be safely gathered in,
   ere the winter storms begin;
   God, our maker, doth provide
   for our wants to be supplied;
   come to God's own temple come;
   raise the song of harvest-home!

2. We ourselves are God's own field,
   fruit unto his praise to yield;
   wheat and tares together sown,
   unto joy or sorrow grown;
   first the blade and then the ear,
   then the full corn shall appear:
   grant, O harvest Lord, that we
   wholesome grain and pure may be.

3. For the Lord our God shall come,
   and shall take his harvest home;
   from his field shall purge away
   all that doth offend, that day,
   give his angels charge at last
   in the fire the tares to cast,
   but the fruitful ears to store
   in his garner evermore.

4. Then, thou Church triumphant,
                          come,
   raise the song of harvest-home;
   all be safely gathered in,
   free from sorrow, free from sin,
   there for ever purified
   in God's garner to abide:
   come, ten thousand angels, come,
   raise the glorious harvest-home!

   *Henry Alford (1810-71)*

# 56

1. Crown him with many crowns,
   the Lamb upon his throne;
   hark, how the heavenly anthem
                          drowns
   all music but its own:
   awake, my soul, and sing
   of him who died for thee,
   and hail him as thy matchless King
   through all eternity.

2. Crown him the Virgin's Son,
   the God incarnate born,
   whose arm those crimson trophies
                          won
   which now his brow adorn;
   fruit of the mystic rose,
   as of that rose the stem,
   the root, whence mercy ever flows,
   the babe of Bethlehem.

3. Crown him the Lord of love;
   behold his hands and side,
   rich wounds, yet visible above,
   in beauty glorified:
   no angel in the sky
   can fully bear that sight,
   but downward bends his burning eye
   at mysteries so bright.

4. Crown him the Lord of peace,
   whose power a sceptre sways,
   from pole to pole, that wars may
                          cease,
   absorbed in prayer and praise:
   his reign shall know no end,
   and round his pierced feet
   fair flowers of Paradise extend
   their fragrance ever sweet.

5. Crown him the Lord of heaven,
   one with the Father known,
   and the blest Spirit through him
                          given
   from yonder triune throne:
   all hail, Redeemer, hail,
   for thou hast died for me;
   thy praise shall never, never fail
   throughout eternity.

   *Matthew Bridges (1800-94)*

# 57

1. Daily, daily, sing to Mary,
   sing my soul, her praises due;
   all her feasts, her actions worship,
   with the heart's devotion true.
   Lost in wond'ring contemplation
   be her majesty confessed:
   call her Mother, call her Virgin,
   happy Mother, Virgin blest.

2. She is mighty to deliver;
   call her, trust her lovingly.
   When the tempest rages round thee,
   she will calm the troubled sea.
   Gifts of heaven she has given,
   noble Lady! to our race:
   she, the Queen, who decks her
                          subjects,
   with the light of God's own grace.

3. Sing, my tongue, the Virgin's
                          trophies,
   who for us her Maker bore;
   for the curse of old inflicted,
   peace and blessings to restore.
   Sing in songs of praise unending,
   sing the world's majestic Queen;
   weary not nor faint in telling
   all the gifts she gives to men.

4. All my senses, heart, affections,
strive to sound her glory forth;
spread abroad the sweet memorials,
of the Virgin's priceless worth,
where the voice of music thrilling,
where the tongues of eloquence,
that can utter hymns beseeming
all her matchless excellence?

5. All our joys do flow from Mary,
all then join her praise to sing;
trembling sing the Virgin Mother,
Mother of our Lord and King,
while we sing her awful glory,
far above our fancy's reach,
let our hearts be quick to offer
love the heart alone can teach.

*Ascribed to St. Bernard of Cluny*
*(12th c.), tr. Henry Bittleston*

# 58

*Day by day in the market place*
*I play my flute all day.*
*I have piped to them all,*
*but nobody dances.*
*Day by day in the market place*
*I play my flute all day,*
*and whoever you be,*
*won't you dance with me.*

1. At Cana, when my mother pleaded
that they were short of wine,
I gave them all the wine they needed;
their happiness was mine.

2. Once, when I found poor Peter
quaking,
I let him walk the sea.
I filled their fishing nets to breaking
that day in Galilee.

3. While all the world despised the
sinner
I showed him hope again,
and gave the honours at that dinner
to Mary Magdalene.

4. Lazarus from the tomb advancing
once more drew life's sweet breath.
You too will leave the churchyard
dancing,
for I have conquered death.

*Aimé Duval*

# 59

1. Day is done, but Love unfailing
dwells ever here;
shadows fall, but hope, prevailing,
calms every fear.
Loving Father, none forsaking,
take our hearts, of Love's own making,
watch our sleeping, guard our waking,
be always near!

2. Dark descends, but Light unending
shines through our night;
you are with us, ever lending
new strength to sight;
one in love, your truth confessing,
one in hope of heaven's blessing,
may we see, in love's possessing,
love's endless light!

3. Eyes will close, but you, unsleeping,
watch by our side;
death may come: in love's safe keeping
still we abide.
God of love, all evil quelling,
sin forgiving, fear dispelling,
stay with us, our hearts indwelling,
this eventide!

*James Quinn, SJ.*

# 60

1. Dear Lord and Father of mankind,
forgive our foolish ways!
Re-clothe us in our rightful mind,
in purer lives thy service find,
in deeper reverence praise,
in deeper reverence praise.

2. In simple trust like theirs who heard
beside the Syrian sea,
the gracious calling of the Lord,
let us, like them, without a word,
rise up and follow thee,
rise up and follow thee.

3. O Sabbath rest by Galilee!
   O calm of hills above,
   where Jesus knelt to share with thee
   the silence of eternity,
   interpreted by love!
   interpreted by love!

4. Drop thy still dews of quietness,
   till all our strivings cease;
   take from our souls the strain and
         stress,
   and let our ordered lives confess
   The beauty of thy peace,
   The beauty of thy peace.

5. Breathe through the heats of our
         desire
   thy coolness and thy balm;
   let sense be dumb, let flesh retire;
   speak through the earthquake, wind
         and fire,
   O still small voice of calm!
   O still small voice of calm!

   *John Greenleaf Whittier (1807-92)*

# 61

1. Dear maker of the starry skies,
   light of believers evermore,
   Jesu, redeemer of mankind,
   be near us who thine aid implore.

2. When man was sunk in sin and death,
   lost in the depth of Satan's snare,
   love brought thee down to cure our
         ills,
   by taking of those ills a share.

3. Thou for the sake of guilty men
   permitting thy pure blood to flow,
   didst issue from thy virgin shrine
   and to the cross a victim go.

4. So great the glory of thy might,
   if we but chance thy name to sound,
   at once all heaven and hell unite
   in bending low with awe profound.

5. Great judge of all, in that last day,
   when friends shall fail and foes
         combine,
   be present then with us, we pray,
   to guard us with thy arm divine.

6. To God the Father with the Son,
   and Holy Spirit, one and three,
   be honour, glory, blessing, praise,
   all through the long eternity.

   *7th c., tr. Edward Caswall*

# 62

1. Ding dong! merrily on high
   in heav'n the bells are ringing,
   ding dong! verily the sky
   is riv'n with angels singing.

   *Gloria, hosanna in excelsis!*

2. E'en so here below, below,
   let steeple bells be swungen,
   and io, io, io,
   by priest and people sungen.

3. Pray you, dutifully prime
   your matin chime, ye ringers;
   may you beautifully rime
   your evetime song, ye singers.

   *George Ratcliffe Woodward*
   *(1848-1934)*

# 63

*Do not worry over what to eat,*
*what to wear or put upon your feet.*
*Trust and pray,*
 *go do your best today,*
*then leave it in the hands*
 *of the Lord.*
*Leave it in the hands of the Lord.*

1. The lilies of the field,
    they do not spin or weave,
   yet Solomon was not
    arrayed like one of these.
   The birds of the air,
    they do not sow or reap,
   but God tends to them,
    like a shepherd tends his sheep.

2. The Lord will guide you
    in his hidden way,
  show you what to do
    and tell you what to say.
  When you pray for rain,
    go build a dam to store
  ev'ry drop of water
    you have asked him for.

3. The Lord knows all your
    needs before you ask.
  Only trust in him
    for he will do the task
  of bringing in your life
    whatever you must know.
  He'll lead you through the darkness
    wherever you must go.

*Sebastian Temple*

# 64

1. Do you know that the Lord
    walks on earth?
  Do you know he is living here now?
  He is waiting for all men
    to recognise him here.
  Do you know that the Lord
    walks on earth?

2. Do you know that he walks
    in disguise?
  Do you know he's in crowds
    ev'rywhere?
  Every place that you go,
    you may find that he is there.
  Do you know that the Lord's
    in disguise?

3. Do you know that the Lord
    thirsts so much?
  Do you know that he's sitting
    in jail?
  Ev'rywhere he is hungry
    and naked in the cold.
  Do you know he's rejected
    without care?

4. Do you know he is crucified
    each day?
  Do you know that he suffers
    and dies?
  Ev'rywhere he is lonely
    and waiting for a call.
  Do you know he is sick
    all alone?

5. Do you know that he wants
    to be free?
  Do you know he wants help
    from you and me?
  He has need of our hands
    and our feet and hearts to serve.
  Do you know he can work
    through men?

6. Do you know that the Lord
    dwells in men?
  Do you know he resides
    in their hearts?
  His face is shining
    in everyone we meet.
  Do you know he's disguised
    as ev'ry man?

7. Do you know that the Lord
    walks on earth?
  Do you know he is living here now?
  He is waiting for all men
    to recognise him here.
  Do you know he's disguised
    as ev'ry man?

*Sebastian Temple*

# 65

1. Draw nigh, and take
    the body of our Lord;
  and drink the holy blood
    for you outpoured;
  saved by that body,
    hallowed by that blood,
  whereby refreshed
    we render thanks to God.

2. Salvation's giver,
    Christ the only Son,
by that his cross and blood
    the victory won,
offered was he for
    greatest and for least;
himself the victim,
    and himself the priest.

3. Victims were offered
    by the law of old,
that, in a type,
    celestial mysteries told.
He, ransomer from
    death and light from shade,
giveth his holy grace
    his saints to aid.

4. Approach ye then with
    faithful hearts sincere,
and take the safeguard
    of salvation here,
he that in this world
    rules his saints and shields,
to all believers
    life eternal yields.

5. With heav'nly bread
    makes them that hunger whole,
gives living waters
    to the thirsty soul,
Alpha and Omega,
    to whom shall bow
all nations at the doom,
    is with us now.

*From the Antiphonary of Bennchar*
*(7th C.), tr. J. M. Neale*

# 66

1. Dust, dust, and ashes
    lie over on my grave.
Dust, dust and ashes
    lie over on my grave.
Dust, dust and ashes
    lie over on my grave,
and the Lord shall bear
    my spirit home,
and the Lord shall bear
    my spirit home.

2 They crucified my saviour
    and nailed him to the cross. . .

3. And Mary came a-running,
    her saviour for to see. . .

4. The angels said: "He's not here,
    he's gone to Galilee. . .

5. He rose, he rose, he rose up,
    he rose up from the dead. . .

*Traditional*

# 67

1. Eternal Father, strong to save,
whose arm doth bind the restless
                       wave,
who bidd'st the mighty ocean deep,
it's own appointed limits keep:
O hear us when we cry to thee
For those in peril on the sea.

2. O Saviour, whose almighty word
the winds and waves submissive
                       heard,
who walkedst on the foaming deep
and calm amid its rage didst sleep:
O hear us when we cry to thee
for those in peril on the sea.

3. O sacred Spirit, who didst brood
upon the waters dark and rude,
and bid their angry tumult cease,
and give, for wild confusion, peace:
O hear us when we cry to thee
for those in peril on the sea.

4. O Trinity of love and power,
our brethren shield in danger's hour.
From rock and tempest, fire and foe,
protect them whereso'er they go,
and ever let there rise to thee
glad hymns of praise from land and
                       sea.

*W. Whiting (1825-78)*

## 68

1. Faith of our fathers, living still
   in spite of dungeon, fire and sword;
   oh, how our hearts
   beat high with joy
   when e'er we hear that glorious
                                word!

   *Faith of our fathers! Holy Faith!*
   *We will be true to thee till death,*
   *we will be true to thee till death.*

2. Our fathers, chained in prisons dark,
   were still in heart
   and conscience free;
   how sweet would be their children's
                                fate,
   if they, like them, could die for thee!

3. Faith of our fathers, Mary's prayers,
   shall win our country back to thee;
   and through the truth
   that comes from God
   England shall then indeed be free.

4. Faith of our fathers, we will love
   both friend and foe in all our strife,
   and preach thee too,
   as love knows how,
   by kindly words and virtuous life.

   *Frederick William Faber (1814-63)*

## 69

1. Father and life-giver,
   grace of Christ impart;
   he, the word incarnate —
   food for mind and heart.
   Children of the promise,
   homage now we pay;
   sacrificial banquet
   cheers the desert way.

2. Wine and bread the symbols —
   love and life convey,
   offered by your people,
   work and joy portray.
   All we own consigning,
   nothing is retained;
   tokens of our service,
   gifts and song contain.

3. Transformation wondrous
   water into wine;
   mingled in the Godhead
   we are made divine.
   Birth into his body
   brought us life anew,
   total consecration —
   fruit from grafting true.

4. Christ, the head and members
   living now as one,
   offered to the Father
   by this holy Son;
   and our adoration
   purified we find,
   through the Holy Spirit
   breathing in mankind.

   *A. J. Newman*

## 70

1. Father most holy,
      merciful and loving,
   Jesu, redeemer,
      ever to be worshipped,
   life-giving Spirit,
      Comforter most gracious,
   God everlasting.

2. Three in a wondrous
      unity unbroken,
   one perfect Godhead,
      love that never faileth,
   light of the angels,
      succour of the needy,
   hope of all living.

3. All thy creation
      serveth its creator,
   thee every creature
      praiseth without ceasing,
   we too would sing thee
      psalms of true devotion:
   hear, we beseech thee.

4. Lord God almighty,
      unto thee be glory,
   one in three persons,
      over all exalted.
   Thine, as is meet,
      be honour, praise and blessing
   now and forever.

   *10th c., tr. A. E. Alston*

# 71

1. Father, within thy house today
   we wait thy kindly love to see:
   since thou hast said in truth that
   they
   who dwell in love are one with thee,
   bless those who for thy blessing
   wait;
   their love accept and consecrate.

2. Blest Spirit, who with life and light
   didst quicken chaos to thy praise,
   whose energy, in sin's despite,
   still lifts our nature up to grace,
   bless those who here in troth
   consent,
   Creator, crown thy sacrament.

3. Great one in three, of whom are
   named
   all families in earth and heaven,
   hear us, who have thy promise
   claimed,
   and let a wealth of grace be given,
   grant them in life and death to be
   each knit to each, and both to thee.

   *Robert Hugh Benson (1871-1914)*

# 72

*Feed us now, O Son of God,
as you fed them long ago.*

1. The people came to hear you,
   the poor, the lame, the blind.
   They asked for food to save them,
   you fed them body and mind.

2. The ones who didn't listen,
   the rich, the safe, the sure,
   they didn't think they needed
   the offering of a cure.

3. It's hard for us to listen,
   things haven't changed at all.
   We've got the things we wanted;
   we don't want to hear your call.

4. Yet millions still have hunger,
   disease, no homes, and fear.
   We offer them so little,
   and it costs them very dear.

5. So help us see the writing,
   written clear upon the wall:
   he who doesn't feed his neighbour
   will get no food at all.

   *Peter Allen*

# 73

1. Fight the good fight with all thy
   might,
   Christ is thy strength, and Christ
   thy right;
   lay hold on life and it shall be
   thy joy and crown eternally.

2. Run the straight race through God's
   good grace,
   lift up thine eyes and seek his face;
   life with its way before us lies,
   Christ is the path, and Christ the
   prize.

3. Cast care aside, upon thy Guide
   lean, and his mercy will provide
   lean, and the trusting soul shall prove
   Christ is its life, and Christ its love.

4. Faint not nor fear, his arms are near,
   he changeth not, and thou art dear;
   only believe, and thou shalt see
   that Christ is all in all to thee.

   *J. S. B. Monsell (1811-75)*

# 74

1. Fill my house unto the fullest.
   Eat my bread and drink my wine.
   The love I bear is held from no-one.

   *All I own
   and all I do
   I give to you.*

2. Take my time unto the fullest.
   Find in me the trust you seek,
   and take my hands to you
   outreaching.

3. Christ our Lord with love enormous
   from the cross his lesson taught
   — to love all men as I have loved you.

4. Join with me as one in Christ-love.
   May our hearts all beat as one,
   and may we give ourselves
                        completely.

*Peter Kearney*

# 75

1. Firmly I believe and truly
   God is three, and God is one,
   and I next acknowledge duly
   manhood taken by the Son.

2. And I trust and hope most fully
   in that manhood crucified;
   and each thought and deed unruly
   do to death, as he has died.

3. Simply to his grace and wholly
   light and life and strength belong;
   and I love supremely, solely,
   him the holy, him the strong.

4. And I hold in veneration,
   for the love of him alone,
   Holy Church, as his creation,
   and her teachings, as his own.

5. Adoration aye be given,
   with and through the angelic host,
   to the God of earth and heaven,
   Father, Son and Holy Ghost.

*John Henry Newman (1801-90)*

# 76

1. Follow Christ and love the world
       as he did,
   when he walked upon the earth.
   Love each friend and enemy
       as he did.
   In God's eyes we have equal worth.

2. Follow Christ and serve the world
       as he did
   when he ministered to ev'ryone.
   Serve each friend and enemy
       as he did
   so that the Father's will be done.

3. He said: "Love each other
       as I love you.
   By this all men will know you're mine.
   As I served you I ask that you do.
   This new commandment I assign."

4. Follow Christ and love the world
       as he did
   when he walked upon the earth.
   Love each friend and enemy
       as he did.
   In God's eyes we have equal worth.

*Sebastian Temple*

# 77

1. For all the saints
       who from their labours rest,
   who thee by faith
       before the world confest,
   thy name, O Jesus
       be for ever blest.

*Alleluia, alleluia!*

2. Thou wast their rock,
       their fortress, and their might;
   thou, Lord, their captain
       in the well-fought fight;
   thou in the darkness drear
       their one true light.

3. O may thy soldiers,
       faithful, true, and bold,
   fight as the saints who
       nobly fought of old,
   and win, with them,
       the victor's crown of gold.

4. O blest communion!
       fellowship divine!
   We feebly struggle,
       they in glory shine;
   yet all are one in thee,
       for all are thine.

5. And when the strife is fierce,
       the warfare long,
   steals on the ear the
       distant triumph-song,
   and hearts are brave again,
       and arms are strong.

6. The golden evening
        brightens in the west;
   soon, soon to faithful
        warriors cometh rest:
   sweet is the calm of
        paradise the blest.

7. But lo! there breaks a
        yet more glorious day;
   the saints triumphant
        rise in bright array:
   the king of glory
        passes on his way.

8. From earth's wide bounds,
        from ocean's farthest coast,
   through gates of pearl streams
        in the countless host,
   singing to Father,
        Son and Holy Ghost.

*William Walsham How (1823-97)*

# 78

1. Forth in the peace of Christ we go;
   Christ to the world with joy
        we bring;
   Christ in our minds, Christ on
        our lips,
   Christ in our hearts, the world's
        true King.

2. King of our hearts, Christ makes
        us kings;
   kingship with him his servants gain;
   with Christ, the Servant-Lord of all,
   Christ's world we serve to share
        Christ's reign.

3. Priests of the world, Christ sends
        us forth
   the world of time to consecrate,
   the world of sin by grace to heal,
   Christ's world in Christ to re-create.

4. Christ's are our lips, his word we
        speak;
   prophets are we whose deeds
        proclaim
   Christ's truth in love that we may be
   Christ in the world, to spread
        Christ's name.

5. We are the Church; Christ bids
        us show
   that in his Church all nations find
   their hearth and home where
        Christ restores
   true peace, true love, to all mankind.

*James Quinn, S.J.*
*(see also hymn 744)*

# 79

1. Forth in thy name, O Lord, I go,
   my daily labour to pursue;
   thee, only thee, resolved to know,
   in all I think or speak or do.

2. The task thy wisdom hath assigned
   O let me cheerfully fulfil;
   in all my works thy presence find,
   and prove thy good and perfect will.

3. Thee may I set at my right hand,
   whose eyes my inmost substance
                              see,
   and labour on at thy command,
   and offer all my works to thee.

4. Give me to bear thy easy yoke,
   and every moment watch and pray,
   and still to things eternal look,
   and hasten to thy glorious day;

5. For thee delightfully employ
   whate'er thy bounteous grace hath
                              given,
   and run my course with even joy,
   and closely walk with thee to
                              heaven.

*Charles Wesley (1707-88)*

# 80

1. Forty days and forty nights
   thou wast fasting in the wild;
   forty days and forty nights
   tempted still, yet unbeguiled:

2. Sunbeams scorching all the day,
   chilly dew-drops nightly shed,
   prowling beasts about thy way,
   stones thy pillow, earth thy bed.

3. Let us thy endurance share
   and from earthly greed abstain
   with thee watching unto prayer,
   with thee strong to suffer pain.

4. Then if evil on us press,
   flesh or spirit to assail,
   victor in the wilderness,
   help us not to swerve or fail!

5. So shall peace divine be ours;
   holier gladness ours shall be,
   come to us angelic powers,
   such as ministered to thee.

6. Keep, O keep us, Saviour dear,
   ever constant by thy side,
   that with thee we may appear
   at the eternal Eastertide.

*George Hunt Smyttan (1822-70)*
*and others*

# 81

1. From the deep I lift my voice,
   hear my cry, O God;
   listen, Lord, to my appeal,
   none but you can help.

2. If you count our grievous sins,
   no man will be spared,
   but your mercy still forgives,
   in your love we trust.

3. Night and day my spirit waits,
   longs to see my God,
   like a watchman, weary, cold,
   waiting for the dawn.

4. Open-handed is the Lord,
   swift to pardon us:
   he will lead his people free,
   clean from all their sins.

5. Glory be to God our Lord,
   merciful and kind,
   Father, Son and Holy Ghost,
   now and evermore.

*Paraphrased from Psalm 129*
*by Luke Connaughton (1919–79)*

# 82

1. From the depths we cry to thee,
   God of sovereign majesty!
   Hear our chants and hymns of
   
   praise;
   bless our Lent of forty days.

2. Though our consciences proclaim
   our transgressions and our shame,
   cleanse us, Lord, we humbly plead,
   from our sins of thought and deed.

3. Lord, accept our Lenten fast
   and forgive our sinful past,
   that we may partake with thee
   in the Easter mystery.

*Based on Psalm 129*
*by Sister M. Teresine*

# 83

1. Give me peace, O Lord, I pray,
   in my work and in my play,
   and inside my heart and mind,
   Lord, give me peace.

2. Give peace to the world, I pray,
   let all quarrels cease today.
   May we spread your light and love.
   Lord, give us peace.

*Estelle White*

# 84

1. Give me joy in my heart,
      keep me praising,
   give me joy in my heart I pray.
   Give me joy in my heart
      keep me praising.
   Keep me praising till the end of day.

   *Sing hosanna! Sing hosanna!*
   *Sing hosanna to the King of Kings!*
   *Sing hosanna! Sing hosanna!*
   *Sing hosanna to the King!*

2. Give me peace in my heart,
      keep me resting,
   give me peace in my heart I pray.
   Give me peace in my heart,
      keep me resting.
   Keep me resting till the end of day.

3. Give me love in my heart,
    keep me serving,
   give me love in my heart, I pray.
   Give me love in my heart,
    keep me serving,
   keep me serving till the end of day.

*Traditional*

# 85

1. Give me yourself
    O Jesus Christ my brother,
   give me yourself
    O Jesus Christ my Lord.

2. Give me your peace,
    O Jesus Christ my brother,
   give me your peace,
    O Jesus Christ my Lord.

3. Give me your love,
    O Jesus Christ my brother,
   give me your love,
    O Jesus Christ my Lord.

4. Give me your heart,
    O Jesus Christ my brother,
   give me your heart,
    O Jesus Christ my Lord.

*Estelle White*

# 86

1. Glorious God, King of creation,
   we praise you, we bless you,
    we worship you in song.
   Glorious God, in adoration,
   at your feet we belong.

   *Lord of life, Father almighty,*
   *Lord of hearts, Christ the King.*
   *Lord of love, Holy Spirit,*
   *to whom we homage bring.*

2. Glorious God, magnificent, holy,
   we love you, adore you,
    and come to you in pray'r.
   Glorious God, mighty, eternal,
   we sing your praise ev'rywhere.

*Sebastian Temple*

# 87

*Glory be to God, the King of kings.*
*Hosanna, hosanna!*
*Raise your voices*
*let the whole world sing.*
*Hosanna, hosanna.*

1. Praise him sun and moon and all that
   gives the world its light,
   planets and the galaxies and
   shooting stars at night.

2. Butterflies and silken moths and
   spiders in their webs,
   praise him streams and rounded
                              stones that
   line a river bed.

3. Praise him concrete, glass and steel
   that form a city's face,
   piston rods and generators,
   satellites in space.

4. Praise him all the oceans and the
   waves upon the shore,
   albatross and kittiwake and
   seagulls as they soar.

5. Praise him all you people from the
   near and distant lands,
   praise him for the fruitful earth,
   his loving gift to man.

   *Glory be to God, the King of kings.*
   *Hosanna, hosanna!*
   *Raise your voices*
    *let the whole world sing.*
   *Hosanna, hosanna, hosanna,*
    *hosanna, hosanna.*

*Estelle White*

# 88

1. Glory be to Jesus,
   who in bitter pains
   poured for me the life-blood,
   from his sacred veins.

2. Grace and life eternal
   in that blood I find:
   blest be his compassion,
   infinitely kind.

3. Blest through endless ages
   be the precious stream,
   which from endless torment
   doth the world redeem.

4. There the fainting spirit
   drinks of life her fill;
   there as in a fountain
   laves herself at will.

5. Abel's blood for vengeance
   pleaded to the skies,
   but the blood of Jesus
   for our pardon cries.

6. Oft as it is sprinkled
   on our guilty hearts,
   Satan in confusion
   terror-struck departs.

7. Oft as earth exulting
   wafts its praise on high,
   hell with horror trembles;
   heaven is filled with joy.

8. Lift ye, then, your voices;
   swell the mighty flood;
   louder still and louder,
   praise the precious blood.

   *18th c., tr. Edward Caswall*

# 89

1. Glory to God, glory to God,
   glory to the Father.
   Glory to God, glory to God,
   glory to the Father.
   To him be glory for ever.
   To him be glory for ever.
   Alleluia, amen.
   Alleluia, amen,
   alleluia, amen,
   alleluia, amen.

2. Glory to God, glory to God,
   Son of the Father.
   Glory to God, glory to God,
   Son of the Father.
   To him be glory for ever.
   To him be glory for ever.
   Alleluia, amen.
   Alleluia, amen,
   alleluia, amen,
   alleluia, amen.

3. Glory to God, glory to God,
   glory to the Spirit.
   Glory to God, glory to God,
   glory to the Spirit.
   To him be glory for ever.
   To him be glory for ever.
   Alleluia, amen.
   Alleluia, amen,
   alleluia, amen,
   alleluia, amen.

   *Peruvian*

# 90

1. Glory to thee, Lord God!
   in faith and hope we sing.
   Through this completed sacrifice
   our love and praise we bring.
   We give thee for our sins
   a price beyond all worth,
   which none could ever fitly pay
   but this thy Son on earth.

2. Here is the Lord of all,
   to thee in glory slain;
   of worthless givers, worthy gift
   a victim without stain.
   Through him we give thee thanks,
   with him we bend the knee,
   in him be all our life, who is
   our one true way to thee.

3. So may this sacrifice
   we offer here this day,
   be joined with our poor lives in all
   we think and do and say.
   By living true to grace,
   for thee and thee alone,
   our sorrows, labours, and our joys
   will be his very own.

*John Greally*

# 91

1. Glory to thee, my God, this night
   for all the blessings of the light;
   keep me, O keep me, King of kings,
   beneath thy own almighty wings.

2. Forgive me, Lord, for thy dear Son,
   the ill that I this day have done,
   that with the world, myself and
   thee,
   I, ere I sleep, at peace may be.

3. Teach me to live, that I may dread
   the grave as little as my bed;
   teach me to die, that so I may
   rise glorious at the awful day.

4. O may my soul on thee repose,
   and with sweet sleep mine eyelids
   close,
   sleep that may me more vigorous
   make
   to serve my God when I awake.

5. Praise God, from whom all blessings
   flow;
   praise him, all creatures here below;
   praise him above, ye heavenly host;
   praise Father, Son, and Holy Ghost.

*T. Ken (1637-1711)*

# 92

*Go, tell it on the mountain,*
*over the hills and ev'rywhere.*
*Go, tell it on the mountain*
*that Jesus Christ is born.*

1. While shepherds kept their watching
   o'er wand'ring flocks by night,
   behold from out of heaven
   there shone a holy light.

2. And lo, when they had seen it,
   they all bowed down and prayed,
   they travelled on together
   to where the Babe was laid.

3. When I was a seeker,
   I sought both night and day:
   I asked my Lord to help me
   and he showed me the way.

4. He made me a watchman
   upon the city wall,
   And if I am a Christian,
   I am the least of all.

*Traditional*

# 93

1. God be in my head, and in my
   understanding;
   God be in mine eyes, and in my
   looking;
   God be in my mouth, and in my
   speaking;
   God be in my heart, and in my
   thinking;
   God be at mine end, and at my
   departing.

*Book of Hours (1514)*

# 94

1. God everlasting, wonderful,
      and holy,
   Father most gracious,
      we who stand before thee
   here at thine altar,
      as thy Son has taught us,
   come to adore thee.

2. Countless the mercies thou hast
      lavished on us,
   source of all blessing
      to all creatures living;
   to thee we render,
      for thy love o'erflowing.
   Humble thanksgiving.

3. Now in remembrance of our
      great redeemer,
   dying on Calvary,
      rising and ascending,
   through him we offer
      what he ever offers,
   sinners befriending.

4. Strength to the living,
      rest to the departed,
   grant, Holy Father,
      through this pure oblation:
   may the life-giving
      bread for ever bring us
   health and salvation.

*Harold Riley*

# 95

1. Godhead here in hiding,
      whom I do adore,
   masked by these bare shadows,
      shape and nothing more,
   see, Lord, at thy service
      low lies here a heart
   lost, all lost in wonder
      at the God thou art.

2. Seeing, touching, tasting
      are in thee deceived;
   how says trusty hearing?
      That shall be believed;
   what God's Son hath told me,
      take for truth I do;
   truth himself speaks truly,
      or there's nothing true.

3. On the cross thy Godhead
      made no sign to men;
   here thy very manhood
      steals from human ken;
   both are my confession,
      both are my belief;
   and I pray the prayer
      of the dying thief.

4. I am not like Thomas,
      wounds I cannot see,
   but can plainly call thee
      Lord and God as he;
   this faith each day deeper
      be my holding of,
   daily make me harder
      hope and dearer love.

5. O thou our reminder
      of Christ crucified,
   living Bread, the life of
      us for whom he died,
   lend this life to me then;
      feed and feast my mind,
   there be thou the sweetness
      man was meant to find.

6. Jesu, whom I look at
      shrouded here below,
   I beseech thee send me
      what I long for so,
   some day to gaze on thee
      face to face in light
   and be blest for ever
      with thy glory's sight.

*Ascribed to St. Thomas Aquinas
(1227-74), tr. Gerard Manley Hopkins*

# 96

1. God is love
   and the one who lives in love
   lives in God,
   and God lives in him.
   And we have come to know
   and have believed
   the love which God has for us.
   God is love
   and the one who lives in love
   lives in God,
   and God lives in him.

2. God is hope . . .

3. God is peace . . .

4. God is joy . . .

*Anonymous*

# 97

1. God is love: his the care,
   tending each, everywhere.
   God is love, all is there!
   Jesus came to show him,
   that mankind might know him!

   *Sing aloud, loud, loud!*
   *Sing aloud, loud, loud!*
   *God is good!*
   *God is truth! God is beauty!*
   *Praise him!*

2. None can see God above;
   all have here man to love;
   thus may we Godward move,
   finding him in others,
   holding all men brothers:

3. Jesus lived here for men:
   strove and died, rose again,
   rules our hearts, now as then;
   for he came to save us
   by the truth he gave us:

4. To our Lord praise we sing,
   light and life, friend and king,
   coming down love to bring,
   pattern for our duty,
   showing God in beauty:

*Percy Dearmer (1867-1936)*

# 98

1. God of mercy and compassion,
   look with pity upon me;
   Father, let me call thee Father,
   'tis thy child returns to thee.

   *Jesus Lord, I ask for mercy;*
   *let me not implore in vain:*
   *all my sins I now detest them,*
   *never will I sin again.*

2. By my sins I have deserved
   death and endless misery,
   hell with all its pain and torments,
   and for all eternity.

3. By my sins I have abandon'd
   right and claim to heaven above,
   where the saints rejoice for ever,
   in a boundless sea of love.

4. See our Saviour, bleeding, dying,
   on the cross of Calvary;
   to that cross my sins have nail'd
   him,
   yet he bleeds and dies for me.

*E. Vaughan (1827-1908)*

# 99

1. God's spirit is in my heart.
   He has called me and set me apart.
   This is what I have to do,
   what I have to do.

   *He sent me to give*
   *the Good News to the poor,*
   *tell prisoners that they are*
   *prisoners no more,*
   *tell blind people that they can see,*
   *and set the downtrodden free,*
   *and go tell ev'ryone*
   *the news that the Kingdom of God*
   *has come,*
   *and go tell ev'ryone*
   *the news that God's kingdom*
   *has come.*

2. Just as the Father sent me,
   so I'm sending you out to be
   my witnesses throughout the world,
   the whole of the world.

3. Don't carry a load in your pack,
   you don't need two shirts on your
                                    back.
   A workman can earn his own keep,
   can earn his own keep.

4. Don't worry what you have to say,
   don't worry because on that day
   God's spirit will speak in your heart,
   will speak in your heart.

*Alan Dale*

# 100

1. Going home, going home,
   I'm a-going home.
   Quiet like, some still day,
   I'm just going home.
   It's not far, just close by,
   through an open door.
   Work all done, care laid by,
   going to fear no more.
   Mother's there expecting me,
   father's waiting too.
   Lots of folk gathered there,
   all the friends I knew,
   all the friends I knew.

2. Morning star lights the way,
   restless dreams all done.
   Shadows gone, break of day,
   real life just begun.
   There's no break, there's no end,
   just a living on,
   wide awake, with a smile,
   going on and on.
   Going home, going home,
   I'm just going home.
   It's not far, just close by,
   through an open door.
   I'm just going home.

*William Arms Fisher*

# 101

1. Gonna lay down
     my sword and shield
   down by the riverside,
   down by the riverside,
   down by the riverside,
   Gonna lay down
     my sword and shield
   down by the riverside.
   I ain't gonna study war no more.

   *I ain't gonna study war no more.*

2. Gonna walk with
     the Prince of Peace
   down by the riverside,
   down by the riverside,
   down by the riverside.
   Gonna walk with
     the Prince of Peace
   down by the riverside.
   I ain't gonna study war no more.

3. Gonna shake hands
     around the world
   down by the riverside,
   down by the riverside,
   down by the riverside.
   Gonna shake hands
     around the world
   down by the riverside.
   I ain't gonna study war no more.

*Traditional Spiritual*

# 102

1. Go, the Mass is ended,
   children of the Lord.
   Take his Word to others
   as you've heard it spoken to you.
   Go, the Mass is ended,
   go and tell the world
   the Lord is good, the Lord is kind,
   and he loves ev'ryone.

2. Go, the Mass is ended,
   take his love to all.
   Gladden all who meet you,
   fill their hearts with hope and
                              courage.
   Go, the Mass is ended,
   fill the world with love,
   and give to all what you've received
   — the peace and joy of Christ.

3. Go, the Mass is ended,
   strengthened in the Lord,
   lighten ev'ry burden,
   spread the joy of Christ around you.
   Go, the Mass is ended,
   take his peace to all.
   This day is yours to change the
                                world
   — to make God known and loved.

   *Sister Marie Lydia Pereira*

# 103

1. Great Saint Andrew, friend of Jesus,
   lover of his glorious cross,
   early by his voice effective
   called from ease to pain and loss,
   strong Saint Andrew, Simon's
                                brother,
   who with haste fraternal flew,
   fain with him to share the treasure
   which, at Jesus' lips, he drew.

2. Blest Saint Andrew, Jesus' herald,
   true apostle, martyr bold,
   who, by deeds his words confirming,
   sealed with blood the truth he told.
   Ne'er to king was crown so
                              beauteous,
   ne'er was prize to heart so dear,
   as to him the cross of Jesus
   when its promised joys drew near.

3. Loved Saint Andrew, Scotland's
                                patron,
   watch thy land with heedful eye,
   rally round the cross of Jesus
   all her storied chivalry!
   To the Father, Son, and Spirit,
   fount of sanctity and love,
   give we glory, now and ever,
   with the saints who reign above.

   *Frederick Oakeley (1802-80)*

# 104

1. Guide me, O thou great redeemer,
   pilgrim through this barren land;
   I am weak, but thou art mighty,
   hold me with thy powerful hand:
   Bread of heaven,
   feed me till I want no more.

2. Open now the crystal fountain,
   whence the healing stream doth
                              flow;
   let the fire and cloudy pillar
   lead me all my journey through;
   strong Deliverer,
   be thou still my strength and shield.

3. When I tread the verge of Jordan,
   bid my anxious fears subside,
   death of death, and hell's
                              destruction,
   land me safe on Canaan's side;
   songs of praises,
   I will ever give to thee.

   *W. Williams (1717-91),*
   *tr. P. and W. Williams*

# 105

1. Hail, glorious Saint Patrick,
      dear saint of our isle,
   on us thy poor children
      bestow a sweet smile;
   and now thou art high
      in the mansions above,
   on Erin's green valleys
   look down in thy love.
   *On Erin's green valleys,*
      *on Erin's green valleys,*
   *on Erin's green valleys*
      *look down in thy love.*

2. Hail, glorious Saint Patrick!
      thy words were once strong
   against Satan's wiles and
      an infidel throng;
   not less is thy might
      where in heaven thou art;
   O, come to our aid,
      in our battle take part.

3. In the war against sin,
      in the fight for the faith,
   dear saint, may thy children
      resist unto death;
   may their strength be in meekness,
      in penance, in prayer,
   Their banner the Cross
      which they glory to bear.

4. Thy people, now exiles
      on many a shore,
   shall love and revere thee
      till time be no more;
   and the fire thou hast kindled
      shall ever burn bright,
   Its warmth undiminished,
      undying its light.

5. Ever bless and defend the sweet
      land of our birth,
   where the shamrock still blooms
      as when thou wert on earth,
   and our hearts shall yet burn,
      wheresoever we roam,
   For God and Saint Patrick,
      and our native home.

*Sister Agnes*

# 106

1. Hail, Queen of heav'n, the ocean
                                    star,
   guide of the wand'rer here below;
   thrown on life's surge, we claim thy
                                    care;
   save us from peril and from woe.
   Mother of Christ, star of the sea,
   pray for the wanderer, pray for me.

2. O gentle, chaste and spotless maid,
   we sinners make our prayers
                              through thee;
   remind thy son that he has paid
   the price of our iniquity.
   Virgin most pure, star of the sea,
   pray for the sinner, pray for me.

3. Sojourners in this vale of tears,
   to thee, blest advocate, we cry;
   pity our sorrows, calm our fears,
   and soothe with hope our misery.
   Refuge in grief, star of the sea,
   pray for the mourner, pray for me.

4. And while to him who reigns above,
   in Godhead One, in Persons Three,
   the source of life, of grace, of love,
   homage we pay on bended knee,
   do thou, bright Queen, star of the
                                    sea,
   pray for thy children, pray for me.

*John Lingard (1771-1851)*

# 107

1. Hail, Redeemer, King divine!
   Priest and Lamb, the throne is thine,
   King, whose reign shall never cease,
   Prince of everlasting peace.

   *Angels, saints and nations sing:*
   *'Praised be Jesus Christ, our King;*
   *Lord of life, earth, sky and sea,*
   *King of love on Calvary.'*

2. King whose name creation thrills,
   rule our minds, our hearts, our wills,
   till in peace each nation rings
   with thy praises, King of kings.

3. King most holy, King of truth,
   guide the lowly, guide the youth;
   Christ thou King of glory bright,
   be to us eternal light.

4. Shepherd-King, o'er mountains steep,
   homeward bring the wandering
                              sheep,
   shelter in one royal fold
   states and kingdoms, new and old.

   *Patrick Brennan, C.Ss.R.,*
   *(1877-1951)*

8. Ever upward let us move,
   wafted on the wings of love;
   looking when our Lord shall come,
   longing, sighing after home.

   *Charles Wesley (1707-88), Thomas*
   *Cotterill (1779-1823) and others*

# 108

1. Hail the day that sees him rise,
                           *alleluia!*
   To his throne above the skies;
                           *alleluia!*
   Christ, the Lamb for sinners given,
                           *alleluia!*
   Enters now the highest heaven,
                           *alleluia!*

2. There for him high triumph waits;
   lift your heads, eternal gates!
   He hath conquered death and sin;
   take the king of glory in!

3. Circled round with angel-powers,
   their triumphant Lord and ours;
   wide unfold the radiant scene,
   take the king of glory in!

4. Lo, the heaven its Lord receives,
   yet he loves the earth he leaves;
   though returning to his throne,
   still he calls mankind his own.

5. See! he lifts his hands above,
   see! he shows the prints of love;
   hark! his gracious lips bestow,
   blessings on his Church below.

6. Still for us he intercedes,
   his prevailing death he pleads;
   near himself prepares our place,
   he the first-fruits of our race.

7. Lord, though parted from our sight,
   far above the starry height,
   grant our hearts may thither rise,
   seeking thee above the skies.

# 109

1. Hail, thou star of ocean,
   portal of the sky;
   ever virgin Mother
   of the Lord most high.
   Oh! by Gabriel's Ave,
   utter'd long ago,
   Eva's name reversing,
   'stablish peace below.

2. Break the captive's fetters,
   light on blindness pour,
   all our ills expelling,
   every bliss implore.
   Show thyself a mother;
   offer him our sighs,
   who for us incarnate
   did not thee despise.

3. Virgin of all virgins,
   to thy shelter take us;
   gentlest of the gentle,
   chaste and gentle make us.
   Still, as on we journey,
   help our weak endeavour;
   till with thee and Jesus
   we rejoice for ever.

4. Through the highest heaven,
   to the almighty Three,
   Father, Son and Spirit,
   One same glory be.

   *9th c., tr. Edward Caswall*

# 110

1. Hail to the Lord's anointed!
   Great David's greater son;
   hail, in the time appointed,
   his reign on earth begun!
   he comes to break oppression,
   to set the captive free;
   to take away transgression,
   and rule in equity.

2. He shall come down like showers
   upon the fruitful earth,
   and love, joy, hope, like flowers,
   spring in his path to birth:
   before him on the mountains
   shall peace the herald go;
   and righteousness in fountains
   from hill to valley flow.

3. Kings shall fall down before him,
   and gold and incense bring;
   all nations shall adore him,
   his praise all people sing;
   to him shall prayer unceasing
   and daily vows ascend;
   his kingdom still increasing
   a kingdom without end.

4. O'er every foe victorious,
   he on his throne shall rest,
   from age to age more glorious,
   all-blessing and all-blest;
   the tide of time shall never
   his covenant remove;
   his name shall stand for ever;
   that name to us is love.

   *James Montgomery (1771-1854)*

# 111

Happy the man
   who wanders with the Lord.
Happy the man
   who knows how to live.
Happy the man
   who never seeks reward,
giving because he loves to give.
He seeks no gold, he wants no gain.

He knows those things
   are all in vain.
He needs no praise nor honour, too.
His only motto:
   'To your own self be true.'
Happy the man
   who learned how to pray.
Happy the man
   who has a burning goal.
Happy the man
   whose service needs no pay.
This man has found his own soul.
Happy the man,
   happy the man of the Lord.

   *Sebastian Temple*

# 112

1. Hark! a herald voice is calling:
   'Christ is nigh' it seems to say;
   'Cast away the dreams of darkness,
   O ye children of the day!'

2. Startled at the solemn warning,
   let the earth-bound soul arise;
   Christ, her sun, all sloth dispelling,
   shines upon the morning skies.

3. Lo! the Lamb, so long expected,
   comes with pardon down from
                              heaven;
   let us haste, with tears of sorrow,
   one and all to be forgiven;

4. So when next he comes with glory,
   wrapping all the earth in fear,
   may he then as our defender
   on the clouds of heaven appear.

5. Honour, glory, virtue, merit,
   to the Father and the Son,
   with the co-eternal Spirit,
   while unending ages run.

   *6th c., tr. Edward Caswall*

# 113

1. Hark, the herald angels sing,
   glory to the new-born King;
   peace on earth and mercy mild,
   God and sinners reconciled:
   joyful all ye nations rise,
   join the triumph of the skies,
   with the angelic host proclaim,
   Christ is born in Bethlehem.

   *Hark, the herald Angels sing,*
   *glory to the new-born King.*

2. Christ, by highest heaven adored,
   Christ, the everlasting Lord,
   late in time behold him come,
   offspring of a Virgin's womb!
   Veiled in flesh the Godhead see,
   hail the incarnate Deity!
   Pleased as man with man to dwell,
   Jesus, our Emmanuel.

3. Hail the heaven-born Prince of
                              peace!
   Hail the Son of Righteousness!
   Light and life to all he brings
   risen with healing in his wings;
   mild he lays his glory by,
   born that man no more may die,
   born to raise the sons of earth,
   born to give them second birth.

   *Charles Wesley (1743),*
   *George Whitefield (1753),*
   *Martin Madan (1760), and others*

# 114

*Haul, haul away.*
*Haul, haul away.*
*Cast the nets wide*
   *and sink the nets deep*
*and it's haul, haul away.*

1. Oh, he sat in the boat
      and he spoke to the crowd.
   Haul, haul away.
   And his voice wasn't soft
      and his voice wasn't loud.
   Haul, haul away.
   And he spoke of the just
      and the pure and the free,
   and his voice caught the air
      like a net in the sea.
   And it's . . .

2. He said: "Cast your nets wide
      where the water is deep."
   Haul, haul away.
   "Oh, cast the nets wide
      and sink the nets deep."
   Haul, haul away.
   "Though we've worked through the
   night and we've nothing to show,
   we will try once again
      just because you say so."
   And it's . . .

3. Oh the catch it was huge
      and the boat it was small.
   Haul, haul away.
   His friends came to help
      when they heard Peter call.
   Haul, haul away.
   "You must leave us," said Peter,
      "for we're men of sin."
   But he said: "Come with me
      and be fishers of men."
   And it's . . .

   *Michael Cockett*

# 115

1. Help, Lord, the souls that thou hast
                                    made,
      the souls to thee so dear,
      in prison for the debt unpaid
      of sin committed here.

2. These holy souls, they suffer on,
   resigned in heart and will,
   until thy high behest is done,
   and justice has its fill.

3. For daily falls, for pardoned crime
they joy to undergo
the shadow of thy cross sublime,
the remnant of thy woe.

4. Oh, by their patience of delay,
their hope amid their pain,
their sacred zeal to burn away
disfigurement and stain;

5. Oh, by their fire of love, not less
in keenness than the flame;
oh, by their very helplessness,
oh, by thy own great name;

6. Good Jesus, help! sweet Jesus aid
the souls to thee most dear,
in prison for the debt unpaid
of sins committed here.

*John Henry Newman (1801-90)*

# 116

1. Here's a child for you, O Lord,
we shall cherish, we shall care.
We'll be faithful to your Word
for we want this child to share
your lovelight.

2. May he hold his head up high,
graceful, joyful, strong of limb.
May his eyes be clear and bright,
seeing beauty in all things
that you've made.

3. We were young ourselves, O Lord,
we were eager, we were fresh
like the opening buds of spring,
and we wanted happiness
in your way.

4. Then, at times, we went astray,
we were foolish, we were weak,
and the innocence we had
vanished like the trace of feet
when snow melts.

5. But we come, O Lord and king,
at your bidding, and we pray
that the precious gift we bring
will grow stronger every day
in your love.

6. By the water poured out here
and our promise, we believe,
he will master every fear,
and at last will come to see
your Godhead.

*Estelle White*

# 117

1. He's got the whole world
in his hand.
He's got the whole world
in his hand.
He's got the whole wide world
in his hand.
He's got the whole world
in his hand.

2. He's got you and me, brother . . .

3. He's got you and me, sister . . .

4. He's got everybody here . . .

5. He's got the whole world . . .

# 118    *Traditional*

1. He was born like you and I
in a body which must die,
yet his death was not for ever,
he lives on.
Who is this, like you and I
who was born to live and die,
yet his death was not for ever,
he lives on?

*Deep, deep, deep,*
*is the mystery I sing.*
*Dark, dark, dark is the riddle.*
*He was born like you and I*
*in a body which must die,*
*yet his death was not for ever:*
*he lives on.*

2. Not a soul, so it is said,
saw him raised up from the dead,
yet by now the story's known
throughout the world.
Who is this whom it is said
no one saw raised from the dead,
yet by now the story's known
throughout the world?

3. His believers, when they've met,
know he's there with them, and yet
he's with God (what makes us
    think that's somewhere else?)
Who is this who, when they've met,
is right there with them, and yet
he's with God (what makes us
    think that's somewhere else?)

*Hubert Richards*

# 119

1. He who would valiant be
'gainst all disaster,
let him in constancy
follow the master
there's no discouragement
shall make him once relent
his first avowed intent
to be a pilgrim.

2. Who so beset him round
with dismal stories,
do'but themselves confound:
his strength the more is.
No foes shall stay his might
though he with giants fight:
he will make good his right
to be a pilgrim.

3. Since, Lord, thou dost defend
us with thy Spirit,
we know we at the end
shall life inherit.
Then fancies flee away!
I'll fear not what men say,
I'll labour night and day
to be a pilgrim.

*Percy Dearmer (1867-1936),*
*after John Bunyan (1628-88)*

# 120

1. Holy Father, God of might,
throned amid the hosts of light,
take our life, our strength, our love,
King of earth and heaven above.

2. Hear the songs your people raise,
songs of joyful thanks and praise,
calling all created things
to adore you, King of kings.

3. Christ, be with us as we go,
let this blind world see and know,
burning in our lives, the sight
of its only saving light.

4. So, all men will bless your name,
and your kingship all proclaim,
praising with the heavenly host
Father, Son and Holy Ghost.

*Anonymous*

# 121

1. Holy God, we praise thy name;
Lord of all, we bow before thee!
All on earth thy sceptre own,
all in heaven above adore thee.
Infinite thy vast domain,
everlasting is thy reign.

2. Hark! the loud celestial hymn,
angel choirs above are raising;
cherubim and seraphim,
in unceasing chorus praising,
fill the heavens with sweet accord,
holy, holy, holy Lord.

3. Holy Father, holy Son,
Holy Spirit, three we name thee.
While in essence only one
Undivided God we claim thee;
and adoring bend the knee,
while we own the mystery.

4. Spare thy people, Lord, we pray,
by a thousand snares surrounded;
keep us without sin to-day;
never let us be confounded.
Lo, I put my trust in thee,
never, Lord, abandon me.

*C. A. Walworth (1820-1900)*

# 122

1. Holy, holy, holy, holy.
   Holy, holy, holy Lord
      God almighty.
   And we lift our hearts before you
      as a token of our love.
   Holy, holy, holy, holy.

2. Gracious Father, gracious Father,
   we are glad to be your children,
      gracious Father.
   And we lift our heads before you
      as a token of our love,
   gracious Father, gracious Father.

3. Precious Jesus, precious Jesus,
   we are glad you have redeemed us,
      precious Jesus.
   And we lift our hands before you
                as a token of our love,
   precious Jesus, precious Jesus.

4. Holy Spirit, Holy Spirit,
   come and fill our hearts anew,
      Holy Spirit.
   And we lift our voice before you
      as a token of our love,
   Holy Spirit, Holy Spirit.

5. Hallelujah, hallelujah,
   hallelujah, hallelujah,
      hallelujah.
   And we lift our hearts before you
      as a token of our love,
   hallelujah, hallelujah.

*Jimmy Owens*

# 123

1. Holy, holy, holy!
      Lord God almighty!
   Early in the morning
      our song shall rise to thee;
   holy, holy, holy!
      Merciful and mighty!
   God in three persons,
      blessed Trinity!

2. Holy, holy, holy!
      All the saints adore thee.
   Casting down their golden crowns
      around the glassy sea;
   Cherubim and seraphim
      falling down before thee,
   which wert, and art,
      and evermore shalt be.

3. Holy, holy, holy!
      Though the darkness hide thee,
   though the eye of sinful man
      thy glory may not see,
   only thou art holy,
      there is none beside thee,
   perfect in power,
      in love, and purity.

4. Holy, holy, holy!
      Lord God almighty!
   All thy works shall praise thy name,
      in earth, and sky, and sea;
   holy, holy, holy!
      Merciful and mighty!
   God in three persons,
      blessed Trinity!

*Reginald Heber (1783-1875)*

# 124

1. Holy Spirit, Lord of light,
   from the clear celestial height,
   thy pure beaming radiance give;
   come, thou Father of the poor,
   come with treasures which endure;
   come, thou light of all that live!

2. Thou, of all consolers best,
   thou, the soul's delightsome guest,
   dost refreshing peace bestow:
   thou in toil art comfort sweet;
   pleasant coolness in the heat;
   solace in the midst of woe.

3. Light immortal, light divine,
   visit thou these hearts of thine,
   and our inmost being fill:
   if thou take thy grace away,
   nothing pure in man will stay;
   all his good is turned to ill.

4. Heal our wounds, our strength
                            renew;
   on our dryness pour thy dew;
   wash the stains of guilt away:
   Bend the stubborn heart and will;
   melt the frozen, warm the chill;
   guide the steps that go astray.

5. Thou, on those who evermore
   thee confess and thee adore,
   in thy sevenfold gifts descend:
   Give them comfort when they die;
   give them life with thee on high;
   give them joys that never end.

*Ascribed to Stephen Langton (d.1228)*
                   *tr. Edward Caswall*

# 125

1. Holy Spirit of fire,
   flame everlasting,
       so bright and clear,
   speak this day in our hearts.
   Lighten our darkness
       and purge us of fear,
   Holy Spirit of fire.

   *The wind can blow or be still,*
   *or water be parched by the sun.*
   *A fire can die into dust:*
   *but here the eternal Spirit of God*
   *tells us a new world's begun.*

2. Holy Spirit of love,
   strong are the faithful
       who trust your pow'r.
   Love who conquer our will,
   teach us the words of
       the gospel of peace,
   Holy Spirit of love.

3. Holy Spirit of God,
   flame everlasting,
       so bright and clear,
   speak this day in our hearts.
   Lighten our darkness
       and purge us of fear,
   Holy Spirit of God.

                        *John Glynn*

# 126

1. Holy Virgin, by God's decree,
   you were called eternally;
   that he could give
       his Son to our race.
   Mary, we praise you,
       hail full of grace.

   *Ave, ave, ave, Maria.*

2. By your faith and loving accord,
   as the handmaid of the Lord,
   you undertook
       God's plan to embrace.
   Mary, we thank you,
       hail full of grace.

3. Refuge for your children so weak,
   sure protection all can seek.
   Problems of life
       you help us to face.
   Mary, we trust you,
       hail full of grace.

4. To our needy world of today
   love and beauty you portray,
   showing the path
       to Christ we must trace.
   Mary, our mother,
       hail, full of grace.

                        *J-P. Lécot*
           *tr. W. Raymond Lawrence*

# 127

1. How dark was the stable
       where Jesus was born?
   How dark was the stable
       that was his first home?
   It was dark as the sky
       on a black winter's night,
   when the stars will not shine
       and the moon gives no light.

2. How cold was the stable
       where Jesus was born?
   How cold was the stable
       that was his first home?
   It was cold as the frost
       on a white window pane;
   it was cold as a heart
       that has known no love.

3. How light was the stable
      when Jesus was born?
   How light was the stable
      he made his first home?
   It was light as the star
      that was shining that night;
   it was light as an angel
      in splendour and might.

4. How warm was the stable
      when Jesus was born?
   How warm was the stable
      he made his first home?
   It was warm as the love
      of that first Christmas morn;
   it was warm as our hearts
      in which Jesus is born.

                    *Michael Cockett*

# 128

1. I am the bread of life.
   He who comes to me
      will never be hungry.
   I will raise him up.
      I will raise him up.
   I will raise him up to eternal life.
   I am the bread of life.

2. I am the spring of life.
   He who hopes in me
      will never be thirsty.
   I will raise him up.
      I will raise him up.
   I will raise him up to eternal life.
   I am the spring of life.

3. I am the way of life.
   He who follows me
      will never be lonely.
   I will raise him up.
      I will raise him up.
   I will raise him up to eternal life.
   I am the way of life.

4. I am the truth of life.
   He who looks for me
      will never seek blindly.
   I will raise him up.
      I will raise him up.
   I will raise him up to eternal life.
   I am the truth of life.

5. I am the life of life.
   He who dies with me
      will never die vainly.
   I will raise him up.
      I will raise him up.
   I will raise him up to eternal life.
   I am the life of life.

                    *David Konstant*

# 129

1. I believe in God almighty,
   who made heav'n and earth.
   I believe in one Lord,
   Jesus Christ, his only Son.
   God from God and Light from Light,
   the one true God above,
   with the Father he is one,
   creator of all things.

   *Oh I believe in God almighty*
   *who made heav'n and earth.*
   *Yes, I believe in God almighty*
   *who made heav'n and earth.*

2. Through the Spirit, born of Mary,
   God became a man.
   For our sake he suffered death.
   They nailed him to a cross.
   But no earthly grave could hold
   the Lord of heav'n and earth;
   bursting forth he rose again,
   just as the prophets said.

3. Forty days he walked the earth,
   a dead man come alive.
   Then he bid his friends farewell,
   returning to his heav'n.
   He will come again to judge
   the living and the dead.
   He is Lord of all the worlds;
   his kingdom has no end.

4. I believe in God the Father,
   Spirit and the Son.
   I believe the Church is holy,
   universal, one.
   And through water all our guilt
   is cleansed—we are made new.
   Dying we will rise again
   to live for ever more.

                    *Kevin Mayhew*

# 130

1. I believe in God, the Father;
   I believe in God, his Son;
   I believe in God, their Spirit;
   each is God, yet God is one.

2. I believe what God has spoken
   through his Church, whose word is
        true;
   boldly she proclaims his Gospel,
   ever old, yet ever new.

3. All my hope is in God's goodness,
   shown for us by him who died,
   Jesus Christ, the world's Redeemer,
   spotless Victim crucified.

4. All my love is Love eternal;
   in that Love I love mankind.
   Take my heart, O Heart once broken,
   take my soul, my strength, my mind.

5. Father, I have sinned against you;
   look on me with eyes of love;
   seek your wand'ring sheep,
        Good Shepherd;
   grant heav'n's peace, O heav'nly Dove.

6. Bless'd be God, the loving Father;
   bless'd be God, his only Son;
   bless'd be God, all-holy Spirit;
   bless'd be God, for ever one.

*James Quinn, SJ.*

# 131

1. I danced in the morning
   when the world was begun,
   and I danced in the moon
   and the stars and the sun,
   and I came down from heaven and
   I danced on the earth,
   at Bethlehem
   I had my birth.

*Dance, then, wherever you may be,*
*I am the Lord of the Dance, said he.*
*And I'll lead you all*
     *wherever you may be,*
*and I'll lead you all*
     *in the dance, said he.*

2. I danced for the scribe
   and the pharisee,
   but they would not dance
   and they wouldn't follow me.
   I danced for the fishermen,
   for James and John;
   they came with me
   and the dance went on.

3. I danced on the Sabbath
   and I cured the lame.
   The holy people they
   said it was a shame.
   They whipped and they stripped
   and they hung me on high,
   and they left me there
   on the cross to die.

4. I danced on a Friday
   when the sky turned black.
   It's hard to dance
   with the devil on your back.
   They buried my body
   and they thought I'd gone
   but I am the dance
   and I still go on.

5. They cut me down
   and I leapt up high.
   I am the life
   that'll never, never die
   I'll live in you
   if you'll live in me.
   I am the Lord
   of the Dance, said he.

*Sydney Carter*

# 132

1. I'll sing a hymn to Mary,
   the Mother of my God,
   the Virgin of all virgins,
   of David's royal blood.
   O teach me, holy Mary,
   a loving song to frame,
   when wicked men blaspheme thee,
   to love and bless thy name.

2. O noble Tower of David,
   of gold and ivory,
   the Ark of God's own promise,
   the gate of heav'n to me,
   to live and not to love thee,
   would fill my soul with shame;
   when wicked men blaspheme thee,
   I'll love and bless thy name.

3. The Saints are high in glory,
   with golden crowns so bright;
   but brighter far is Mary,
   upon her throne of light.
   O that which God did give thee,
   let mortal ne'er disclaim;
   when wicked men blaspheme thee,
   I'll love and bless thy name.

4. But in the crown of Mary,
   there lies a wondrous gem,
   as Queen of all the Angels,
   which Mary shares with them:
   no sin hath e'er defiled thee,
   so doth our faith proclaim;
   when wicked men blaspheme thee,
   I'll love and bless thy name.

   *John Wyse (1825-98)*

# 133

1. Immaculate Mary!
   Our hearts are on fire,
   that title so wondrous
   fills all our desire.

   *Ave, ave, ave Maria!*
   *Ave, ave, ave Maria!*

2. We pray for God's glory,
   may his kingdom come!
   We pray for his vicar,
   our father, and Rome.

3. We pray for our mother
   the church upon earth,
   and bless, sweetest Lady,
   the land of our birth.

4. O Mary! O mother!
   Reign o'er us once more,
   be England thy 'dowry'
   as in days of yore.

5. We pray for all sinners,
   and souls that now stray
   from Jesus and Mary,
   in heresy's way.

6. For poor, sick, afflicted
   thy mercy we crave;
   and comfort the dying
   thou light of the grave.

7. There is no need, Mary,
   nor ever has been,
   which thou canst not succour,
   Immaculate Queen.

8. In grief and temptation,
   in joy or in pain,
   we'll ask thee, our mother,
   nor seek thee in vain.

9. O bless us, dear Lady,
   with blessings from heaven.
   And to our petitions
   let answer be given.

10. In death's solemn moment,
    our mother, be nigh;
    as children of Mary –
    O teach us to die.

11. And crown thy sweet mercy
    with this special grace,
    to behold soon in heaven
    God's ravishing face.

12. Now to God be all glory
    and worship for aye,
    and to God's virgin mother
    an endless Ave.

    *Anonymous*

# 134

1. Immortal, invisible,
      God only wise,
   in light inaccessible
      hid from our eyes,
   most blessed, most glorious,
      the Ancient of Days,
   almighty, victorious,
      thy great name we praise.

2. Unresting, unhasting,
      and silent as light;
   nor wanting, nor wasting,
      thou rulest in might —
   thy justice like mountains
      high-soaring above
   thy clouds which are fountains
      of goodness and love.

3. To all life thou givest,
      to both great and small;
   in all life thou livest,
      the true life of all;
   we blossom and flourish
      as leaves on the tree,
   and wither and perish;
      but naught changeth thee.

4. Great Father of glory,
      pure Father of light,
   thine angels adore thee,
      all veiling their sight;
   all laud we would render:
      O help us to see
   'tis only the splendour
      of light hideth thee.

   *W. Chalmers Smith (1825-1908)*
   *Based on 1 Tim. 1: 17*

# 135

1. In bread we bring you, Lord,
      our bodies' labour.
   In wine we offer you
      our spirits' grief.
   We do not ask you, Lord,
      who is my neighbour?
   But stand united now,
      one in belief.

Oh we have gladly heard
   your Word, your holy Word,
and now in answer, Lord,
   our gifts we bring.
Our selfish hearts make true,
   our failing faith renew,
our lives belong to you,
   our Lord and King.

2. The bread we offer you
      is blessed and broken,
   and it becomes for us
      our spirits' food.
   Over the cup we bring
      your Word is spoken;
   make it your gift to us,
      your healing blood.
   Take all that daily toil
      plants in our heart's poor soil
   take all we start and spoil,
      each hopeful dream,
   the chances we have missed,
      the graces we resist,
   Lord, in thy Eucharist,
      take and redeem.

   *Kevin Nichols*

# 136

1. In Christ there is no east or west,
   in him no south or north,
   but one great fellowship of love
   throughout the whole wide earth.

2. In him shall true hearts ev'rywhere
   their high communion find.
   His service is the golden cord
   close-binding all mankind.

3. Join hands, then, brothers of the
                              faith
   whate'er your race may be.
   Who serves my Father as a son
   is surely kin to me.

4. In Christ now meet both east and
                              west,
   in him meet south and north.
   All Christly souls are one in him
   throughout the whole wide earth.

   *John Oxenham (1852-1941)*

# 137

1. In the bleak midwinter,
   frosty wind made moan,
   earth stood hard as iron,
   water like a stone;
   snow had fallen, snow on snow,
   snow on snow,
   in the bleak midwinter
   long ago.

2. Our God, heaven cannot hold him
   nor earth sustain;
   Heaven and earth shall flee away,
   when he comes to reign.
   In the bleak midwinter
   a stable-place sufficed
   the Lord God Almighty,
   Jesus Christ.

3. Enough for him, whom Cherubim
   worship night and day,
   a breastful of milk,
   and a mangerful of hay:
   enough for him, whom angels
   fall down before,
   the ox and ass and camel
   which adore.

4. Angels and archangels
   may have gathered there,
   Cherubim and Seraphim
   thronged the air.
   But only his mother
   in her maiden bliss
   worshipped the beloved
   with a kiss.

5. What can I give him,
   poor as I am?
   If I were a shepherd
   I would bring a lamb;
   if I were a wise man
   I would do my part;
   yet what I can I give him —
   give my heart.

   *Christina G. Rossetti (1830-94)*

# 138

1. In the earth the small seed
      is hidden and
   lies unseen until
      it is bidden by
   springtime stirrings up
      to the sunlight and
   summer ripening.
   Golden is the harvest
      and precious the
   bread that you are,
   and give to us, Lord.

2. In the vineyard branches
      are cut away
   so that fresh young shoots
      may, with ev'ry day,
   bend beneath the fruit
      as it ripens and
   fills with promise.
   Golden is the harvest
      and precious the
   wine that you are
   and give to us, Lord.

3. In me, Oh my Lord, plant
      the seed of love
   nourished by your body
      and by your blood.
   May my soul take wings
      and rise upwards to
   new awakenings!
   Golden is the light of
      your Godhead that
   by love you have,
   and give to us, Lord.

   *Estelle White*

# 139

1. Into one we all are gathered
    through the love of Christ.
   Let us then rejoice with gladness.
       In him we find love.
   Let us fear and love the living God,
   and love and cherish all mankind.

   *Where charity and love are,*
       *there is God.*

2. Therefore, when we are together
    in the love of Christ,
   let our minds know no division,
       strife or bitterness;
   may the Christ our God be in our
                           midst.
   Through Christ our Lord all love is
                           found.

3. May we see your face in glory,
    Christ our loving God.
   With the blessed saints of heaven
    give us lasting joy.
   We will then possess true happiness,
   and love for all eternity.

   *Adapted from "Ubi Caritas et Amor"*
                   *by Michael Cockett*

# 140

1. I saw the grass, I saw the trees
    and the boats along the shore.
   I saw the shapes of many things
    I had only sensed before.
   And I saw the faces of men
       more clearly
   than if I had never been blind,
   the lines of envy around their lips
   and the greed
       and the hate in their eyes.
   And I turned away,
       yes, I turned away,
   for I had seen the perfect face
       of a real and proper man,
   the man who brought me
       from the dark
   into light, where life began.

2. I hurried then away from town
    to a quiet, lonely place.
   I found a clear, unruffled pool
    and I gazed upon my face.
   And I saw the image of me
       more clearly
   than if I had never been blind.
   The lines of envy around the lips
   and the greed
       and the hate in the eyes.
   And I turned away,
       yes, I turned away,
   for I had seen the perfect face
       of a real and proper man,
   the man who'd brought me
       from the dark
   into light, where life began.

3. I made my way into the town,
    to the busy, crowded streets,
   the shops and stalls and alley-ways,
    to the squalor and the heat.
   And I saw the faces of men
       more clearly
   than if I had never been blind,
   the lines of sorrow around their lips
   and the child
       looking out from their eyes,
   and I turned to them,
       yes, I turned to them,
   remembering the perfect face
       of a real and proper man,
   the man who'd brought me
       from the dark
   into light, where life began.

                           *Estelle White*

# 141

*I sing a song to you, Lord,*
*a song of love and praise.*
*All glory be to you, Lord,*
*through everlasting days.*

1. Holy, holy, holy,
    mighty Lord and God.
   He who was and is now,
   and who is to come.

2. Worthy is the slain Lamb,
   honour him and praise.
   We rejoice with gladness,
   sing our love today.

3. He has used his power,
   has begun his reign.
   So rejoice, you heavens,
   and proclaim his name.

4. Shine your light on us, Lord,
   let us know your way.
   Be our guide for ever,
   make us yours today.

*Richard Beaumont*

# 142

1. I sing the Lord God's praises,
   I answer to his call.
   His servant-girl he raises,
   she will be blessed by all.
   The Lord God gives his power
   to her who loves his name;
   o'er her his strength will tower,
   his mercies will remain.

2. Proud-hearted men he scatters,
   the strong will pass away;
   and for the kind and gentle
   there dawns the Lord's own day.
   Woe to the rich and mighty!
   He feeds and satisfies
   those who for justice hunger,
   and to him turn their eyes.

3. A Saviour he had promised
   to Abram long ago;
   and now to his own people
   his mercy he will show.
   Come let us praise our Father,
   for he fulfils his word,
   and sends his Holy Spirit
   through Jesus Christ our Lord.

*W. F. Harwood*

# 143

1. It came upon the midnight clear,
   that glorious song of old,
   from angels bending near the earth
   to touch their harps of gold;
   'Peace on the earth, good will to men,
   from heaven's all-gracious King!

The world in solemn stillness lay
to hear the angels sing.

2. Yet with the woes of sin and strife
   the world has suffered long;
   beneath the angel-strain have rolled
   two thousand years of wrong;
   and man, at war with man, hears not
   the love-song which they bring:
   O hush the noise, ye men of strife,
   and hear the angels sing!

3. For lo, the days are hastening on,
   by prophets seen of old,
   when with the ever-circling years
   shall come the time foretold,
   when the new heaven and earth
                              shall own
   the prince of peace their king,
   and all the world send back the song
   which now the angels sing.

*E. H. Sears (1810-76)*

# 144

*It's me, it's me, it's me, O Lord,
standin' in the need of pray'r.
It's me, it's me it's me, O Lord,
standin' in the need of pray'r.*

1. Not my brother or my sister,
       but it's me, O Lord,
   standin' in the need of prayer.
   Not my brother or my sister,
       but it's me, O Lord,
   standin' in the need of pray'r.

2. Not my mother or my father,
       but it's me, O Lord,
   standin' in the need of prayer.
   Not my mother or my father,
       but it's me, O Lord,
   standin' in the need of pray'r.

3. Not the stranger or my neighbour,
       but it's me, O Lord,
   standin' in the need of prayer.
   Not the stranger or my neighbour,
       but it's me, O Lord,
   standin' in the need of pray'r.

*Traditional Spiritual*

# 145

1. I watch the sunrise
lighting the sky,
casting its shadows near.
And on this morning
bright though it be,
I feel those shadows near me.

*But you are always*
*close to me*
*following all my ways.*
*May I be always*
*close to you*
*following all your ways, Lord.*

2. I watch the sunlight
shine through the clouds,
warming the earth below.
And at the mid-day
life seems to say:
"I feel your brightness near me."
*For you are always ...*

3. I watch the sunset
fading away,
lighting the clouds with sleep.
And as the evening
closes its eyes
I feel your presence near me.
*For you are always ...*

4. I watch the moonlight
guarding the night,
waiting till morning comes.
The air is silent,
earth is at rest —
only your peace is near me.
*Yes, you are always ...*

*John Glynn*

# 146

1. I will give you glory,
O God, my King.
I will bless your name for ever.
I will bless you day, after day.

*Day after day, after day, after day,*
*after day, after day, after day.*

2. I will sing your praises,
O God, my King.
I will bless your name for ever.
I will bless you day, after day.

3. I will give you honour,
O God, my King.
I will bless your name for ever.
I will bless you day, after day.

*Malcolm Campbell-Carr*

# 147

1. I wonder as I wander
out under the sky,
how Jesus the Saviour
did come for to die
for poor ord'n'ry people
like you and like I.
I wonder as I wander
out under the sky.

2. When Mary birthed Jesus,
'twas in a cow's stall
with wise men and farmers
and shepherds and all.
But high from God's heaven
a star's light did fall,
and the promise of ages
it did then recall.

3. If Jesus had wanted
for any wee thing,
a star in the sky, or
a bird on the wing,
or all of God's angels
in heav'n for to sing,
he surely could have it,
'cause he was the king.

*Traditional*

# 148

1. January brings the snow,
   and the white frost glistens;
   I'm a child full of love,
   speak, Lord, and I'll listen.

2. March means sun and wind and rain,
   springtime flowers dancing.
   I am young, growing fast,
   wanting all the answers.

3. Maytime blossoms fill the air,
   here's a time for pleasure!
   Keep me safe, O my Lord,
   in my work and leisure.

4. In July the trees are tall,
   butterflies are roving.
   In my prime, may I be
   faithful in my loving.

5. In September's golden fields
   harvesters are reaping,
   and my mind gathers in
   mem'ries worth the keeping.

6. In November there are mists
   jewelling the grasses.
   Now my steps lose their spring;
   how each moment passes!

7. Come December days grow short
   and they say my life's through;
   but, my Lord, it's been good,
   and I want to thank you.

*Estelle White*

# 149

1. Jerusalem the golden,
   with milk and honey blest,
   beneath thy contemplation
   sink heart and voice oppressed.
   I know not, ah, I know not
   what joys await us there,
   what radiancy of glory,
   what bliss beyond compare.

2. They stand, those halls of Sion,
   all jubilant with song,
   and bright with many an angel,
   and all the martyr throng;
   the prince is ever in them,
   the daylight is serene;
   the pastures of the blessed
   are decked in glorious sheen.

3. There is the throne of David;
   and there, from care released,
   the shout of them that triumph,
   the song of them that feast;
   and they, who with their leader
   have conquered in the fight,
   for ever and for ever
   are clad in robes of white.

4. O sweet and blessed country,
   the home of God's elect!
   O sweet and blessed country
   that eager hearts expect!
   Jesus, in mercy bring us
   to that dear land of rest;
   who art, with God the Father
   and Spirit, ever blest.

*From 'De Contemptu Mundi'*
*Bernard of Cluny (12th C.)*
*tr. J.M. Neale*

# 150

1. Jesu, lover of my soul!
   Let me to thy bosom fly,
   while the nearer waters roll,
   while the tempest still is high;
   hide me, O my Saviour, hide,
   till the storm of life is past;
   safe into the haven guide,
   O receive my soul at last.

2. Other refuge have I none;
   hangs my helpless soul on thee;
   leave, ah! leave me not alone,
   still support and comfort me.
   All my trust on thee is stayed,
   all my help from thee I bring;
   cover my defenceless head
   with the shadow of thy wing.

3. Thou, O Christ, art all I want;
   more than all in thee I find;
   raise the fallen, cheer the faint,
   heal the sick and lead the blind,
   just and holy is thy name;
   I am all unrighteousness;
   false and full of sin I am,
   thou art full of truth and grace.

4. Plenteous grace with thee is found,
   grace to cover all my sin
   let the healing streams abound;
   make and keep me pure within.
   Thou of life the fountain art,
   freely let me take of thee;
   spring thou up within my heart,
   rise to all eternity.

   *Charles Wesley (1707-88)*

# 151

1. Jesu, meek and lowly,
   Saviour, pure and holy,
   on thy love relying,
   come I to thee flying.

2. Prince of life and power,
   my salvation's tower,
   on the cross I view thee,
   calling sinners to thee.

3. There behold me gazing
   at the sight amazing;
   bending low before thee,
   helpless I adore thee.

4. See the red wounds streaming,
   with Christ's life-blood gleaming,
   blood for sinners flowing,
   pardon free bestowing,

5. Fountains rich in blessing,
   Christ's fond love expressing,
   thou my aching sadness
   turnest into gladness.

6. Lord in mercy guide me,
   be thou e'er beside me,
   In thy ways direct me,
   'neath thy wings protect me.

   *A. H. Collins (1827-1919)*

# 152

1. Jesu, the very thought of thee
   with sweetness fills my breast;
   but sweeter far thy face to see,
   and in thy presence rest.

2. Nor voice can sing, nor heart can
                                 frame,
   nor can the memory find,
   a sweeter sound than thy blest name,
   O Saviour of mankind.

3. O hope of every contrite heart,
   O joy of all the meek,
   to those who fall, how kind thou art,
   how good to those who seek!

4. But what to those who find? Ah, this
   nor tongue nor pen can show;
   the love of Jesus, what it is
   none but his lovers know.

5. Jesu, our only joy be thou,
   as thou our prize wilt be;
   Jesu, be thou our glory now,
   and through eternity.

   *11th c.,tr. Edward Caswall*

# 153

1. Jesus Christ is risen today,
      alleluia!
   Our triumphant holy day,
      alleluia!
   Who did once, upon the cross,
      alleluia!
   Suffer to redeem our loss,
      alleluia!

2. Hymns of praise then let us sing,
      alleluia!
   Unto Christ, our heavenly king,
      alleluia!
   Who endured the cross and grave,
      alleluia!
   Sinners to redeem and save,
      alleluia!

3. But the pains that he endured,
      alleluia!
   Our salvation have procured;
      alleluia!

Now above the sky he's king,
alleluia!
Where the angels ever sing,
alleluia!

*Lyra Davidica (1708) and the
Supplement (1816).
Based partly on 'Surrexit Christus
hodie. (14th c.)*

# 154

1. Jesus, gentlest Saviour,
   God of might and power,
   thou thyself art dwelling
   in us at this hour.
   Nature cannot hold thee,
   heav'n is all too strait
   for thine endless glory,
   and thy royal state.

2. Yet the hearts of children,
   hold what worlds cannot,
   and the God of wonders
   loves the lowly spot.
   Jesus, gentlest Saviour,
   thou art in us now,
   fill us full of goodness,
   till our hearts o'erflow.

3. Pray the prayer within us
   that to heaven shall rise;
   sing the song that angels
   sing above the skies;
   multiply our graces,
   chiefly love and fear;
   and, dear Lord, the chiefest,
   grace to persevere.

*Frederick William Faber (1814-63)*

# 155

1. Jesus, Lord, I'll sing a song
   that's soft and low for you,
   so you can join with me
   and sing it too.
   You have said that when we pray,
   then you are praying too,
   and when your Father hears us,
   he hears you.

*Our Father who art in heaven,
hallowed be thy name,
hallowed be thy name.*

2. I believe that you are here
   with me and praying too.
   Your Father loves me
   because I love you.
   Jesus, Lord, I'll sing a song that's
   soft and low for you,
   so you can join with me
   and sing it too.

*Briege O'Hare*

# 156

1. Jesus is God! The solid earth,
   the ocean broad and bright,
   the countless stars, the golden dust,
   that strew the skies at night,
   the wheeling storm, the dreadful
   fire,
   the pleasant wholesome air,
   the summer's sun, the winter's frost,
   his own creations were.

2. Jesus is God! the glorious bands
   of golden angels sing
   songs of adoring praise to him,
   their maker and their king.
   He was true God in Bethlehem's
   crib,
   on Calvary's cross true God,
   he who in heaven eternal reigned,
   in time on earth abode.

3. Jesus is God! Let sorrow come,
   and pain and every ill;
   all are worth while, for all are means
   his glory to fulfil;
   worth while a thousand years of life
   to speak one little word,
   if by our Credo we might own
   the Godhead of our Lord.

*Frederick William Faber (1814-63)*

# 157

1. Jesus, my Lord, my God, my all,
   how can I love thee as I ought?
   And how revere this wondrous gift
   so far surpassing hope or thought?

   *Sweet Sacrament, we thee adore;*
   *Oh, make us love thee more and*
   *more.*

2. Had I but Mary's sinless heart
   to love thee with, my dearest King,
   Oh, with what bursts of fervent
   praise
   thy goodness, Jesus, would I sing!

3. Ah, see! within a creature's hand
   the vast Creator deigns to be,
   reposing, infant-like, as though
   on Joseph's arm, or Mary's knee.

4. Thy body, soul, and Godhead, all;
   O mystery of love divine!
   I cannot compass all I have,
   for all thou hast and art are mine;

5. Sound, sound, his praises higher
   still,
   and come, ye angels, to our aid;
   'tis God, 'tis God, the very God
   whose power both man and angels
   made.

   *Frederick William Faber (1814-63)*

# 158

1. Jesus! thou art coming,
   holy as thou art,
   thou, the God who made me,
   to my sinful heart.
   Jesus! I believe it,
   on thy only word;
   kneeling, I adore thee,
   as my king and Lord.

2. Who am I, my Jesus,
   that thou com'st to me?
   I have sinned against thee,
   often grievously;
   I am very sorry
   I have caused thee pain.
   I will never, never,
   wound thy heart again.

3. Put thy kind arms round me,
   feeble as I am;
   thou art my Good Shepherd,
   I, thy little lamb;
   since thou comest, Jesus,
   now to be my guest,
   I can trust thee always,
   Lord, for all the rest.

4. Dearest Lord, I love thee,
   with my whole heart,
   not for what thou givest,
   but for what thou art.
   Come, oh, come, sweet Saviour!
   Come to me, and stay,
   for I want thee, Jesus,
   more than I can say.

5. Ah! what gift or present,
   Jesus, can I bring?
   I have nothing worthy
   of my God and King;
   but thou art my shepherd:
   I, thy little lamb,
   take myself, dear Jesus,
   all I have and am.

6. Take my body, Jesus,
   eyes, and ears and tongue;
   never let them, Jesus,
   help to do thee wrong.
   Take my heart, and fill it
   full of love for thee;
   all I have I give thee,
   give thyself to me.

   *'S.N.D.'*

## 159

1. Just a closer walk with thee,
   grant it, Jesus if you please;
   daily walking close to thee,
   let it be, dear Lord, let it be.

2. Through the day of toil that's near,
   if I fall, dear Lord, who cares.
   Who with me my burden share?
   None but thee, dear Lord, none but
   thee.

3. When my feeble life is o'er,
   time for me will be no more.
   Guide me gently, safely on
   to the shore, dear Lord, to the
   shore.

*Traditional*

## 160

1. Keep we the fast that men of old
   learned from on high in mystic
   ways,
   till yonder sun hath duly told
   his hallowed tale of forty days.

2. This covenant, long since revealed
   to patriarchs and ardent seers,
   Christ by his own example sealed,
   author of time, and Lord of years.

3. More wisely therefore let us walk,
   sparing of food and wine and sleep;
   over our trifles and our talk
   more jealous be the watch we keep.

4. Still by our sins, O Lord, we grieve
   thy love, so full of pardon free:
   author of mercy, still reprieve
   the souls that turn again to thee.

5. Remember whence our fashion
   came,
   frail creatures, yet thy creatures still,
   crush, for the glory of thy name,
   the murm'rings of our stubborn will.

6. The guilt that dooms us put away,
   with larger grace our prayers
   requite,
   at last, and ever from this day,
   teach us to live as in thy sight.

7. Hear us, O Trinity sublime,
   and undivided unity;
   so let this consecrated time
   bring forth thy fruits abundantly.

*St. Gregory the Great (540-604)*
*tr. R. A. Knox*

## 161

1. King of glory, king of peace,
   I will love thee;
   and that love may never cease,
   I will move thee.
   Thou hast granted my request,
   thou hast heard me;
   thou didst note my working breast,
   thou hast spared me.

2. Wherefore with my utmost art,
   I will sing thee.
   And the cream of all my heart
   I will bring thee,
   though my sins against me cried,
   thou didst clear me;
   and alone, when they replied,
   thou didst hear me.

3. Seven whole days, not one in seven,
   I will praise thee;
   in my heart, though not in heaven,
   I can raise thee.
   Small it is, in this poor sort
   to enrol thee:
   e'en eternity's too short
   to extol thee.

*George Herbert (1593-1633)*

# 162

1. Kum ba yah, my Lord,
   kum ba yah,
   kum ba yah, my Lord,
   kum ba yah!
   Kum ba yah, my Lord,
   kum ba yah!
   O Lord, kum ba yah.

2. Someone's crying, Lord,
   kum ba yah,
   someone's crying, Lord,
   kum ba yah!
   Someone's crying, Lord,
   kum ba yah!
   O Lord, kum ba yah.

3. Someone's singing, Lord,
   kum ba yah,
   someone's singing, Lord,
   kum ba yah!
   Someone's singing, Lord,
   kum ba yah!
   O Lord, kum ba yah.

4. Someone's praying, Lord,
   kum ba yah,
   someone's praying, Lord,
   kum ba yah!
   Someone's praying, Lord,
   kum ba yah!
   O Lord, kum ba yah.

*Spiritual*

# 163

1. Leader now on earth no longer,
   soldier of th'eternal king,
   victor in the fight for heaven,
   we thy loving praises sing.

   *Great Saint George,*
   *our patron, help us,*
   *in the conflict be thou nigh;*
   *help us in that daily battle,*
   *where each one must win or die.*

2. Praise him who in deadly battle
   never shrank from foeman's sword,
   proof against all earthly weapon,
   gave his life for Christ the Lord.

3. Who, when earthly war was over,
   fought, but not for earth's renown;
   fought, and won a nobler glory,
   won the martyr's purple crown.

4. Help us when temptation presses,
   we have still our crown to win,
   help us when our soul is weary
   fighting with the powers of sin.

5. Clothe us in thy shining armour,
   place thy good sword in our hand;
   teach us how to wield it, fighting
   onward towards the heavenly land.

6. Onward, till, our striving over,
   on life's battlefield we fall,
   resting then, but ever ready,
   waiting for the angel's call.

*Joseph W. Reeks (1849-1900)*

# 164

1. Lead, kindly light
         amid th'encircling gloom,
   lead thou me on;
      the night is dark,
         and I am far from home,
   lead thou me on.
   Keep thou my feet;
         I do not ask to see
   the distant scene;
         one step enough for me.

2. I was not ever thus,
         nor prayed that thou
   shouldst lead me on;
   I loved to choose
         and see my path; but now
   lead thou me on.
   I loved the garish day,
         and, spite of fears,
   pride ruled my will;
         remember not past years.

3. So long thy power
   hath blest me, sure it still
   will lead me on
   o'er moor and fen,
      o'er crag and torrent, till
   the night is gone,
   and with the morn
      those angel faces smile
   which I have loved
      long since, and lost awhile.

   *John Henry Newman (1801-90)*

# 165

1. Lead us, heav'nly Father, lead us
   o'er the world's tempestuous sea:
   guard us, guide us, keep us, feed us,
   for we have no help but thee;
   yet possessing ev'ry blessing
   if our God our Father be.

2. Saviour, breathe forgiveness o'er us,
   all our weakness thou dost know,
   thou didst tread this earth before us,
   thou didst feel its keenest woe;
   lone and dreary, faint and weary,
   through the desert thou didst go.

3. Spirit of our God, descending,
   fill our hearts with heavenly joy,
   love with every passion blending,
   pleasure that can never cloy;
   thus provided, pardoned, guided,
   nothing can our peace destroy.

   *J. Edmeston (1791-1867)*

# 166

1. Let all mortal flesh keep silence
   and with fear and trembling stand,
   ponder nothing earthly-minded:
   for with blessing in his hand,
   Christ our God on earth descendeth,
   our full homage to demand.

2. King of kings, yet born of Mary,
   as of old on earth he stood
   Lord of lords, in human vesture –
   in the Body and the Blood.
   He will give to all the faithful
   his own Self for heavenly Food.

3. Rank on rank the host of heaven
   spreads its vanguard on the way,
   as the Light of Light descendeth
   from the realms of endless day,
   that the powers of hell may vanish
   as the darkness clears away.

4. At his feet the six-winged Seraph;
   Cherubim with sleepless eye,
   veil their faces to the Presence,
   as with ceaseless voice they cry,
   alleluia, alleluia,
   alleluia, Lord most high.

   *Liturgy of St. James (5th Century)*
   *tr. G. Moultrie (1829–85)*

# 167

1. Let all that is within me cry holy.
   Let all that is within me cry holy.
   Holy, holy, holy
      is the Lamb that was slain.

2. Let all that is within me cry mighty.
   Let all that is within me cry mighty.
   Mighty, mighty, mighty
      is the Lamb that was slain.

3. Let all that is within me cry worthy.
   Let all that is within me cry worthy.
   Worthy, worthy, worthy
      is the Lamb that was slain.

4. Let all that is within me cry blessed.
   Let all that is within me cry blessed.
   Blessed, blessed, blessed
      is the Lamb that was slain.

5. Let all that is within me cry Jesus.
   Let all that is within me cry Jesus.
   Jesus, Jesus, Jesus
      is the Lamb that was slain.

   *Traditional*

# 168

1. Let all the world
   in every corner sing,
   my God and King!
   The heav'ns are not too high,
   his praise may thither fly;
   the earth is not too low,
   his praises there may grow.
   Let all the world
   in every corner sing,
   my God and King!

2. Let all the world
   in every corner sing,
   my God and King!
   The church with psalms must shout,
   no door can keep them out;
   but, above all, the heart
   must bear the longest part.
   Let all the world
   in every corner sing,
   my God and King!

   *George Herbert (1593-1633)*

# 169

1. Let us break bread together
   on our knees.
   Let us break bread together
   on our knees.
   When I fall on my knees
   with my face to the rising sun,
   Oh Lord, have mercy on me.

2. Let us drink wine together . . .

3. Let us praise God together . . .

   *Traditional*

# 170

1. Let's make peace in our hearts.
   Let's make peace in our hearts.
   Let's make true peace in our hearts.
   Let's make true peace in our hearts.

2. Let's take peace into the world.
   Let's take peace into the world.
   Let's take true peace into the world.
   Let's take true peace into the world.

3. Let's share peace with ev'ryone.
   Let's share peace with ev'ryone.
   Let's share true peace with ev'ryone.
   Let's share true peace with ev'ryone.

4. My peace I leave with you.
   My peace I give to you.
   Not as the world gives do I give,
   but true peace I give unto you.

   *Sebastian Temple*

# 171

1. Let us, with a gladsome mind,
   praise the Lord, for he is kind;

   *For his mercies aye endure,
   ever faithful, ever sure.*

2. Let us blaze his name abroad,
   for of gods he is the God;

3. He, with all-commanding might,
   filled the new-made world with
   light;

4. He the golden-tressed sun
   caused all day his course to run:

5. And the horned moon at night,
   'mid her spangled sisters bright:

6. All things living he doth feed,
   his full hand supplies their need:

7. Let us, with a gladsome mind,
   praise the Lord, for he is kind.

   *John Milton (1608-75),
   based on Ps. 136*

# 172

1. Light of our darkness, Word of God,
   sent to illumine our earthly night,
   you we salute with singing hearts,
   bathed in the splendour of your
   light.

2. Sword that can pierce the inmost
   soul,
   stripping whatever thoughts are
   there,
   cut to the marrow of our minds,
   enter our hearts and lay them bare.

3. Vessel of God's abundant life,
   bearer of truth that sets us free,
   breaking the deadly grasp of sin,
   work in our hearts your mystery.

4. Word that has overcome the world,
   seed of immortal destiny,
   grow in our hearts, that we may live
   sharing your deathless victory.

*Richard Connolly*

# 173

1. Little flower in the ground,
   petals falling all around.
   Summer's past and Autumn's here
   and now we know your end is near.

2. Seeds that fall on to the ground
   by the winds are scattered round.
   Some will feed the Winter birds,
   and some will nestle in the earth.

3. Some will last the Winter through
   'till the Spring makes all things new.
   See the flower newly grown
   from seeds the Winter wind has
   sown.

4. Praise the Lord in heav'n above,
   who shows us all the way of love.
   Praise him for the dying year.
   If Winter comes then Spring is near.

*Michael Cockett*

# 174

1. Little Jesus, sweetly sleep,
   do not stir;
   we will lend a coat of fur,
   we will rock you,
   rock you, rock you,
   we will rock you,
   rock you, rock you,
   see the fur to keep you warm
   snugly round your tiny form.

2. Mary's little baby sleep,
   sweetly sleep,
   sleep in comfort, slumber deep;
   we will rock you,
   rock you, rock you,
   we will rock you,
   rock you, rock you,
   we will serve you all we can,
   darling , darling little man.

*Czech., tr. O.B.C.*

# 175

1. Long ago in Bethlehem,
   you were lying in a manger
   in the midst of human danger,
   at your mother's knee.
   Hosanna, alleluia,
   hosanna, alleluia,
   hosanna, alleluia,
   at your mother's knee.

2. Now as King we hail the baby,
   living faith proclaims the story
   of that humble manger glory,
   stabled in the hay.
   Hosanna, alleluia,
   hosanna, alleluia,
   hosanna, alleluia,
   Christ is King today.

*Ian Sharp*

## 176

1. Look down, O Mother Mary,
   from thy bright throne above;
   cast down upon thy children
   one only glance of love;
   and if a heart so tender
   with pity flows not o'er,
   then turn away, O Mother,
   and look on us no more.

   *Look down O Mother Mary,*
   *from thy bright throne above,*
   *cast down upon thy children,*
   *one only glance of love.*

2. See how, ungrateful sinners,
   we stand before thy Son;
   his loving heart upbraids us
   the evil we have done,
   but if thou wilt appease him,
   speak for us but one word;
   for thus thou canst obtain us
   the pardon of Our Lord.

3. O Mary, dearest Mother,
   if thou wouldst have us live,
   say that we are thy children,
   and Jesus will forgive.
   Our sins make us unworthy
   that title still to bear,
   but thou art still our mother;
   then show a mother's care.

4. Unfold to us thy mantle,
   there stay we without fear;
   what evil can befall us
   if, mother, thou art near?
   O kindest, dearest mother
   thy sinful children save;
   look down on us with pity,
   who thy protection crave.

   *St. Alphonsus (1696-1787),*
   *tr. Edmund Vaughan*

## 177

1. Lord accept the gifts we offer
   at this Eucharistic feast,
   bread and wine to be transformed
                                   now
   through the action of thy priest
   take us too, Lord, and transform us,
   be thy grace in us increased.

2. May our souls be pure and spotless
   as the host of wheat so fine;
   may all stain of sin be crushed out,
   like the grape that forms the wine,
   as we, too, become partakers,
   in this sacrifice divine.

3. Take our gifts, almighty Father,
   living God, eternal, true,
   which we give through Christ, our
                                   Saviour,
   pleading here for us anew
   grant salvation to all present,
   and our faith and love renew.

   *Sister M. Teresine*

## 178

1. Lord, for tomorrow and its needs
   I do not pray;
   keep me, my God, from stain of sin,
   just for today.

2. Let me both diligently work
   and duly pray;
   let me be kind in word and deed,
   just for today.

3. Let me be slow to do my will,
   prompt to obey;
   help me to mortify my flesh,
   just for today.

4. Let me no wrong or idle word
   unthinking say;
   set thou a seal upon my lips,
   just for today.

5. Let me in season, Lord, be grave,
   in season, gay;
   let me be faithful to thy grace,
   just for today.

6. And if today my tide of life
   should ebb away,
   give me thy sacraments divine,
   sweet Lord, today.

7. So, for tomorrow and its needs
   I do not pray;
   but keep me, guide me, love me,
                                   Lord,
   just for today.

   *Sister M. Xavier*

# 179

1. Lord, Jesus Christ,
   you have come to us
   you are one with us, Mary's son.
   Cleansing our souls from all their sin,
   pouring your love and goodness in,
   Jesus our love for you we sing,
   living Lord.

2. Lord Jesus Christ,
   now and ev'ry day
   teach us how to pray, Son of God.
   You have commanded us to do
   this in remembrance, Lord, of you
   Into our lives your pow'r breaks
                                  through,
   living Lord.

3. Lord Jesus Christ,
   you have come to us,
   born as one of us, Mary's Son.
   Led out to die on Calvary,
   risen from death to set us free,
   living Lord Jesus, help us see
   you are Lord.

4. Lord Jesus Christ,
   I would come to you,
   live my life for you, Son of God.
   All your commands I know are true,
   your many gifts will make me new,
   into my life your pow'r breaks
                                  through,
   living Lord.

   *Patrick Appleford*

# 180

1. Lord Jesus, think on me,
   and purge away my sin;
   from earthborn passions set me free,
   and make me pure within.

2. Lord Jesus, think on me,
   with care and woe oppressed;
   let me thy loving servant be,
   and taste thy promised rest.

3. Lord Jesus, think on me
   amid the battle's strife;
   in all my pain and misery
   be thou my health and life.

4. Lord Jesus, think on me,
   nor let me go astray;
   through darkness and perplexity
   point thou the heavenly way.

5. Lord Jesus, think on me,
   when flows the tempest high:
   when on doth rush the enemy,
   O Saviour, be thou nigh.

6. Lord Jesus, think on me,
   that, when the flood is past,
   I may the eternal brightness see,
   and share thy joy at last.

   *Bishop Synesius (375-430)*
   *tr. A. W. Chatfield*

# 181

1. Lord of all hopefulness,
   Lord of all joy,
   whose trust, ever child-like,
   no cares could destroy,
   be there at our waking,
   and give us, we pray,
   your bliss in our hearts, Lord,
   at the break of the day.

2. Lord of all eagerness,
   Lord of all faith,
   whose strong hands were skilled
   at the plane and the lathe,
   be there at our labours,
   and give us, we pray,
   your strength in our hearts, Lord,
   at the noon of the day.

3. Lord, of all kindliness,
   Lord of all grace,
   your hands swift to welcome,
   your arms to embrace,
   be there at our homing,
   and give us, we pray,
   your love in our hearts, Lord,
   at the eve of the day.

4. Lord of all gentleness,
   Lord of all calm,
   whose voice is contentment,
   whose presence is balm,
   be there at our sleeping,
   and give us, we pray,
   your peace in our hearts, Lord,
   at the end of the day.

   *Jan Struther (1901-53)*

# 182

1. Lord, we pray for golden peace,
   peace all over the land,
   may all men dwell in liberty,
   all walking hand in hand.

   *Banish fear and ignorance,*
   *hunger, thirst and pain.*
   *Banish hate and poverty,*
   *let no man live in vain,*
   *let no man live in vain.*

2. Keep all men for ever one,
   one in love and in grace.
   And wipe away all war and strife,
   give freedom to each race.

3. Let your justice reign supreme.
   Righteousness always done.
   Let goodness rule the hearts of men
   and evil overcome.

   *Sebastian Temple*

# 183

1. Lord, who throughout these forty
                              days
   for us didst fast and pray,
   teach us with thee to mourn our sins,
   and at thy side to stay.

2. As thou with Satan didst contend,
   and didst the victory win,
   O give us strength in thee to fight,
   in thee to conquer sin.

3. As thirst and hunger thou didst bear,
   so teach us, gracious Lord,
   to die to self, and daily live
   by thy most holy word.

4. And through these days of
                              penitence,
   and through thy Passiontide,
   yea, evermore, in life and death,
   Lord Christ, with us abide.

   *Claudia Frances Hernaman (1838-98)*

# 184

1. Love divine, all loves excelling,
   joy of heaven, to earth come down,
   fix in us thy humble dwelling,
   all thy faithful mercies crown.

2. Jesus, thou art all compassion,
   pure unbounded love thou art;
   visit us with thy salvation,
   enter every trembling heart.

3. Come, almighty to deliver,
   let us all thy life receive;
   suddenly return, and never,
   never more thy temples leave.

4. Thee we would be always blessing,
   serve thee as thy hosts above;
   pray, and praise thee without
                              ceasing,
   glory in thy perfect love.

5. Finish then thy new creation,
   pure and sinless let us be;
   let us see thy great salvation
   perfectly restored in thee.

6. Changed from glory into glory,
   till in heaven we take our place,
   till we cast our crowns before thee,
   lost in wonder, love, and praise.

   *Charles Wesley (1707-88)*

# 185

1. Love is his word, love is his way,
feasting with men, fasting alone,
living and dying, rising again,
love, only love, is his way.

*Richer than gold
is the love of my Lord:
better than splendour and wealth.*

2. Love is his way, love is his mark,
sharing his last Passover feast,
Christ at his table, host to the
Twelve,
love, only love, is his mark.

3. Love is his mark, love is his sign,
bread for our strength, wine for our
joy,
"This is my body, this is my blood,"
love, only love, is his sign.

4. Love is his sign, love is his news,
"Do this," he said, "lest you forget
all my deep sorrow, all my dear
blood,"
love, only love, is his news.

5. Love is his news, love is his name,
we are his own, chosen and called,
family, brethren, cousins and kin.
Love, only love, is his name.

6. Love is his name, love is his law.
Hear his command, all who are his:
"Love one another, I have loved
you."
Love, only love, is his law.

7. Love is his law, love is his word:
love of the Lord, Father and Word,
love of the Spirit, God ever one,
love, only love, is his word.

*Luke Connaughton (1919–79)*

# 186

1. Loving Father, from thy bounty
choicest gifts unnumbered flow:
all the blessings of salvation,
which to Christ thy Son we owe,
all the gifts that by thy bidding
nature's hands on us bestow!

2. Here thy grateful children gather,
offering gifts of bread and wine;
these we give to thee in homage,
of our love the loving sign,
and restore to thee creation,
given to man, yet ever thine!

3. Soon will come Christ's loving
presence,
on our love to set his seal!
Body broken, Blood shed for us,
bread and wine will then reveal!
bread and wine, though these no
longer,
flesh and blood will yet conceal!

*James Quinn, S.J.*

# 187

1. Loving shepherd of thy sheep,
keep me, Lord, in safety keep;
nothing can thy pow'r withstand,
none can pluck me from thy hand.

2. Loving shepherd, thou didst give
thine own life that I might live;
may I love thee day by day,
gladly thy sweet will obey.

3. Loving shepherd, ever near,
teach me still thy voice to hear;
suffer not my steps to stray
from the strait and narrow way.

4. Where thou leadest may I go,
walking in thy steps below;
then before thy Father's throne,
Jesu, claim me for thine own.

*Jane E. Leeson (1807-82)*

# 188

1. Maiden, yet a mother,
   daughter of thy Son,
   high beyond all other,
   lowlier is none;
   thou the consummation
   planned by God's decree,
   when our lost creation
   nobler rose in thee!

2. Thus his place prepared,
   he who all things made
   'mid his creatures tarried,
   in thy bosom laid;
   there his love he nourished,
   warmth that gave increase
   to the root whence flourished
   our eternal peace.

3. Noon on Sion's mountain
   is thy charity;
   hope its living fountain
   finds, on earth, in thee:
   lady, such thy power,
   he, who grace would buy
   not as of thy dower,
   without wings would fly.

   *Dante Alighieri (1265-1321)*
   *tr. R. A. Knox*

# 189

1. Make me a channel of your peace.
   Where there is hatred,
       let me bring your love.
   Where there is injury,
       your pardon, Lord.
   And where there's doubt,
       true faith in you.

2. Make me a channel of your peace.
   Where there's despair in life,
       let me bring hope.
   Where there is darkness
       only light,
   and where there's sadness
       ever joy.

3. Oh, Master,
       grant that I may never seek
   so much to be consoled
       as to console,
   to be understood as to understand,
   to be loved, as to love,
       with all my soul.

4. Make a channel of your peace.
   It is in pardoning
       that we are pardoned,
   in giving to all men
       that we receive,
   and in dying that we're
       born to eternal life.

   *Sebastian Temple*

# 190

1. Man of Galilee
   will you come and stand by me
   through the length of each working
       day?
   Bless, O Lord, my efforts, I pray.

2. Man who healed the blind
   open up the eyes of my mind
   to the needs of my fellow man.
   Help me give with open hands.

3. Man of bread and of wine
   show me by the means of this sign
   that I share your life and your light
   with the neighbour here at my side.

4. Man of Calvary
   give me strength and will to be free
   of the weight of self-pity's chains,
   then my trials will be but gains.

5. Man at God's right hand,
   will you help me understand
   that in you, when my breath is
       stilled,
   all my longings will be fulfilled?

   *Estelle White*

# 191

1. Many times I have turned
     from the way of the Lord,
   many times
     I have chosen the darkness.
   In the light of the day,
     when the shadows are gone,
   all I see is my sin
     in its starkness.

   *Jesus came to bring us mercy.*
   *Jesus came to bring us life again.*
   *He loves us, he loves us, he loves us!*

2. I confess I have sinned
     in the sight of the Lord,
   through my pride,
     through my malice and weakness.
   I've rejected the promise
     that comes from the cross
   **where the Lord hung above**
     **us in meekness.**

3. With a word, with a deed,
     with a failure to act,
   with a thought
     that was evil and hateful,
   I confess to you,
     brothers and sisters of mine,
   I have sinned and
     been proven ungrateful.

4. Through my fault, through my fault,
     through my serious fault,
   I confess to you,
     Lord, all my sinning.
   But look down on me, Lord,
     grant your pardon and peace;
   with your help, I've a
     new life beginning.

                          *Willard F. Jabusch*

# 192

1. Mary immaculate,
     star of the morning,
   chosen before
     the creation began,
   chosen to bring,
     for thy bridal adorning,
   woe to the serpent
     and rescue to man.

2. Here, in an orbit
     of shadow and sadness
   veiling thy splendour,
     thy course thou hast run;
   now thou art throned in all glory
     and gladness,
   crowned by the hand
     of thy saviour and Son.

3. Sinners, we worship
     thy sinless perfection,
   fallen and weak,
     for thy pity we plead;
   grant us the shield
     of thy sovereign protection,
   measure thine aid
     by the depth of our need.

4. Frail is our nature,
     and strict our probation,
   watchful the foe
     that would lure us to wrong,
   succour our souls
     in the hour of temptation,
   Mary immaculate
     tender and strong.

5. See how the wiles
     of the serpent assail us,
   see how we waver
     and flinch in the fight;
   let thine immaculate
     merit avail us,
   make of our weakness
     a proof of thy might.

6. Bend from thy throne
     at the voice of our crying;
   bend to this earth
     which thy footsteps have trod;
   stretch out thine arms
     to us living and dying,
   Mary immaculate,
     mother of God.

                          *F. W. Weatherell*

## 193

May the peace of Christ
    be with you today,
may the peace of Christ
    be with you today,
may the love of Christ,
the joy of Christ,
may the peace of Christ be yours.

*Kevin Mayhew*


## 194

1. Merrily on, merrily on
    flow the bright waters
        that carry a song,
    a song that is sung
        of the love of the Lord,
    a love that is endless
        and ever outpoured.

2. Father above, Father above,
    source of our life and
        our strength and our love,
    as fresh as the spring
        that is limpid and clear,
    your presence is young
        and will always be near.

3. Son from on high, Son from on high,
    you who united
        the earth and the sky,
    Oh, cleanse us with water
        and fill us with peace,
    our river of mercy
        who never will cease.

4. Spirit of God, Spirit of God,
    breathe on the waters
        and flow in the flood,
    and open the flood-gates
        that lead to the sea
    – the ocean is open
        and boundless and free!

5. Merrily on, merrily on
    flow the bright waters
        that carry a song,
    a song that is sung
        of the love of the Lord,
    a love that is endless
        and ever outpoured.

*John Glynn*


## 195

1. Mine eyes have seen the glory
    of the coming of the Lord.
He is trampling out the vintage
    where the grapes of wrath are stored.
He has loosed the fateful lightning
    of his terrible swift sword.
His truth is marching on.

*Glory, glory halleluja!*
*Glory, glory halleluja!*
*Glory, glory halleluja!*
*His truth is marching on.*

2. I have seen him in the watchfires
    of a hundred circling camps.
They have gilded him an altar
    in the evening dews and damps.
I can read his righteous sentence
    by the dim and flaring lamps.
His day is marching on.

3. He has sounded forth the trumpet
    that shall never sound retreat.
He is sifting out the hearts of men
    before his judgement seat.
O, be swift my soul to answer him,
    be jubilant my feet!
Our God is marching on.

4. In the beauty of the lilies
    Christ was born across the sea
with a glory in his bosom
    that transfigures you and me.
As he died to make men holy,
    let us die to make men free.
Whilst God is marching on.

*Julia Ward Howe (1819-1910)*

# 196

1. Morning has broken
   like the first morning,
   blackbird has spoken
   like the first bird.
   Praise for the singing!
   Praise for the morning!
   Praise for them, springing
   fresh from the Word!

2. Sweet the rain's new fall
   sunlit from heaven,
   like the first dew-fall
   on the first grass.
   Praise for the sweetness
   of the wet garden,
   sprung in completeness
   where his feet pass.

3. Mine is the sunlight!
   Mine is the morning
   born of the one light
   Eden saw play!
   Praise with elation,
   praise ev'ry morning,
   God's re-creation
   of the new day!

   *Eleanor Farjeon (1881-1965)*

# 197

1. "Moses I know you're the man,"
   the Lord said.
   "You're going to work out my
      plan,"
   the Lord said.
   "Lead all the Israelites
   out of slavery."
   And I shall make them a
      wandering race
   called the people of God."

   *So ev'ry day we're on our way,*
   *for we're a travelling,*
      *wandering race*
   *called the people of God.*

2. "Don't get too set in your ways,"
   the Lord said.
   "Each step is only a phase,"
   the Lord said.
   "I'll go before you and
      I shall be a sign
   to guide my travelling,
      wandering race.
   You're the people of God."

3. "No matter what you may do,"
   the Lord said,
   "I shall be faithful and true,"
   the Lord said.
   "My love will strengthen you
      as you go along,
   for you're my travelling,
      wandering race.
   You're the people of God."

4. "Look at the birds in the air,"
   the Lord said,
   "They fly unhampered by care,"
   the Lord said.
   "You will move easier
      if you're travelling light,
   for you're a wandering,
      vagabond race.
   You're the people of God."

5. "Foxes have places to go,"
   the Lord said.
   "But I've no home here below,"
   the Lord said.
   "So if you want to be
      with me all your days,
   keep up the moving and
      travelling on.
   You're the people of God."

   *Estelle White*

# 198

1. Most ancient of all mysteries,
   before thy throne we lie;
   have mercy now, most merciful,
   most Holy Trinity.

2. When heaven and earth were yet
                           unmade,
   when time was yet unknown,
   thou, in thy bliss and majesty,
   didst live and love alone.

3. Thou wert not born; there was no
                           fount,
   from which thy being flowed;
   there is no end which thou canst
                           reach:
   but thou art simply God.

4. How wonderful creation is,
   the work that thou didst bless;
   and oh, what then must thou be like,
   Eternal Loveliness!

5. Most ancient of all mysteries,
   still at thy throne we lie;
   have mercy now, most merciful,
   most Holy Trinity.

   *Frederick William Faber (1814-63)*

2. Though poverty and work and woe
   the masters of my life may be,
   when times are worst, who does not
                           know
   darkness is light with love of thee?
   darkness is light with love of thee?

3. But scornful men have coldly said
   thy love was leading me from God;
   and yet in this I did but tread
   the very path my Saviour trod,
   the very path my Saviour trod.

4. They know but little of thy worth
   who speak these heartless words to
                           me;
   for what did Jesus love on earth
   one half so tenderly as thee?
   one half so tenderly as thee?

5. Get me the grace to love thee more;
   Jesus will give if thou wilt plead;
   and, Mother! when life's cares are
                           o'er,
   oh, I shall love thee then indeed!
   oh, I shall love thee then indeed!

6. Jesus, when his three hours were run,
   bequeath'd thee from the cross to me,
   and oh! how can I love thy Son,
   sweet Mother! if I love not thee?
   sweet Mother! if I love not thee?

   *Frederick William Faber (1814-63)*

# 200

1. *My glory and the lifter of my head,*
   *my glory and the lifter of my head,*
   *for thou, O Lord, art a shield to me,*
   *my glory and the lifter of my head.*
   I cried unto the Lord with my voice,
   I cried unto the Lord with my voice,
   I cried unto the Lord with my voice,
   and he heard me out of his holy hill.

   *From Scripture*

# 199

1. Mother of Mercy, day by day
   my love of thee grows more and
                           more;
   thy gifts are strewn upon my way,
   like sands upon the great seashore,
   like sands upon the great seashore.

# 201

1. My God accept my heart this day,
   and make it wholly thine,
   that I from thee no more may stray,
   no more from thee decline.

2. Before the cross of him who died,
   behold, I prostrate fall;
   let every sin be crucified,
   and Christ be all in all.

3. Anoint me with thy heavenly grace,
   and seal me for thine own,
   that I may see thy glorious face,
   and worship at thy throne.

4. Let every thought, and work and
   word
   to thee be ever given,
   then life shall be thy service, Lord,
   and Death the gate of heaven.

5. All glory to the Father be,
   all glory to the Son,
   all glory, Holy Ghost, to thee,
   while endless ages run.

   *Matthew Bridges (1800-94)*

# 202

1. My God, and is thy table spread,
   and does thy cup with love o'erflow?
   Thither be all thy children led,
   and let them all thy sweetness know.

2. Hail, sacred feast, which Jesus
   makes!
   Rich banquet of his flesh and blood!
   Thrice happy he, who here partakes
   that sacred stream, that heavenly
   food.

3. O let thy table honoured be,
   and furnished well with joyful
   guests;
   and may each soul salvation see,
   that here its sacred pledges tastes.

   *Philip Doddridge (1702-51)*

# 203

1. My God, how wonderful thou art,
   thy majesty how bright
   how beautiful thy mercy-seat
   in depths of burning light.

2. How dread are thine eternal years
   O everlasting Lord!
   By prostrate spirits day and night
   incessantly adored.

3. How beautiful, how beautiful
   the sight of thee must be,
   thine endless wisdom, boundless
   power
   and awful purity!

4. Oh, how I fear thee, living God!
   with deepest, tenderest fears,
   and worship thee with trembling hope
   and penitential tears.

5. Yet I may love thee too, O Lord,
   almighty as thou art,
   for thou hast stooped to ask of me
   the love of my poor heart.

6. No earthly father loves like thee,
   no mother e'er so mild
   bears and forbears as thou hast done
   with me thy sinful child.

7. Father of Jesus, love's reward,
   what rapture will it be,
   prostrate before thy throne to lie,
   and gaze and gaze on thee!

   *Frederick William Faber (1814-63)*

# 204

1. My God I love thee, not because
   I hope for heav'n thereby;
   nor yet that those who love thee not
   are lost eternally.

2. Thou, O my Jesus, thou didst me
   upon the cross embrace;
   for me didst bear the nails and spear
   and manifold disgrace.

3. And griefs and torments numberless
   and sweat of agony;
   e'en death itself — and all for one
   who was thine enemy.

4. Then why, O Blessed Jesu Christ
   should I not love thee well;
   not for the sake of winning heaven,
   or of escaping hell;

5. Not with the hope of gaining aught;
   not seeking a reward,
   but, as thyself hast loved me
   O ever-loving Lord?

6. E'en so I love thee, and will love,
   and in thy praise will sing;
   solely because thou art my God
   and my eternal king.

   *17th c., tr. Edward Caswall*


# 205

1. My God loves me.
   His love will never end.
   He rests within my heart
   for my God loves me.

2. His gentle hand
   he stretches over me.
   Though storm-clouds
       threaten the day
   he will set me free.

3. He comes to me
   in sharing bread and wine.
   He brings me life that will reach
   past the end of time.

4. My God loves me,
   his faithful love endures.
   And I will live like a child
   held in love secure.

5. The joys of love
   as offerings now we bring.
   The pains of love will be lost
   in the praise we sing.

   **Verse 1** *Anonymous*
   **Verses 2-5** *Sandra Joan Billington*


# 206

1. My song is love unknown,
   my Saviour's love to me,
   love to the loveless shown,
   that they might lovely be.
   O who am I,
   that for my sake,
   my Lord should take
   frail flesh and die?

2. He came from his blest throne,
   salvation to bestow;
   but men made strange, and none
   the longed-for Christ would know,
   but O, my friend,
   my friend indeed,
   who at my need
   his life did spend!

3. Sometimes they strew his way,
   and his sweet praises sing;
   resounding all the day
   hosannas to their King;
   then 'Crucify!'
   is all their breath,
   and for his death
   they thirst and cry.

4. Why, what hath my Lord done?
   What makes this rage and spite?
   He made the lame to run,
   he gave the blind their sight.
   Sweet injuries!
   Yet they at these
   themselves displease,
   and 'gainst him rise.

5. They rise, and needs will have
   my dear Lord made away;
   a murderer they save,
   the Prince of Life they slay.
   Yet cheerful he
   to suffering goes,
   that he his foes
   from thence might free.

6. In life, no house, no home
my Lord on earth might have:
in death no friendly tomb
but what a stranger gave.
What may I say?
Heaven was his home;
but mine the tomb
wherein he lay.

7. Here might I stay and sing,
no story so divine,
never was love, dear King,
never was grief like thine.
This is my Friend,
in whose sweet praise
I all my days
could gladly spend.

*Samuel Crossman (c. 1624-84)*

# 207

1. New praises be given
to Christ newly crowned,
who back to his heaven
a new way hath found;
God's blessedness sharing
before us he goes,
what mansions preparing,
what endless repose!

2. His glory still praising
on thrice holy ground
the apostles stood gazing,
his mother around;
with hearts that beat faster,
with eyes full of love,
they watched while their master
ascended above.

3. "No star can disclose him",
the bright angels said;
"Eternity knows him,
your conquering head;
those high habitations,
he leaves not again,
till, judging all nations,
on earth he shall reign".

4. Thus spoke they and straightway,
where legions defend
heaven's glittering gateway,
their Lord they attend,
and cry, looking thither,
"Your portals let down
for him who rides hither
in peace and renown".

5. They asked, who keep sentry
in that blessed town,
"Who thus claimeth entry,
a king of renown?"
"The Lord of all valiance",
that herald replied,
"Who Satan's battalions
laid low in their pride".

6. Grant, Lord, that our longing
may follow thee there,
on earth who are thronging
thy temples with prayer;
and unto thee gather,
Redeemer, thine own
where thou with thy Father
dost sit on the throne.

*St. Bede the Venerable (673-735)*
*tr. R. A. Knox*

# 208

1. Now come to me all you who seek
and place your trust in me.
For I have comfort for the weak,
the strength to set you free.
And, just as gentle blades of grass
can crack the hardened earth,
creation will be yours at last
when love is brought to birth.

2. Now come to me all you who seek
and place your trust in me.
For I will comfort those who mourn
and make the blind to see.
However dark the stormy night
the sun will raise the dawn,
and you will live beneath the light
of love in darkness born.

3. Now come to me all you who seek
   and place your trust in me.
   For I bring peace to those at war
   and set the captives free.
   Just as in cutting sun-ripe wheat
   we count the summer's worth,
   so shall all those who justice seek
   be there at love's new birth.

*Michael Cockett*

# 209

1. Now Jesus said:
      "We'll bake some bread,
   so bring me flour and water.
   Then bring me salt
         and bring me yeast;
   I'll bake for you a splendid feast,
   and we will join and drink a toast
   to friendship ever after."

2. They found the flour,
         they found the salt,
   they found a jug of water.
   But, though they searched
         around the town,
   an ounce of yeast
         could not be found.
   They came to him
         with eyes cast down
   and told him of their failure.

3. Then Jesus said:
         "Do not be sad,
   we'll mix the flour and water.
   And though we bake
         unleavened bread,
   if you will be the yeast instead,
   the bread will rise up from the dead
   and feed you ever after."

*Michael Cockett*

# 210

1. Now Jesus said:
   "You must love one another,
   pass it on, pass it on,"
   And Jesus said:
   "Call all men your brother,
   come to me, learn to love,
   pass it on, pass it on."

2. So Peter said:
   "You must love one another,
   pass it on, pass it on,"
   So Peter said:
   "Call all men your brother,
   come to me, learn to love,
   pass it on, pass it on."

3. The people said . . .

4. My Father said . . .

5. Now I can say . . .

*Michael Cockett*

# 211

1. Now thank we all our God,
   with heart and hands and voices,
   who wondrous things hath done,
   in whom this world rejoices;
   who from our mother's arms
   hath blessed us on our way
   with countless gifts of love,
   and still is ours today.

2. O may this bounteous God
   through all our life be near us
   with ever joyful hearts
   and blessed peace to cheer us;
   and keep us in his grace,
   and guide us when perplexed,
   and free us from all ills
   in this world and the next.

3. All praise and thanks to God
   the Father now be given
   the Son and him who reigns
   with them in highest heaven,
   the one Eternal God,
   whom earth and heaven adore;
   for thus it was, is now,
   and shall be evermore.

*Martin Rinkart (1586-1649),*
*tr. Catherine Winkworth*

# 212

1. Now with the fast-departing light,
   maker of all! We ask of thee,
   of thy great mercy, through the
   night
   our guardian and defence to be.

2. Far off let idle visions fly;
   no phantom of the night molest:
   curb thou our raging enemy,
   that we in chaste repose may rest.

3. Father of mercies! hear our cry:
   hear us, O sole-begotten Son!
   Who, with the Holy Ghost most
   high,
   reignest while endless ages run.

   *7th c., tr. Edward Caswall*

# 213

1. O bread of heaven, beneath this veil
   thou dost my very God conceal;
   my Jesus, dearest treasure, hail;
   I love thee and adoring kneel;
   each loving soul by thee is fed
   with thine own self in form of bread.

2. O food of life, thou who dost give
   the pledge of immortality;
   I live; no, 'tis not I that live;
   God gives me life, God lives in me:
   he feeds my soul, he guides my ways,
   and every grief with joy repays.

3. O bond of love, that dost unite
   the servant to his living Lord;
   could I dare live, and not requite
   such love — then death were meet
   reward:
   I cannot live unless to prove
   some love for such unmeasured love.

4. Beloved Lord in heaven above,
   there, Jesus, thou awaitest me;
   to gaze on thee with changeless love,
   yes, thus I hope, thus shall it be:
   for how can he deny me heaven
   who here on earth himself hath
   given?

   *St. Alphonsus (1696-1787)*
   *tr. Edward Vaughan*

# 214

1. O come, all ye faithful,
   joyful and triumphant,
   O come ye, O come ye to Bethlehem;
   come and behold him,
   born the king of angels:

   *O come, let us adore him,*
   *O come, let us adore him,*
   *O come, let us adore him,*
   *Christ the Lord.*

2. God of God,
   light of light,
   lo! he abhors not the virgin's womb;
   very God,
   begotten not created:

3. Sing, choirs of angels,
   sing in exultation,
   sing all ye citizens of heaven above:
   glory to God
   in the highest:

4. Yea, Lord, we greet thee,
   born this happy morning,
   Jesu, to thee be glory given;
   word of the Father,
   now in flesh appearing:

   *18th c., tr. Frederick Oakeley*

# 215

1. O come and mourn with me awhile;
   see, Mary calls us to her side;
   O come and let us mourn with her;

   *Jesus our love, Jesus our love,*
   *is crucified.*

2. Have we no tears to shed for him,
   while soldiers scoff and men deride?
   Ah! look how patiently he hangs;

3. How fast his feet and hands are
   nailed,
   his blessed tongue with thirst is tied;
   his failing eyes are blind with blood;

4. Seven times he spoke, seven words
   of love,
   and all three hours his silence cried
   For mercy on the souls of men;

5. O break, O break, hard heart of
   mine:
   thy weak self-love and guilty pride
   his Pilate and his Judas were:

6. A broken heart, a fount of tears,
   ask, and they will not be denied;
   a broken heart, love's cradle is;

7. O love of God! O sin of man!
   In this dread act your strength is
   tried;
   and victory remains with love;

   *Frederick William Faber (1814-63)*

# 216

1. O come, O come, Emmanuel,
   and ransom captive Israel,
   that mourns in lonely exile here
   until the Son of God appear:

   *Rejoice, rejoice! Emmanuel*
   *shall come to thee, O Israel.*

2. O come, thou Rod of Jesse, free
   thine own from Satan's tyranny;
   from depths of hell thy people save,
   and give them vict'ry o'er the grave:

3. O come, thou dayspring, come and
   cheer
   our spirits by thine advent here;
   disperse the gloomy clouds of night,
   and death's dark shadows put to
   flight:

4. O come, thou key of David, come
   and open wide our heavenly home;
   make safe the way that leads on high,
   and close the path to misery.

5. O come, O come, thou Lord of
   might,
   who to thy tribes on Sinai's height
   in ancient times didst give the law
   in cloud and majesty and awe:

   *From the 'Great O Antiphons'*
   *(12th-13th c.), tr. John Mason Neale*

# 217

1. O Father, now the hour has come,
   so glorify your Son,
   that he may give eternal life
   to those who hope in him.

2. Through Jesus Christ, your only Son,
   the Word has now been sown,
   so honour him with glory now,
   the saviour of the world.

3. O Father of the Word of Truth,
   the world has known you not,
   but through the Son that you have
   sent
   your love is in our hearts.

4. He is no longer in this world,
   he has returned to you.
   So, holy Father, make us one
   as he is one with you.

5. May all good men be joined as one,
   as Father with the Son,
   that through the unity of love,
   the whole world may believe.

6. Through glory given to the Son,
   the Father will reveal
   the joy complete, the bond of love,
   mysterious Three in One.

   *Michael Cockett*

# 218

1. O Father, take in sign of love
these gifts of bread and wine!
With them we give our very selves,
to be for ever thine!

2. These gifts another gift will be,
thy Son in very deed,
for us a willing victim made,
the Lamb on whom we feed!

3. These are the gifts thy Son did bless
the night before he died.
By which he showed himself a priest
and victim crucified!

4. He now has given us as our own
his offering made to thee:
his body broken, Blood outpoured,
for us on Calvary!

5. This bread his Body will become,
this wine his Blood will be!
Our humble gifts will be the gift
that is most dear to thee!

6. This perfect gift thou wilt restore
to greatest and to least,
to make all one in love and joy
in thy communion-feast!

*James Quinn, S.J.*

# 219

1. Of the glorious body telling,
O my tongue, its myst'ries sing,
and the blood, all price excelling,
which the world's eternal king,
in a noble womb once dwelling,
shed for this world's ransoming.

2. Giv'n for us, for us descending,
of a virgin to proceed,
man with man in converse blending,
scattered he the gospel seed,
'till his sojourn drew to ending,
which he closed in wondrous deed.

3. At the last great supper lying,
circled by his brethren's band,
meekly with the law complying,
first, he finished its command.

Then, immortal food supplying,
gave himself with his own hand.

4. Word made flesh, by word he
maketh
very bread his flesh to be;
man in wine Christ's blood
partaketh,
and if senses fail to see,
faith alone the true heart waketh,
to behold the mystery.

5. Therefore, we before him bending,
this great sacrament revere;
types and shadows have their ending,
for the newer rite is here;
faith, our outward sense befriending,
makes the inward vision clear.

6. Glory let us give, and blessing,
to the Father and the Son;
honour, might and praise addressing,
while eternal ages run;
ever too his love confessing,
who from both, with both is one.

*St. Thomas Aquinas (1127-74),*
*tr. J. M. Neale, E. Caswall and others*

# 220

1. O Godhead hid, devoutly I adore
thee,
who truly art within the forms
before me;
to thee my heart I bow with
bended knee,
as failing quite in contemplating
thee.

2. Sight, touch, and taste in thee are
each deceived,
the ear alone most safely is
believed:
I believe all the Son of God has
spoken;
than truth's own word there is no
truer token.

3. God only on the cross lay hid from
view;
but here lies hid at once the
manhood too:

and I, in both professing my belief,
make the same prayer as the
repentant thief.

4. Thy wounds, as Thomas saw, I do
not see;
yet thee confess my Lord and God
to be;
make me believe thee ever more and
more,
In thee my hope, in thee my love to
store.

5. O thou memorial of our Lord's own
dying!
O bread that living art and vivifying!
Make ever thou my soul on thee to
live;
ever a taste of heavenly sweetness
give.

6. O loving Pelican! O Jesus, Lord!
Unclean I am, but cleanse me in thy
blood;
of which a single drop, for sinners
spilt,
is ransom for a world's entire guilt.

7. Jesus, whom for the present veiled
I see,
what I so thirst for, oh, vouchsafe
to me:
that I may see thy countenance
unfolding,
and may be blest thy glory in
beholding.

*St. Thomas Aquinas (1227-74),*
*tr. Edward Caswall*

# 221

1. O God of earth and altar,
bow down and hear our cry,
our earthly rulers falter,
our people drift and die;
the walls of gold entomb us,
the swords of scorn divide,
take not thy thunder from us,
but take away our pride.

2. From all that terror teaches,
from lies of tongue and pen,
from all the easy speeches
that comfort cruel men,
from sale and profanation
of honour and the sword,
from sleep and from damnation,
deliver us, good Lord!

3. Tie in a living tether
the prince and priest and thrall,
bind all our lives together,
smite us and save us all;
in ire and exultation
aflame with faith, and free,
lift up a living nation,
a single sword to thee.

*G. K. Chesterton (1874-1936)*

# 222

1. O God, our help in ages past,
our hope for years to come,
our shelter from the stormy blast,
and our eternal home;

2. Beneath the shadow of thy throne,
thy saints have dwelt secure;
sufficient is thine arm alone,
and our defence is sure.

3. Before the hills in order stood,
or earth received her frame,
from everlasting thou art God,
to endless years the same.

4. A thousand ages in thy sight,
are like an evening gone;
short as the watch that ends the
night
before the rising sun.

5. Time, like an ever-rolling stream,
bears all its sons away;
they fly forgotten, as a dream
dies at the opening day.

6. O God, our help in ages past,
our hope for years to come,
be thou our guard while troubles
last,
and our eternal home.

*Isaac Watts (1674-1748)*

# 223

1. O God, thy people gather,
   obedient to thy word,
   around thy holy altar,
   to praise thy name, O Lord;
   for all thy loving kindness
   our grateful hearts we raise;
   but pardon first the blindness
   of all our sinful ways.

2. Thou art our loving Father,
   thou art our holiest Lord,
   but we have sinned against thee,
   by thought and deed and word.
   Before the court of heaven
   we stand and humbly pray
   our sins may be forgiven,
   our faults be washed away.

3. Though sinful, we implore thee
   to turn and make us live,
   that so we may adore thee,
   and our due offering give,
   and may the prayers and voices
   of thy glad people rise,
   as thy whole Church rejoices
   in this great sacrifice.

*Anthony Nye*

# 224

1. O God, we give ourselves today
   with this pure host to thee,
   the selfsame gift which thy dear Son
   gave once on Calvary.

2. Entire and whole, our life and love
   with heart and soul and mind,
   for all our sins and faults and needs,
   thy Church and all mankind.

3. With humble and with contrite heart
   this bread and wine we give
   because thy Son once gave himself
   and died that we might live.

4. Though lowly now, soon by thy
   word
   these offered gifts will be
   the very body of our Lord,
   his soul and deity.

5. His very body, offered up
   a gift beyond all price,
   he gives to us, that we may give
   in loving sacrifice.

6. O Lord, who took our human life,
   as water mixed with wine,
   grant through this sacrifice that we
   may share thy life divine.

*Anthony Nye*

# 225

*Oh living water, refresh my soul.*
*Oh living water, refresh my soul*
*Spirit of joy, Lord of creation.*
*Spirit of hope, Spirit of peace.*

1. Spirit of God,
   Spirit of God.

2. Oh set us free,
   Oh set us free.

3. Come, pray in us,
   come, pray in us.

*Rosalie Vissing*

# 226

1. Oh Lord,
   all the world belongs to you,
   and you are always making
   all things new.
   What is wrong you forgive,
   and the new life you give
   is what's turning the world
   upside down.

2. The world's
   only loving to its friends,
   but you have brought us love that
   never ends;
   loving enemies too,
   and this loving with you
   is what's turning the world
   upside down.

3. This world
   lives divided and apart.
   You draw all men together
   and we start
   in your body to see
   that in fellowship we

can be turning the world
upside down.

4. The world
wants the wealth to live in state,
but you show us a new way
to be great:
like a servant you came,
and if we do the same,
we'll be turning the world
upside down.

5. Oh Lord
all the world belongs to you,
and you are always making
all things new.
Send your Spirit on all
in your Church whom you call
to be turning the world
upside down.

*Patrick Appleford*

# 227

1. O Lord, my God,
when I in awesome wonder,
consider all the worlds
thy hand has made,
I see the stars,
I hear the rolling thunder,
thy pow'r throughout
the universe displayed.

*Then sings my soul,*
*my Saviour God to thee:*
*How great thou art,*
*how great thou art.*
*Then sings my soul,*
*my Saviour God to thee:*
*How great thou art,*
*how great thou art.*

2. And when I think
that God, his Son not sparing,
sent him to die, I
scarce can take it in
that on the cross,
my burden gladly bearing,
he bled and died
to take away my sin.

3. When Christ shall come
with shout of acclamation
and take me home,
what joy shall fill my heart;
when I shall bow
in humble adoration,
and there proclaim;
my God, how great thou art.

*Carl Boberg (1850–1940)*
*tr. Stuart K. Hine*

# 228

1. O holy Lord, by all adored,
our trespasses confessing,
to thee this day thy children pray,
our holy faith professing!
Accept, O king, the gifts we bring,
our songs of praise, the prayers we
raise,
and grant us, Lord, thy blessing.

2. To God on high be thanks and
praise,
who deigns our bond to sever;
his care shall guide us all our days,
and harm shall reach us never,
on him we rest with faith assured;
of all that live he is the Lord,
for ever and for ever.

*M. F. Bell (1862-1947)*

# 229

1. Oh sinner man,
where you going to run to?
Oh, sinner man,
where you going to run to?
Oh, sinner man,
where you going to run to?
all on that day?

2. Run to the moon,
moon won't you hide me?
Run to the sea,
sea won't you hide me?
Run to the sun,
sun won't you hide me?
all on that day?

3. Lord said: "Sinner Man,
   the moon'll be a-bleeding."
   Lord said: "Sinner Man,
   the sea'll be a-sinking."
   Lord said: "Sinner Man,
   the sun'll be a-freezing."
   all on that day.

4. Run to the Lord:
   "Lord, won't you hide me?"
   Run to the Lord:
   "Lord, won't you hide me?"
   Run to the Lord:
   "Lord, won't you hide me?"
   all on that day.

5. Lord said: "Sinner Man,
   you should have been a-praying!"
   Lord said: "Sinner Man,
   you should have been a-praying!"
   Lord said: "Sinner Man,
   you should have been a-praying!"
   all on that day.

*Traditional*

# 230

1. Oh, the Lord looked down
   from his window in the sky,
   said: "I created man
   but I can't remember why!
   Nothing but fighting
   since creation day.
   I'll send a little water
   and wash them all away."
   Oh, the Lord came down
   and looked around a spell.
   There was Mister Noah
   behaving mighty well.
   And that is the reason
   the Scriptures record
   Noah found grace
   in the eyes of the Lord.

   *Noah found grace*
   *in the eyes of the Lord.*
   *Noah found grace*
   *in the eyes of the Lord.*
   *Noah found grace*
   *in the eyes of the Lord*
   *and he left him high and dry.*

2. The Lord said: "Noah,
   there's going to be a flood,
   there's going to be some water,
   there's going to be some mud,
   so take off your hat, Noah,
   take off your coat,
   get Sham, Ham and Japhat
   and build yourself a boat."
   Noah said: "Lord,
   I don't believe I could."
   The Lord said: "Noah,
   get yourself some wood.
   You never know what
   you can do till you try.
   Build it fifty cubits wide
   and thirty cubits high."

3. Noah said: "There she is,
   there she is Lord!"
   The Lord said: "Noah,
   it's time to get aboard.
   Take of each creature
   a he and a she
   and of course take Mrs Noah
   and the whole family."
   Noah said: "Lord,
   it's getting mighty dark."
   The Lord said: "Noah,
   get those creatures in the ark."
   Noah said: "Lord,
   it's beginning to pour."
   The Lord said: "Noah,
   hurry up and close the door."

4. The ark rose up
   on the bosom of the deep.
   After forty days
   Mr Noah took a peep.
   He said: "We're not moving, Lord,
   where are we at?"
   The Lord said: "You're sitting
   right on Mount Ararat."
   Noah said: "Lord,
   it's getting nice and dry."
   The Lord said: "Noah,
   see my rainbow in the sky.
   Take all your creatures
   and people the earth
   and be sure that you're not
   more trouble than you're worth."

*Traditional*

## 231

1. Oh, the love of my Lord
      is the essence
   of all that I love here on earth.
   All the beauty I see
   he has given to me
   and his giving is gentle as silence.

2. Every day, every hour,
      every moment
   have been blessed by
      the strength of his love.
   At the turn of each tide
   he is there at my side,
   and his touch is as gentle as silence.

3. There've been times when I've turned
      from his presence,
   and I've walked other paths,
      other ways.
   But I've called on his name
   in the dark of my shame,
   and his mercy was gentle as silence.

*Estelle White*

## 232

1. Oh when the saints go marching in,
   oh when the saints go marching in,
   I want to be in that number,
   when the saints go marching in.

2. Oh when the drums begin to bang,
   oh when the drums begin to bang,
   I want to be in that number,
   when the drums begin to bang.

3. Oh when the stars fall from the sky,
   oh when the stars fall from the sky,
   I want to be in that number,
   when the stars fall from the sky.

4. Oh when the moon turns into blood,
   oh when the moon turns into blood,
   I want to be in that number,
   when the moon turns into blood.

5. Oh when the sun turns into fire,
   oh when the sun turns into fire,
   I want to be in that number,
   when the sun turns into fire.

6. Oh when the fires begin to blaze,
   oh when the fires begin to blaze,
   I want to be in that number,
   when the fires begin to blaze.

7. Oh when the Lord calls out the
                              names,
   oh when the Lord calls out the
                              names,
   I want to be in that number,
   when the Lord calls out the names.

*Traditional*

## 233

1. O Jesus Christ, remember,
   when thou shalt come again,
   upon the clouds of heaven,
   with all thy shining train;
   when every eye shall see thee
   in deity revealed,
   who now upon this altar
   in silence art concealed.

2. Remember then, O Saviour,
   I supplicate of thee,
   that here I bowed before thee
   upon my bended knee;
   that here I owned thy presence,
   and did not thee deny,
   and glorified thy greatness
   though hid from human eye.

3. Accept, divine Redeemer,
   the homage of my praise;
   be thou the light and honour
   and glory of my days.
   Be thou my consolation
   when death is drawing nigh;
   be thou my only treasure
   through all eternity.

*Edward Caswall (1814-78)*

## 234

1. O king of might and splendour
   creator most adored,
   this sacrifice we render
   to thee as sov'reign Lord.
   May these our gifts be pleasing
   unto thy majesty,

mankind from sin releasing
who have offended thee.

2. Thy body thou hast given,
thy blood thou hast outpoured,
that sin might be forgiven,
O Jesus, loving Lord.
As now with love most tender,
thy death we celebrate,
our lives in self-surrender
to thee we consecrate.

*Dom Gregory Murray, O.S.B.*

# 235

1. O little town of Bethlehem,
how still we see thee lie!
Above thy deep and dreamless sleep
the silent stars go by.
Yet, in thy dark streets shineth
the everlasting light;
the hopes and fears of all the years
are met in thee tonight.

2. O morning stars, together
proclaim the holy birth,
and praises sing to God the King,
and peace to men on earth;
for Christ is born of Mary;
and, gathered all above,
while mortals sleep, the angels keep
their watch of wondering love.

3. How silently, how silently,
the wondrous gift is given!
So God imparts to human hearts
the blessings of his heaven.
No ear may hear his coming;
but in this world of sin,
where meek souls will receive him, still
the dear Christ enters in.

4. Where children pure and happy
pray to the blessed Child,
where misery cries out to thee,
Son of the mother mild;
where charity stands watching
and faith holds wide the door,
the dark night wakes, the glory
breaks,
and Christmas comes once more.

*Phillips Brooks (1835-93)*

# 236

1. O Mother blest, whom God bestows
on sinners and on just,
what joy, what hope thou givest
those
who in thy mercy trust.

*Thou art clement, thou art chaste,*
*Mary, thou art fair;*
*of all mothers sweetest, best;*
*none with thee compare.*

2. O heavenly mother, mistress sweet!
It never yet was told
that suppliant sinner left thy feet
unpitied, unconsoled.

3. O mother pitiful and mild,
cease not to pray for me;
for I do love thee as a child,
and sigh for love of thee.

4. Most powerful mother, all men
know
thy Son denies thee nought;
thou askest, wishest it, and lo!
his power thy will hath wrought.

5. O mother blest, for me obtain
ungrateful though I be,
to love that God who first could
deign
to show such love for me.

*St. Alphonsus Liguori (1699–1787),*
*tr. Edmund Vaughan*

# 237

1. O my Lord, within my heart
pride will have no home,
every talent that I have
comes from you alone.

*And like a child at rest*
*close to its mother's breast,*
*safe in your arms*
*my soul is calmed.*

2. Lord, my eyes do not look high
nor my thoughts take wings,
for I can find treasures in
ordinary things.

3. Great affairs are not for me,
   deeds beyond my scope,
   in the simple things I do
   I find joy and hope.

   *Estelle White*

# 238

1. Once in royal David's city
   stood a lowly cattle shed,
   where a Mother laid her baby
   in a manger for his bed:
   Mary was that Mother mild,
   Jesus Christ her little child.

2. He came down to earth from
                   heaven,
   who is God and Lord of all,
   and his shelter was a stable
   and his cradle was a stall;
   with the poor, and mean, and lowly,
   lived on earth our Saviour holy.

3. And through all his wondrous
                   childhood
   he would honour and obey,
   love, and watch the lowly maiden
   in whose gentle arms he lay;
   Christian children all must be
   mild, obedient, good as he.

4. For he is our childhood's pattern,
   day by day like us he grew;
   he was little, weak and helpless,
   tears and smiles like us he knew;
   and he feeleth for our sadness,
   and he shareth in our gladness.

5. And our eyes at last shall see him
   through his own redeeming love,
   for that child so dear and gentle
   is our Lord in heaven above;
   and he leads his children on
   to the place where he is gone.

6. Not in that poor lowly stable,
   with the oxen standing by,
   we shall see him; but in heaven,
   set at God's right hand on high;
   when like stars his children crowned
   all in white shall wait around.

   *Cecil Francis Alexander (1818-95)*

# 239

1. On Jordan's bank the Baptist's cry
   announces that the Lord is nigh,
   come then and hearken, for he
                   brings
   glad tidings from the King of kings.

2. Then cleansed be every Christian
                   breast,
   and furnished for so great a guest!
   Yea, let us each our hearts prepare,
   for Christ to come and enter there.

3. For thou art our salvation, Lord,
   our refuge and our great reward;
   without thy grace our souls must
                   fade,
   and wither like a flower decayed.

4. Stretch forth thy hand, to heal our
                   sore,
   and make us rise, to fall no more;
   once more upon thy people shine,
   and fill the world with love divine.

5. All praise, eternal Son, to thee
   whose advent sets thy people free,
   whom, with the Father, we adore,
   and Holy Ghost, for evermore.

   *C. Coffin (1676-1749), tr. J. Chandler*

# 240

1. On this house your blessing, Lord.
   On this house your grace bestow.
   On this house your blessing, Lord.
   May it come and never go.
   Bringing peace and joy
   and happiness,
   bringing love that knows no end.
   On this house your blessing Lord.
   On this house your blessing send.

2. On this house your loving, Lord.
   May it overflow each day.
   On this house your loving, Lord.
   May it come and with us stay.
   Drawing us in love
   and unity
   by the love received from you.
   On this house your loving, Lord.
   May it come each day anew.

3. On this house your giving, Lord.
   May it turn and ever flow.
   On this house your giving, Lord.
   On this house your wealth bestow.
   Filling all our hopes
   and wishes, Lord,
   in the way you know is best.
   On this house your giving, Lord.
   May it come and with us rest.

4. On this house your calling, Lord.
   May it come to us each day.
   On this house your calling, Lord.
   May it come to lead the way.
   Filling us with nobler
   yearnings, Lord,
   calling us to live in you.
   On this house your calling, Lord.
   May it come each day anew.

*Sister Marie Lydia Pereira*

# 241

1. Onward, Christian soldiers,
   marching as to war,
   with the Cross of Jesus
   going on before.
   Christ the royal Master
   leads against the foe;
   forward into battle,
   see, his banners go!

   *Onward, Christian soldiers,*
   *marching as to war,*
   *with the Cross of Jesus*
   *going on before.*

2. At the sign of triumph
   Satan's legions flee;
   on then, Christian soldiers,
   on to victory.
   Hell's foundations quiver
   at the shout of praise;
   brothers, lift your voices,
   loud your anthem raise.

3. Like a mighty army
   moves the Church of God.
   Brothers, we are treading
   where the Saints have trod;
   we are not divided,
   all one body we,
   one in hope and doctrine,
   one in charity.

4. Crowns and thrones may perish,
   kingdoms rise and wane,
   but the Church of Jesus
   constant will remain;
   gates of hell can never
   'gainst that Church prevail;
   we have Christ's own promise,
   and that cannot fail.

5. Onward, then, ye people,
   join our happy throng,
   blend with ours your voices
   in the triumph song;
   glory, laud, and honour
   unto Christ the King;
   this through countless ages
   men and angels sing.

*S. Baring-Gould (1834-1924)*

# 242

1. Open your ears, O Christian people,
   open your ears and hear Good News.
   Open your hearts
        O royal priesthood
   God has come to you.
   *God has spoken to his people,*
   *alleluia.*
   *And his words are words of wisdom,*
   *alleluia.*

2. Israel comes to greet the Saviour,
   Judah is glad to see his day.
   From East and West the
        the peoples travel,
   he will show the way.

3. He who has ears to hear his message;
   he who has ears, then let him hear.
   He who would learn
        the way of wisdom,
   let him hear God's words.

                              *W. F. Jabusch*

# 243

1. O perfect love,
        all human thought transcending,
   lowly we kneel
        in prayer before thy throne.
   That theirs may be
        the love which knows no ending
   whom thou for evermore
        dost join in one.

2. O perfect life,
        be thou their full assurance
   of tender charity
        and steadfast faith,
   of patient hope,
        and quiet, brave endurance,
   with childlike trust
        that fears nor pain nor death.

3. Grant them the joy
        which brightens earthly sorrow,
   grant them the peace
        which calms all earthly strife;
   and to life's day
        the glorious unknown morrow
   that dawns upon
        eternal love and life.

*Dorothy Francis Gurney (1858-1932)*

# 244

1. O praise ye the Lord!
        praise him in the height;
   rejoice in his word,
        ye angels of light;
   ye heavens, adore him,
        by whom ye were made,
   and worship before him,
        in brightness arrayed.

2. O praise ye the Lord!
        praise him upon earth,
   in tuneful accord,
        ye sons of new birth.
   Praise him who hath brought you
        his grace from above,
   praise him who hath taught you
        to sing of his love.

3. O praise ye the Lord,
        all things that give sound;
   each jubilant chord
        re-echo around;
   loud organs, his glory
        forth tell in deep tone,
   and, sweet harp, the story
        of what he hath done.

4. O praise ye the Lord!
        thanksgiving and song
   to him be outpoured
        all ages along;
   for love in creation,
        for heaven restored,
   for grace of salvation,
        O praise ye the Lord!

*Henry Williams Baker (1821-77),*
*based on Psalms 148 and 150*

## 245

*See also no.373*

1. O Priest and Victim, Lord of life,
   throw wide the gates of paradise!
   We face our foes in mortal strife;
   thou art our strength:
       O heed our cries!

2. To Father, Son and Spirit blest,
   one only God, be ceaseless praise!
   May he in goodness grant us rest
   in heav'n, our home,
       for endless days!

*St Thomas Aquinas (1227-74)*
*tr. James Quinn, S.J.*

## 246

1. O purest of creatures!
       Sweet mother, sweet maid;
   the one spotless womb
       wherein Jesus was laid.
   Dark night hath come down
       on us, mother, and we
   look out for thy shining,
       sweet star of the sea.

2. Deep night hath come down on
       this rough-spoken world.
   And the banners of darkness
       are boldly unfurled;
   and the tempest-tossed Church,
       all her eyes are on thee.
   They look to thy shining,
       sweet star of the sea.

3. He gazed on thy soul,
       it was spotless and fair;
   for the empire of sin,
       it had never been there;
   none ever had owned thee,
       dear mother, but he,
   and he blessed thy clear shining,
       sweet star of the sea.

4. Earth gave him one lodging;
       'twas deep in thy breast,
   and God found a home where
       the sinner finds rest;
   his home and his hiding-place,
       both were in thee;
   he was won by thy shining,
       sweet star of the sea.

5. Oh, blissful and calm
       was the wonderful rest
   that thou gavest thy God
       in thy virginal breast;
   for the heaven he left
       he found heaven in thee,
   and he shone in thy shining,
       sweet star of the sea.

*Frederick William Faber (1814-63)*

## 247

1. O sacred head sore wounded,
   defiled and put to scorn,
   O kingly head surrounded
   with mocking crown of thorn,
   what sorrow mars thy grandeur?
   Can death thy bloom deflower?
   O countenance whose splendour
   the hosts of heaven adore.

2. Thy beauty, long-desirèd,
   hath vanished from our sight;
   thy power is all expired,
   and quenched the light of light.
   Ah me! for whom thou diest,
   hide not so far thy grace:
   show me, O love most highest,
   the brightness of thy face.

3. I pray thee, Jesu, own me,
   me, shepherd good, for thine;
   who to thy fold hast won me,
   and fed with truth divine.
   Me guilty, me refuse not;
   incline thy face to me,
   this comfort that I lose not
   on earth to comfort thee.

4. In thy most bitter passion
   my heart to share doth cry,
   with thee for my salvation
   upon the cross to die.
   Ah, keep my heart thus movèd
   to stand thy cross beneath,
   to mourn thee, well-beloved,
   yet thank thee for thy death.

5. My days are few, O fail not,
   with thine immortal power,
   to hold me that I quail not
   in death's most fearful hour:
   that I may fight befriended,
   and see in my last strife
   to me thine arms extended
   upon the cross of life.

   *Paulus Gerhardt (1607-76),*
   *tr. Robert Bridges*

# 248

1. O Sacred Heart,
   our home lies deep in thee;
   on earth thou art an exile's rest,
   in heav'n the glory of the blest,
   O Sacred Heart.

2. O Sacred Heart,
   thou fount of contrite tears;
   where'er those living waters flow,
   new life to sinners they bestow,
   O Sacred Heart.

3. O Sacred Heart,
   bless our dear native land;
   may England's sons in truth e'er
                              stand,
   with faith's bright banner still in
                              hand,
   O Sacred Heart.

4. O Sacred Heart,
   our trust is all in thee,
   for though earth's night be dark
                        and drear,
   thou breathest rest where thou art
                        near,
   O Sacred Heart.

5. O Sacred Heart,
   when shades of death shall fall,
   receive us 'neath thy gentle care,
   and save us from the tempter's snare,
   O Sacred Heart.

6. O Sacred Heart,
   lead exiled children home,
   where we may ever rest near thee,
   in peace and joy eternally,
   O Sacred Heart.

   *Francis Stanfield (1835-1914)*

# 249

1. O thou, who at
      thy Eucharist didst pray
   that all thy Church
      might be for ever one,
   grant us at every
      Eucharist to say
   with longing heart and soul,
      "Thy will be done".
   O may we all one bread,
      one body be,
   one through this sacrament of unity.

2. For all thy Church,
      O Lord, we intercede;
   make thou our sad
      divisions soon to cease;
   draw us the nearer
      each to each, we plead,
   by drawing all to thee,
      O Prince of peace;
   thus may we all one
      bread, one body be,
   one through this sacrament of unity.

3. We pray thee too
      for wanderers from thy fold,
   O bring them back,
      good shepherd of the sheep,
   back to the faith which
      saints believed of old,
   back to the Church which still
      that faith doth keep;
   soon may we all one bread,
      one body be,
   one through this sacrament of unity.

4. So, Lord, at length
   When sacraments shall cease,
   may we be one
      with all thy Church above,
   one with thy saints in
      one unbroken peace,
   one with thy saints in one
      unbounded love:
   more blessed still, in peace
      and love to be
   one with the Trinity in unity.

   *William Harry Turton (1856-1938)*

# 250

1. O Trinity, most blessed light,
   O unity of sovereign might,
   as now the fiery sun departs,
   shed thou thy beams within our
                              hearts.

2. To thee our morning song of praise,
   to thee our evening prayer we raise;
   thee may our souls for evermore,
   in lowly reverence adore.

3. All praise to God the Father be,
   all praise, eternal Son, to thee,
   whom with the Spirit we adore,
   for ever and for evermore.

*St. Ambrose (340-397), tr. J. M. Neale*

# 251

1. Our Father, who art in heaven,
   hallowed be thy name.
   Thy kingdom come thy will be
                              done,
   hallowed be thy name,
   hallowed be thy name.

2. On earth as it is in heaven,
   hallowed be thy name.
   Give us this day our daily bread,
   hallowed be thy name,
   hallowed be thy name.

3. Forgive us our trespasses,
   hallowed be thy name,
   as we forgive those who trespass
                              against us,
   hallowed be thy name,
   hallowed be thy name.

4. And lead us not into temptation,
   hallowed be thy name,
   but deliver us from all that is evil,
   hallowed be thy name,
   hallowed be thy name.

5. For thine is the kingdom, the power
                              and the glory,
   hallowed be thy name,
   for ever, and for ever and ever,
   hallowed be thy name,
   hallowed be thy name.

6. Amen, amen, it shall be so,
   hallowed be thy name.
   Amen, amen, it shall be so,
   hallowed be thy name,
   hallowed be thy name.

*Traditional Caribbean*

# 252

1. Out and away
      the mountains are calling!
   Voices are clear
      and wide as the sky!
   Where is the music
      I hear in my heart:
   soars over valleys
      as swift as a lark;
   echoes the joy that has
      scattered the dark: I am free.

2. Hear the wind sigh
      through leaves that are falling;
   see the wind sway
      the trees that are dry.
   Silent the darkness
      where thunder-clouds form;
   still is the world as
      it waits for the storm:
   now comes the lightning that
      heralds the dawn of the rain.

3. Water is clear,
    as clear as the moonlight;
dew on the ground,
    a tear in the eye.
Rivers and torrents
    have vanished before;
oceans have coastlines
    and continents shores:
Boundless the flow that's
    unlocking the doors of my heart.

4. Free as the day
    my spirit is flying:
eagles have wings,
    but none strong as these!
Where have I found it,
    this life newly-grown?
Gently, my heart says
    it's not of my own:
deeper beyond me the Spirit
    has blown — he is love.

*John Glynn*


# 253

1. O worship the King
all glorious above;
O gratefully sing
his power and his love:
our shield and defender,
the ancient of days,
pavilioned in splendour,
and girded with praise.

2. O tell of his might,
O sing of his grace,
whose robe is the light,
whose canopy space.
His chariots of wrath,
the deep thunder-clouds form,
and dark is his path
on the wings of the storm.

3. This earth, with its store
of wonders untold,
almighty, thy power
hath founded of old;
hath stablished it fast
by a changeless decree,
and round it hath cast,
like a mantle, the sea.

4. Thy bountiful care
what tongue can recite?
It breathes in the air,
it shines in the light;
it streams from the hills,
it descends to the plain,
and sweetly distils
in the dew and the rain.

5. Frail children of dust,
and feeble as frail,
in thee do we trust,
nor find thee to fail;
thy mercies how tender!
How firm to the end!
Our maker, defender,
redeemer, and friend.

6. O measureless might,
ineffable love,
while angels delight
to hymn thee above,
thy humbler creation,
though feeble their lays,
with true adoration
shall sing to thy praise.

*Robert Grant (1779-1838)*

# 254

1. Peace is flowing like a river,
flowing out through you and me,
spreading out into the desert,
setting all the captives free.

2. Love is flowing like a river . . .

3. Joy is flowing like a river . . .

4. Hope is flowing like a river . . .

*Anonymous*

## 255

1. Peace is the gift of heaven to earth,
   softly enfolding our fears.
   Peace is the gift of
       Christ to the world,
   given for us.
   He is the Lamb who bore
       the pain of peace.

2. Peace is the gift of Christ
       to his Church,
   wound of the lance of his love.
   Love is the pain he
       suffered for man,
   offered to us:
   Oh, to accept the wound
       that brings us peace!

3. Joy is the gift the Spirit imparts,
   born of the heavens and earth.
   We are his children,
       children of joy,
   people of God:
   He is our Lord, our peace,
       our love, our joy!

*John Glynn*

## 256

*Peacemakers to be called
    the sons of God.
Peacemakers to be called
    the sons of God.*

1. Seeing the crowd,
   Jesus went up to the hill.
   There he sat down
   and was joined by his friends.
   Then he began to speak to them,
   and this is what he said:
   You must be . . .

2. Happy the gentle,
   for I give to them the earth.
   Happy the mourners,
   I will comfort their distress.
   Happy are those who thirst and
   hunger after what is right.
   They shall be . . .

*Malcolm Campbell-Carr*

## 257

1. Peace, perfect peace,
       is the gift of Christ our Lord.
   Peace, perfect peace,
       is the gift of Christ our Lord.
   Thus, says the Lord
       will the world know my friends.
   Peace, perfect peace,
       is the gift of Christ our Lord.

2. Love, perfect love . . .

3. Faith, perfect faith . . .

4. Hope, perfect hope . . . .

5. Joy, perfect joy . . .

*Kevin Mayhew*

## 258

1. People of God,
       give praise to his name,
   praise everlasting is his,
   brought to his feast
       as guests in his house,
   praise everlasting is his,
   enter with joy, the Spirit is here,
   praise everlasting is his,
   gladly receive the word that is life,
   praise everlasting is his.

2. Sing with one voice,
       one love in your heart,
   praise everlasting is his,
   love that the Saviour
       bears to us all;
   praise everlasting is his,
   friend for the friendless, neighbour
       for foe,
   praise everlasting is his,
   Christ for all peoples, we are his sign
   praise everlasting is his.

3. All that we have
   and all that we are,
   praise everlasting is his,
   all is his gift,
   his token of love,
   praise everlasting is his,
   all to be loved, made profit for love,
   praise everlasting is his,
   all to be taken home to the Lord,
   praise everlasting is his.

4. Praise for his glory,
   thanks for his gifts,
   praise everlasting is his,
   God everlasting, one that is three,
   praise everlasting is his,
   offer him praise,
   the Lord of all might,
   praise everlasting is his,
   majesty, glory, age upon age,
   praise everlasting is his.

*Luke Connaughton*
*(1919–79)*

# 259

1. Praise him, praise him,
   praise him in the morning,
   praise him in the noontime.
   Praise him, praise him,
   praise him when the sun goes down.

2. Love him, . . .

3. Trust him, . . .

4. Serve him, . . .

5. Jesus, . . .

*Anonymous*

# 260

1. Praise, my soul, the king of heaven!
   To his feet thy tribute bring.
   Ransomed, healed, restored, forgiven,
   who like me his praise should sing?
   Praise him! Praise him!
   Praise him! Praise him!
   Praise the everlasting king!

2. Praise him for his grace and favour
   to our fathers in distress;
   praise him still the same for ever,
   slow to chide and swift to bless.
   Praise him! Praise him!
   Praise him! Praise him!
   Glorious in his faithfulness!

3. Father-like he tends and spares us;
   well our feeble frame he knows;
   in his hands he gently bears us,
   rescues us from all our foes.
   Praise him! Praise him!
   Praise him! Praise him!
   Widely as his mercy flows!

4. Angels, help us to adore him;
   ye behold him face to face;
   sun and moon bow down before
   him,
   dwellers all in time and space.
   Praise him! Praise him!
   Praise him! Praise him!
   Praise with us the God of grace!

*Henry Francis Lyte (1793-1847)*

# 261

*Praise the Lord, and sing hallelujah,*
*hallelujah, hallelujah.*
*Praise the Lord, and sing hallelujah,*
*hallelujah, hallelujah.*

1. Praise him for the sun and
   for the stars above,
   hallelujah, hallelujah.
   Praise him with your brothers
   for he is the God of love,
   hallelujah, hallelujah.

2. Praise him when you're happy,
   praise him when you're sad,
   hallelujah, hallelujah.
   He's the God who saves us
   and his message makes us glad,
   hallelujah, hallelujah.

3. Praise him in the morning,
   praise him in the night,
   hallelujah, hallelujah.
   Praise him in the thunder
   for he is the God of might,
   hallelujah, hallelujah.

*Gerald O'Mahony*

# 262

1. Praise to the Holiest in the height,
   and in the depth be praise,
   in all his words most wonderful,
   most sure in all his ways.

2. O loving wisdom of our God!
   When all was sin and shame,
   a second Adam to the fight,
   and to the rescue came.

3. O wisest love! that flesh and blood
   which did in Adam fail,
   should strive afresh against the foe,
   should strive and should prevail;

4. And that a higher gift than grace
   should flesh and blood refine,
   God's presence and his very self,
   and Essence all divine.

5. O generous love! that he who smote
   in man for man the foe,
   the double agony in man
   for man should undergo.

6. And in the garden secretly
   and on the Cross on high,
   should teach his brethren, and
   inspire
   to suffer and to die.

7. Praise to the Holiest in the height,
   and in the depth be praise,
   in all his words most wonderful,
   most sure in all his ways.

*John Henry Newman (1801-90)*

# 263

Praise to the Lord our God,
let us sing together,
lifting our hearts and our voices
to sing with joy and gladness.
Come along, along, along,
and sing with . . .

*Estelle White*

# 264

1. Praise to the Lord, the Almighty,
   the King of creation!
   O my soul, praise him,
   for he is your health and
   salvation.
   All you who hear,
   now to his altar draw near,
   join in profound adoration.

2. Praise to the Lord, let us offer
   our gifts at his altar;
   let not our sins and transgressions
   now cause us to falter.
   Christ, the High Priest,
   bids us all join in his feast.
   Victims with him on the altar.

3. Praise to the Lord, oh, let all that
   is in us adore him!
   All that has life and breath,
   come now in praises before him.
   Let the Amen sound from
   his people again,
   now as we worship before him.

*Joachim Neander (1650-80),*
*tr. C. Winkworth*

# 265

1. Praise we now the Lord our God,
   all mankind in chorus;
   ceaselessly let seraphim,
   angels, pow'rs and cherubim
   sing with joy their praise of him,
   holy, Lord of Sabaoth.

2. All the earth and sea and sky,
   glorify their maker,
   blessed martyrs, prophets grand,
   Christ's beloved apostle-band,
   holy Church in every land.
   Sing his praise for ever.

3. Hail thou king of glory, Christ,
   born before all ages!
   Born of Mary, Virgin pure,
   thou didst us from death secure,
   opening wide to mankind poor,
   stores of heavenly treasure.

4. Seated now at God's right hand,
   bless thy chosen people;
   rule o'er us, dear Lord, we pray,
   keep us free from sin this day,
   save us, Lord, without delay,
   lest we be confounded.

5. In the solemn day of doom,
   we shall hear thy judgment;
   but remember, Lord, we cry,
   in that day when we shall die,
   how thy blood on us did lie,
   signing us thy people.

6. Praise we yet the Lord our God,
   throned in triune splendour:
   praise the Father, Lord of might,
   praise the Son, redeemer bright,
   praise the Spirit, source of light,
   through eternal ages.

*D. McRoberts*

# 266

1. Praise we our God with joy
   and gladness never ending;
   angels and saints with us
   their grateful voices blending.
   He is our Father dear,
   o'er filled with parent's love;
   mercies unsought, unknown,
   he showers from above.

2. He is our shepherd true;
   with watchful care unsleeping,
   on us, his erring sheep
   an eye of pity keeping;
   he with a mighty arm
   the bonds of sin doth break,
   and to our burden'd hearts
   in words of peace doth speak.

3. Graces in copious stream
   from that pure fount are welling,
   where, in our heart of hearts,
   our God hath set his dwelling.
   His word our lantern is;
   his peace our comfort still;
   his sweetness all our rest;
   our law, our life, his will.

*Frederick Oakeley (1802-80) and others*

# 267

1. Promised Lord, and Christ is he,
   may we soon his kingdom see.

   *Come, O Lord, quickly come,
   come in glory, come in glory,
   come in glory, quickly come.*

2. Teaching, healing once was he,
   may we soon his kingdom see.

3. Dead and buried once was he,
   may we soon his kingdom see.

4. Risen from the dead is he,
   may we soon his kingdom see.

5. Soon to come again is he,
   may we soon his kingdom see.
   *Come, O Lord, quickly come,
   in our lifetime, in our lifetime,
   in our lifetime may it be.*

*Roger Ruston,
based on a Jewish Passover Song*

# 268

1. Reap me the earth
      as a harvest to God,
   gather and bring it again,
   all that is his,
      to the Maker of all.
   Lift it and offer it high.
   *Bring bread, bring wine,
   give glory to the Lord;
   whose is the earth but God's,
   whose is the praise but his?*

2. Go with your song
      and your music with joy,
   go to the altar of God.
   Carry your offerings,
      fruits of the earth,
   work of your labouring hands.

3. Gladness and pity
      and passion and pain,
   all that is mortal in man,
   lay all before him,
      return him his gift,
   God, to whom all shall go home.

*Peter Icarus*

## 269

Rejoice in the Lord always,
and again I say rejoice.
Rejoice in the Lord always,
and again I say rejoice.
Rejoice, rejoice,
and again I say rejoice.
Rejoice, rejoice,
and again I say rejoice.

*from Scripture*

## 270

1. Rejoice! the Lord is King!
Your Lord and King adore;
mortals, give thanks and sing,
and triumph evermore:

   *Lift up your heart,
   lift up your voice;
   rejoice, again I say, rejoice.*

2. Jesus the Saviour reigns,
the God of truth and love;
when he had purged our stains,
he took his seat above:

3. His kingdom cannot fail;
he rules o'er earth and heaven;
the keys of death and hell
are to our Jesus given:

4. He sits at God's right hand
till all his foes submit,
and bow to his command,
and fall beneath his feet:

   *Charles Wesley (1707-88)*

## 271

1. Ride on! ride on in majesty!
Hark, all the tribes hosanna cry;
thy humble beast pursued his road
with palms and scattered garments
strowed.

2. Ride on! ride on in majesty!
In lowly pomp ride on to die;
O Christ, thy triumphs now begin
o'er captive death and conquered
sin.

3. Ride on! ride on in majesty!
The wingèd squadrons of the sky,
look down with sad and wondering
eyes

   to see the approaching sacrifice.

4. Ride on! ride on in majesty!
Thy last and fiercest strife is nigh;
the Father, on his sapphire throne
expects his own anointed Son.

5. Ride on! ride on in majesty!
In lowly pomp ride on to die;
bow thy meek head to mortal pain,
then take, O God, thy power, and
reign.

   *H. H. Milman (1791-1868)*

## 272

1. Round me falls the night,
Saviour be my light;
through the hours in darkness
shrouded
let me see thy face unclouded.
Let thy glory shine
in this heart of mine.

2. Earthly work is done,
earthly sounds are none;
rest in sleep and silence seeking,
let me hear thee softly speaking;
in my spirit's ear
whisper: "I am near".

3. Blessed heav'nly light
shining through earth's night;
voice that oft of love has told me,
arms, so strong, to clasp and hold
me;
thou thy watch will keep,
Saviour o'er my sleep.

   *W. Romanis (1824–99)*

# 273

1. Seasons come, seasons go,
   moon-struck tides will ebb and flow;
   when I forget my constant one
   he draws me back, he brings me
                    home.

   O love, my love,
      I hear you far away.
   a distant storm
      that will refresh the day.

2. Seasons come, seasons go,
   petals fall though flowers grow;
   and when I doubt love lifts a hand
   and scatters stars like grains of sand.
   Oh love, my love,
      I see you passing by
   like birds that fearlessly
      possess the sky.

3. Seasons come, seasons go,
   times to reap and times to sow;
   but you are love, a fruitful vine,
   in ev'ry season yielding wine.
   I hear my love
      in laughter and in song,
   no day too short,
      no winter night too long.

   *Michael Cockett*

# 274

1. See, amid the winter's snow,
   born for us on earth below,
   see, the tender lamb appears,
   promised from eternal years.

   *Hail, thou ever-blessed morn,*
   *hail, redemption's happy dawn!*
   *Sing through all Jerusalem,*
   *Christ is born in Bethlehem.*

2. Lo, within a manger lies
   he who built the starry skies;
   he who, throned in heights sublime,
   sits amid the cherubim.

3. Say, ye holy shepherds, say,
   what your joyful news today?
   Wherefore have ye left your sheep
   on the lonely mountain steep?

4. 'As we watched at dead of night,
   lo, we saw a wondrous light;
   angels, singing peace on earth,
   told us of the Saviour's birth.'

5. Sacred infant, all divine,
   what a tender love was thine,
   thus to come from highest bliss,
   down to such a world as this!

6. Virgin mother, Mary blest,
   by the joys that fill thy breast,
   pray for us, that we may prove
   worthy of the Saviour's love.

   *Edward Caswall (1814-78)*

# 275

1. See us, Lord, about thine altar;
   though so many, we are one;
   many souls by love united
   in the heart of Christ thy Son.

2. Hear our prayers, O loving Father,
   hear in them thy Son, our Lord;
   hear him speak our love and worship,
   as we sing with one accord.

3. Once were seen the blood and water;
   now he seems but bread and wine;
   then in human form he suffered,
   now his form is but a sign.

4. Wheat and grape contain the
                    meaning;
   food and drink he is to all;
   one in him, we kneel adoring,
   gathered by his loving call.

5. Hear us yet; so much is needful
   in our frail, disordered life;
   stay with us and tend our weakness
   till that day of no more strife.

6. Members of his mystic body
   now we know our prayer is heard,
   heard by thee, because thy children
   have received th' eternal word.

   *John Greally*

# 276

Shalom, my friend,
  shalom my friend, shalom, shalom,
the peace of Christ
  I give you today, shalom, shalom.

*Sandra Joan Billington*

# 277

1. Silent night, holy night,
   all is calm, all is bright,
   round yon virgin mother and child;
   holy infant so tender and mild:
   sleep in heavenly peace,
   sleep in heavenly peace.

2. Silent night, holy night.
   Shepherds quake at the sight,
   glories stream from heaven afar,
   heavenly hosts sing alleluia:
   Christ, the Saviour is born,
   Christ, the Saviour is born.

3. Silent night, holy night.
   Son of God, love's pure light
   radiant beams from thy holy face,
   with the dawn of redeeming grace:
   Jesus, Lord, at thy birth,
   Jesus, Lord, at thy birth.

*Joseph Mohr (1792-1848),*
*tr. J. Young*

# 278

*Sing, my soul. Sing, my soul.*
*Sing, my soul, of his mercy.*
*Sing, my soul. Sing, my soul.*
*Sing, my soul, of his mercy.*

1. The Lord is good to me.
   His light will shine on me.
   When city lights would blind my
                              eyes.
   He hears my silent call.
   His hands help when I fall.
   His gentle voice stills my sighs.

2. The Lord is good to me.
   His word will set me free
   when men would tie me to the
                              ground.

He mocks my foolish ways
with love that never fails.
When I'm most lost then I'm found.

3. The Lord is good to me.
   I hear him speak to me.
   His voice is in the rain that falls.
   He whispers in the air
   of his unending care.
   If I will hear, then he calls.

*Michael Cockett*

# 279

1. Sing, my tongue, the glorious battle,
   sing the last, the dread affray;
   o'er the cross, the victor's trophy,
   sound the high triumphal lay;
   how, the pains of death enduring,
   earth's redeemer won the day.

2. Faithful cross! above all other,
   one and only noble tree!
   None in foliage, none in blossom,
   none in fruit thy peer may be;
   sweetest wood and sweetest iron!
   Sweetest weight is hung on thee.

3. Bend, O lofty tree, thy branches,
   thy too rigid sinews bend;
   and awhile the stubborn hardness,
   which thy birth bestowed, suspend;
   and the limbs of heaven's high
                              monarch,
   gently on thine arms extend.

4. Thou alone wast counted worthy
   this world's ransom to sustain,
   that by thee a wrecked creation
   might its ark and haven gain,
   with the sacred blood anointed
   of the Lamb that hath been slain.

5. Praise and honour to the Father,
   praise and honour to the Son,
   praise and honour to the Spirit,
   ever three and ever one,
   one in might and one in glory,
   while eternal ages run.

*Venantius Fortunatus (530-609),*
*tr. J. M. Neale*

## 280

1. Sing of the bride
   and sing of the groom,
   and the wine that was flowing free,
   when the Lord was a guest
   at the wedding feast
   in a town in Galilee.

   *Fill the pots with water*
   *and raise the glasses high,*
   *for the Lord has come to Cana*
   *and changed water into wine.*

2. Sing of the bride
   and sing of the groom,
   and the feasting all night and day,
   with the wine running short
   at the wedding feast
   to the stewards' sad dismay.

3. "Please will you help,
   they have no more wine,"
   said a mother to her only son.
   He said: "Woman, don't you know
   you can't turn to me,
   for my time has not yet come."

4. "Wait till the day
   and wait till the time
   for the cross and for Calvary,
   but until that time
   here's a fine new wine
   with a taste that's fine and free."

5. Drink to the bride
   and drink to the groom
   at the wedding in Galilee,
   and drink to the life
   that is like new wine
   to all men who wish to be free.

   *Michael Cockett*

## 281

1. Sing of Mary, pure and lowly,
   virgin mother undefiled.
   Sing of God's own Son most holy,
   who became her little child.
   Fairest child of fairest mother,
   God, the Lord, who came to earth,
   Word made flesh, our very brother,
   takes our nature by his birth.

2. Sing of Jesus, son of Mary,
   in the home at Nazareth.
   Toil and labour cannot weary
   love enduring unto death.
   Constant was the love he gave her,
   though he went forth from her side,
   forth to preach and heal and suffer,
   till on Calvary he died.

3. Glory be to God the Father,
   glory be to God the Son;
   glory be to God the Spirit,
   glory to the three in one.
   From the heart of blessed Mary,
   from all saints the song ascends
   and the Church the strain re-echoes
   unto earth's remotest ends.

   *Roland F. Palmer, SSJE*

## 282

*Sing, sing, sing, sing, sing, sing!*
*Sing! people of God, sing!*
*Sing with one accord.*
*Sing! people of God,*
*sing your praises to the Lord.*

1. O Lord, how glorious over all
   the good earth is your name.
   You have exalted your majesty
   over ev'ry hill and plain.
   From the mouths of the little ones
   you fashion endless praise
   to silence all the vengeful ones
   and glorify your ways.

2. When we behold the heavens
   where your creation shines,
   the moon and stars you set in place
   to stand the test of time,
   what is man that you should mind,
   his sons that you should care?
   A little less than angels
   you have crowned him ev'rywhere.

3. You've given us dominion
over all that you have made.
We're masters of your handiwork
and rule them unafraid.
We're lords of the fish and birds,
of beasts both wild and tame.
O Lord, how glorious over all
the good earth is your name.

*Sebastian Temple*

# 283

1. Sing praises to God, sing praises,
sing praises to God, sing praises,
for he is the king of all the earth,
sing praises to his name.

2. Give glory to God, give glory,
give glory to God, give glory,
for he is the king of all the earth,
give glory to his name.

3. Give honour to God, give honour,
give honour to God, give honour,
for he is the king of all the earth,
give honour to his name.

*Anonymous*

# 284

1. Sing praises to the living God,
glory, hallelujah.
Come, adore the living God,
glory, hallelujah.
Though sun and moon may pass away
his words will ever stay.
His power is for evermore,
glory, hallelujah.

*Glory to the Trinity.
The undivided Unity,
the Father, Son and Spirit one,
from whom all life
and greatness come.*

2. And to the living God we sing,
glory hallelujah.
Let our love and praises ring,
glory hallelujah.
To all his sons he always gives
his mercy and his love.
So praise him now for evermore,
glory hallelujah.

3. And to the God who cannot die,
glory hallelujah.
To the living God we cry,
glory hallelujah.
He promised to be with us and
he lives in ev'ry one.
We love him now for evermore,
glory hallelujah.

*Sebastian Temple*

# 285

1. Sleep, holy babe,
upon thy mother's breast;
great Lord of earth and sea and sky,
how sweet it is to see thee lie
in such a place of rest.

2. Sleep, holy babe;
thine angels watch around,
all bending low, with folded wings,
before th'incarnate King of kings,
in reverent awe profound.

3. Sleep, holy babe,
while I with Mary gaze
in joy upon that face awhile,
upon the loving infant smile,
which there divinely plays.

4. Sleep, holy babe,
ah, take thy brief repose,
too quickly will thy slumbers break,
and thou to lengthen'd pains awake,
that death alone shall close.

5. O lady blest,
sweet Virgin, hear my cry;
forgive the wrong that I have done
to thee, in causing thy dear Son
upon the cross to die.

*Edward Caswall (1814-78)*

# 286

1. Songs of thankfulness and praise,
Jesus, Lord to thee we raise,
manifested by the star
to the sages from afar;
branch of royal David's stem,
in thy birth at Bethlehem;
anthems be to thee addressed;
God in man made manifest.

2. Manifest at Jordan's stream,
prophet, Priest and King supreme,
and at Cana wedding-guest,
in thy Godhead manifest,
manifest in power divine,
changing water into wine;
anthems be to thee addressed;
God in man made manifest.

3. Manifest in making whole,
palsied limbs and fainting soul,
manifest in valiant fight,
quelling all the devil's might,
manifest in gracious will,
ever bringing good from ill;
anthems be to thee addressed;
God in man made manifest.

4. Sun and moon shall darkened be,
stars shall fall, the heavens shall flee.
Christ will then like lightning shine.
All will see his glorious sign.
All will see the judge appear;
all will then the trumpet hear;
thou by all wilt be confessed;
God in man made manifest.

5. Grant us grace to see thee, Lord,
mirrored in thy holy word;
may we imitate thee now
and be pure, as pure art thou;
that we like to thee may be
at thy great Epiphany,
and may praise thee, ever blest,
God in man made manifest.

*Christopher Wordsworth (1807-85)*

# 287

*Sons of God, hear his holy Word!*
*Gather round the table of the Lord!*
*Eat his Body, drink his Blood,*
*and we'll sing a song of love.*
*Allelu, allelu, allelu, alleluia.*

1. Brothers, sisters, we are one,
and our life has just begun.
In the Spirit we are young.
We can live for ever.

2. Shout together to the Lord
who has promised our reward:
happiness a hundredfold,
and we'll live forever.

3. Jesus gave a new command
that we love our fellow man
till we reach the promised land,
where we'll live forever.

4. If we want to live with him;
we must also die with him;
die to selfishness and sin,
and we'll rise forever.

5. Make the world a unity,
make all men one family
till we meet the Trinity
and live with them forever.

6. With the Church we celebrate;
Jesus' coming we await,
so we make a holiday,
so we'll live forever.

*James Thiem*
© *1966 F.E.L. Publications*

# 288

1. Soul of my Saviour,
      sanctify my breast;
   Body of Christ,
      be thou my saving guest;
   Blood of my Saviour,
      bathe me in thy tide,
   wash me with water
      flowing from thy side.

2. Strength and protection
      may thy Passion be;
   O Blessed Jesus
      hear and answer me;
   deep in thy wounds, Lord,
      hide and shelter me;
   so shall I never,
      never part from thee.

3. Guard and defend me
      from the foe malign;
   in death's dread moments
      make me only thine;
   call me, and bid me
      come to thee on high,
   when I may praise thee
      with thy saints for aye.

*Ascribed to John XXII (1249-1334),*
*tr. Anonymous*

# 289

   Spirit of the living God,
      fall afresh on me.
   Spirit of the living God,
      fall afresh on me.
   Break me, melt me,
      mould me, fill me.
   Spirit of the living God,
      fall afresh on me.

*Daniel Iverson*

# 290

1. Star of ocean, lead us;
      God for mother claims thee,
   ever Virgin names thee;
   gate of heaven, speed us.

2. Ave to thee crying
   Gabriel went before us;
   peace do thou restore us,
   Eva's knot untying.

3. Loose the bonds that chain us,
   darkened eyes enlighten,
   clouded prospects brighten,
   heavenly mercies gain us.

4. For thy sons thou carest;
   offer Christ our praying —
   still thy word obeying —
   whom on earth thou barest.

5. Purer, kinder maiden
   God did never fashion;
   pureness and compassion
   grant to hearts sin-laden.

6. From that sin release us,
   shield us, heavenward faring,
   heaven, that is but sharing
   in thy joy with Jesus.

7. Honour, praise and merit
   to our God address we;
   Three in One confess we,
   Father, Son and Spirit.

*9th c., tr. R. A. Knox*

# 291

   *Steal away, steal away,*
   *steal away to Jesus.*
   *Steal away, steal away home.*
   *I ain't got long to stay here.*

1. My Lord, he calls me.
   He calls me by the thunder.
   The trumpet sounds within my soul;
   I ain't got long to stay here.

2. Green trees are bending,
   the sinner stands a-trembling.
   The trumpet sounds within my soul;
   I ain't got long to stay here.

3. My Lord, he calls me,
   he calls me by the lightning.
   The trumpet sounds within my soul;
   I ain't got long to stay here.

*Traditional Spiritual*

## 292

*Suffer little children*
  *to come unto me,*
*for theirs is the kingdom of heaven.*
*Suffer little children*
  *to come unto me.*
*for theirs is the kingdom*
  *of the Lord.*

1. There came unto him
   children, little children,
   that he might lay his hands
     upon them,
   pray for and bless them,
   children, little children,
   gathered round our Lord.

2. The disciples said:
   "Children, little children,
   leave the Master to his prayer.
   Begone and stay not,
   children, little children,
   gathered round our Lord."

3. But Jesus said:
   "Children, little children,
   stay my blessing to receive.
   Forbid you not that
   children, little children,
   shall gather round the Lord."

4. "For you must be like
   children, little children,
   humble, simple, pure in heart.
   For it is to these
   children, little children,
   the kingdom of heav'n belongs."

*Philip Green*

## 293

1. Sweet heart of Jesus,
     fount of love and mercy,
   today we come,
     thy blessing to implore;
   O touch our hearts,
     so cold and so ungrateful,
   and make them, Lord,
     thine own for evermore.

*Sweet heart of Jesus, we implore,*
*O make us love thee more and more.*

2. Sweet heart of Jesus,
     make us know and love thee,
   unfold to us
     the treasures of thy grace;
   that so our hearts,
     from things of earth uplifted,
   may long alone
     to gaze upon thy face.

3. Sweet heart of Jesus,
     make us pure and gentle,
   and teach us how
     to do thy blessed will;
   to follow close
     the print of thy dear footsteps,
   and when we fall
     — sweet heart, oh, love us still.

4. Sweet heart of Jesus,
     bless all hearts that love thee,
   and may thine own
     heart ever blessed be,
   bless us, dear Lord,
     and bless the friends we cherish,
   and keep us true
     to Mary and to thee.

*Traditional*

## 294

1. Sweet sacrament divine,
   hid in thy earthly home,
   lo! round thy lowly shrine,
   with suppliant hearts we come;
   Jesus, to thee our voice we raise,
   in songs of love and heartfelt praise,
   sweet sacrament divine.

2. Sweet sacrament of peace,
   dear home of every heart,
   where restless yearnings cease,
   and sorrows all depart,
   there in thine ear all trustfully
   we tell our tale of misery,
   sweet sacrament of peace.

3. Sweet sacrament of rest,
   Ark from the ocean's roar,
   within thy shelter blest
   soon may we reach the shore,
   save us, for still the tempest raves;
   save, lest we sink beneath the waves
   sweet sacrament of rest.

4. Sweet sacrament divine,
   earth's light and jubilee,
   in thy far depths doth shine
   thy Godhead's majesty;
   sweet light, so shine on us, we pray,
   that earthly joys may fade away,
   sweet sacrament divine.

   *Francis Stanfield (1835-1914)*

## 295

1. Sweet Saviour, bless us ere we go,
   thy word into our minds instil;
   and make our lukewarm hearts to
   glow
   with lowly love and fervent will.

   *Through life's long day
       and death's dark night,
   O gentle Jesus, be our light.*

2. The day is done; its hours have run,
   and thou hast taken count of all,
   the scanty triumphs grace has won,
   the broken vow, the frequent fall.

3. Grant us, dear Lord, from evil ways,
   true absolution and release;
   and bless us more than in past days
   with purity and inward peace.

4. Do more than pardon; give us joy,
   sweet fear and sober liberty,
   and loving hearts without alloy,
   that only long to be like thee.

5. Labour is sweet, for thou hast toiled,
   and care is light, for thou hast cared;
   let not our works with self be soiled.
   Nor in unsimple ways ensnared.

6. For all we love − the poor, the sad,
   the sinful − unto thee we call;
   oh let thy mercy make us glad,
   thou art our Jesus and our all.

   *Frederick William Faber (1814-63)*

## 296

1. Take my hands
       and make them as your own,
   and use them for your
       Kingdom here on earth.
   Consecrate them to your care,
   anoint them for
       your service where
   you may need your gospel to be sown.

2. Take my hands.
       They speak now for my heart,
   and by their actions
       they will show their love.
   Guard them on their daily course,
   be their strength
       and guiding force
   to ever serve the Trinity above.

3. Take my hands.
       I give them to you, Lord.
   Prepare them for the
       service of your name.
   Open them to human need
   and by their love
       they'll sow your seed
   so all may know
       the love and hope you give.

   *Sebastian Temple*

## 297

*Take our bread, we ask you,*
*take our hearts, we love you,*
*take our lives, oh Father,*
*we are yours, we are yours.*

1. Yours as we stand
       at the table you set,
   yours as we eat the bread
       our hearts can't forget.
   We are the signs
       of your life with us yet;
   we are yours, we are yours.

2. Your holy people
       stand washed in your blood,
   Spirit filled, yet hungry,
       we await your food.
   Poor though we are,
       we have brought ourselves to you:
   we are yours, we are yours,

*Joseph Wise*

## 298

1. Thank you
       for giving me the morning.
   Thank you for ev'ry day that's new.
   Thank you
       that I can know my worries
   can be cast on you.

2. Thank you
       for all my friends and brothers.
   Thank you for all the men that live.
   Thank you
       for even greatest enemies
   I can forgive.

3. Thank you,
       I have my occupation.
   Thank you
       for ev'ry pleasure small.
   Thank you
       for music, light and gladness.
   Thank you for them all.

4. Thank you
       for many little sorrows.
   Thank you for ev'ry kindly word.
   Thank you
       for ev'rywhere your guidance
   reaches ev'ry land.

5. Thank you,
       I see your Word has meaning.
   Thank you, I know your Spirit here.
   Thank you
       because you love all people,
   those both far and near.

6. Thank you,
       O Lord, you spoke unto us.
   Thank you that for our words you car
   Thank you,
       O Lord, you came among us,
   bread and wine to share.

7. Thank you,
       O Lord, your love is boundless.
   Thank you that I am full of you.
   Thank you,
       you made me feel so glad and
   thankful as I do.

*Walter van der Haas*
*and Peter-Paul van Lelyveld*

## 299

1. The bakerwoman
       in her humble lodge
   received a grain of wheat from God.
   For nine whole months
       the grain she stored.
   Behold the handmaid of the Lord.
   Make us the bread, Mary, Mary.
   Make us the bread,
       we need to be fed.

2. The bakerwoman took
       the road which led
   to Bethlehem, the house of bread.
   To knead the bread she laboured
       through the night,
   and brought it forth about midnight.
   Bake us the bread, Mary, Mary.
   Bake us the bread,
       we need to be fed.

3. She baked the bread for thirty years
   by the fire of her love
      and the salt of her tears,
   by the warmth of a heart
      so tender and bright,
   and the bread was golden
      brown and white.
   Bring us the bread, Mary, Mary.
   Bring us the bread,
      we need to be fed.

4. After thirty years
      the bread was done.
   It was taken to town
      by her only son;
   the soft white bread to be given free
   to the hungry people of Galilee.
   Give us the bread, Mary, Mary.
   Give us the bread,
      we need to be fed.

5. For thirty coins the bread was sold,
   and a thousand teeth so cold,
      so cold
   tore it to pieces on a Friday noon
   when the sun turned black
      and red the moon.
   Break us the bread, Mary, Mary.
   Break us the bread,
      we need to be fed.

6. And when she saw
      the bread so white,
   the living bread she had made
      at night,
   devoured as wolves might
      devour a sheep,
   the bakerwoman began to weep.
   Weep for the bread, Mary, Mary.
   Weep for the bread,
      we need to be fed.

7. But the bakerwoman's only son
   appeared to his friends
      when three days had run
   on the road which to Emmaus led,
   and they knew him in
      the breaking of bread.
   Lift up your head, Mary, Mary.
   Lift up your head,
      for now we've been fed.

*Hubert Richards*

# 300

1. The Church's one foundation,
   is Jesus Christ, her Lord;
   she is his new creation,
   by water and the Word;
   from heav'n he came and sought her
   to be his holy bride,
   with his own blood he bought her,
   and for her life he died.

2. Elect from every nation,
   yet one o'er all the earth,
   her charter of salvation
   one Lord, one faith, one birth;
   one holy name she blesses,
   partakes one holy food,
   and to one hope she presses,
   with every grace endued.

3. 'Mid toil, and tribulation,
   and tumult of her war,
   she waits the consummation
   of peace for evermore;
   till with the vision glorious
   her longing eyes are blest,
   and the great Church victorious
   shall be the Church at rest.

4. Yet she on earth hath union
   with God the Three in One,
   and mystic sweet communion
   with those whose rest is won:
   O happy ones and holy!
   Lord, give us grace that we
   like them, the meek and lowly
   on high may dwell with thee.

*S. J. Stone (1830-1900)*

# 301

1. The coming of our God
   our thoughts must now employ;
   then let us meet him on the road
   with songs of holy joy.

2. The co-eternal Son,
   a maiden's offspring see;
   a servant's form Christ putteth on,
   to set his people free.

3. Daughter of Sion, rise
to greet thine infant king,
nor let thy stubborn heart despise
the pardon he doth bring.

4. In glory from his throne
again will Christ descend,
and summon all that are his own
to joys that never end.

5. Let deeds of darkness fly
before the approaching morn,
for unto sin 'tis ours to die,
and serve the virgin-born.

6. Our joyful praises sing
to Christ, that set us free;
like tribute to the Father bring,
and, Holy Ghost, to thee.

*Charles Coffin (1676-1749),*
*tr. R. Campbell*

# 302

1. The day of resurrection!
Earth, tell it out abroad;
the Passover of gladness
the Passover of God!
From death to life eternal,
from earth unto the sky,
our Christ hath brought us over
with hymns of victory.

2. Our hearts be pure from evil,
that we may see aright
the Lord in rays eternal
of resurrection-light;
And listening to his accents,
may hear so calm and plain
his own 'All hail' and, hearing,
may raise the victor strain.

3. Now let the heavens be joyful,
and earth her song begin,
the round world keep high triumph,
and all that is therein;
Let all things seen and unseen
their notes of gladness blend,
for Christ the Lord hath risen,
our joy that hath no end.

*St. John Damascene (d. c.754)*
*tr. J.M. Neale*

# 303

1. The day thou gavest Lord, is ended:
the darkness falls at thy behest;
to thee our morning
hymns ascended;
thy praise shall sanctify our rest.

2. We thank thee that thy Church
unsleeping,
while earth rolls onward into light,
through all the world her
watch is keeping,
and rests not now by day or night.

3. As o'er each continent and island
the dawn leads on another day,
the voice of prayer is
never silent,
nor dies the strain of praise away.

4. The sun that bids us rest is waking
our brethren 'neath the western sky
and hour by hour fresh
lips are making
thy wondrous doings heard on high.

5. So be it, Lord; thy throne shall
never,
like earth's proud empire, pass away;
thy kingdom stands, and
grows for ever,
till all thy creatures own thy sway.

*John Ellerton (1826-93)*

# 304

1. The farmer in the fertile field is
   sowing, sowing.
   The seed is good,
       the shoots of corn are
   growing, growing, growing, growing.

2. An enemy with darnel seed is
   sowing, sowing.
   The weed that fights
       the growing corn is
   choking, choking, choking, choking.

3. Together till the harvest they'll be
   growing, growing.
   But then what has
       been sown we will be
   reaping, reaping, reaping, reaping.

4. The corn is taken to the barn for
   storing, storing.
   The weed is cast
       into the fire for
   burning, burning, burning, burning.

*Michael Cockett*

# 305

1. The first Nowell the angel did say
       was to certain poor shepherds in
       fields as they lay:
   in fields where they lay keeping
       their sheep,
   on a cold winter's night that was
       so deep.

   *Nowell, Nowell, Nowell, Nowell,*
   *born is the King of Israel!*

2. They looked up and saw a star,
       shining in the east, beyond them
       far,
   and to the earth it gave great light,
   and so it continued both day and
       night.

3. And by the light of that same star,
       three wise men came from country
       far.
   To seek for a king was their intent,
   and to follow the star wherever it
       went.

4. This star drew nigh to the north-
       west,
   o'er Bethlehem it took its rest,
   and there it did both stop and stay
   right over the place where Jesus lay

5. Then entered in those wise men
       three,
   full reverently upon their knee,
   and offered there in his presence,
   their gold and myrrh and
       frankincense.

6. Then let us all with one accord
   sing praises to our heavenly Lord,
   that hath made heaven and earth of
       nought,
   and with his blood mankind hath
       bought.

*Traditional Old English*

# 306

1. The God whom earth,
       and sea, and sky,
   adore and laud and magnify,
   who o'er their threefold fabric
                               reigns,
   the Virgin's spotless womb contains.

2. The God whose will
       by moon and sun,
   and all things in due course is done,
   is borne upon a maiden's breast
   by fullest heavenly grace possessed.

3. How blest that mother,
       in whose shrine
   the great Artificer divine,
   whose hand contains the earth and
                                  sky,
   vouchsafed, as in his ark, to lie!

4. Blest, in the message Gabriel brought;
   blest, by the work the Spirit wrought;
   from whom the great desire of earth,
   took human flesh and human birth.

5. All honour, laud and glory be,
   O Jesus, virgin-born, to thee!
   All glory, as is ever meet
   to Father and to Paraclete.

*Ascribed to Venantius Fortunatus*
*(530-609), tr. J. M. Neale*

# 307

1. The green life rises from the earth,
   the life of sun and rain and soil,
   in seed and shoot, in grain and grape,
   in food and drink for men.

   *Praise be to God for all his gifts,*
   *praise for the bread and wine.*

2. The Lord of Spring, the Lord of Life,
   made bread his body, wine his blood.
   The life of earth, the life of God,
   becomes the life of man.

3. We take in hand the bread and wine,
   reminder of the dying Lord.
   This food, this drink, this feast of joy
   gives Christ's own life to us.

4. "The Son of Man must die," said he,
   "my death will raise you all to life.
   No blade is born, no harvest reaped,
   until the seed has died.

5. "These are the signs of death and life,
   the bread you break, the cup you share:
   my dying gift in which I live,
   my death is life to you."

6. Give praise to God who gave this gift,
   his very Son, to bring us life.
   The Father's life in him is ours,
   his Spirit breathes in us.

*Luke Connaughton (1919–79)*

# 308

1. The head that once was crowned
                           with thorns
   is crowned with glory now:
   a royal diadem adorns
   the mighty victor's brow.

2. The highest place that heaven
                           affords
   is his, is his by right.
   The King of kings and Lord of lords,
   and heaven's eternal light;

3. The joy of all who dwell above,
   the joy of all below,
   to whom he manifests his love,
   and grants his name to know.

4. To them the cross, with all its shame
   with all its grace is given;
   their name an everlasting name,
   their joy the joy of heaven.

5. They suffer with their Lord below,
   they reign with him above,
   their profit and their joy to know
   the mystery of his love.

6. The cross he bore is life and health,
   though shame and death to him;
   his people's hope, his people's
                           wealth,
   their everlasting theme.

*Thomas Kelly (1769-1854)*

# 309

1. The heav'nly Word, proceeding forth
   yet leaving not the Father's side,
   accomplishing his work on earth
   had reached at length life's eventide.

2. By false disciple to be giv'n
   to foemen for his life athirst,
   himself, the very bread of heav'n,
   he gave to his disciples first.

3. He gave himself in either kind,
   he gave his flesh, he gave his blood;
   in love's own fullness thus designed,
   of the whole man to be the food.

4. O saving victim, opening wide
   the gate of heav'n to man below,
   our foes press on from every side;
   thine aid supply, thy strength
                              bestow.

5. To thy great name be endless praise,
   Immortal Godhead, one in three;
   O grant us endless length of days
   in our true native land with thee.

*St. Thomas Aquinas (1227-74),*
*tr. J. M. Neale*

# 310

*The King of glory comes*
*the nation rejoices*
*open the gates before him,*
*lift up your voices.*

1. Who is the King of glory
   how shall we call him?
   He is Emmanuel,
   the promised of ages.

2. In all of Galilee,
   in city and village,
   he goes among his people,
   curing their illness.

3. Sing then of David's Son,
   our Saviour and brother;
   in all of Galilee
   was never another.

4. He gave his life for us,
   the pledge of salvation.
   He took upon himself
   the sins of the nation.

5. He conquered sin and death;
   he truly has risen.
   And he will share with us
   his heavenly vision.

*W. F. Jabusch*

# 311

1. The King of love my Shepherd is,
   whose goodness faileth never;
   I nothing lack if I am his
   and he is mine for ever.

2. Where streams of living water flow
   my ransomed soul he leadeth,
   and where the verdant pastures grow
   with food celestial feedeth.

3. Perverse and foolish oft I strayed
   but yet in love he sought me,
   and on his shoulder gently laid,
   and home, rejoicing, brought me.

4. In death's dark vale I fear no ill
   with thee, dear Lord, beside me;
   thy rod and staff my comfort still,
   thy cross before to guide me.

5. Thou spread'st a table in my sight,
   thy unction grace bestoweth:
   and O what transport of delight
   from thy pure chalice floweth!

6. And so through all the length of
                                 days
   thy goodness faileth never;
   good Shepherd, may I sing thy praise
   within thy house for ever.

*Henry Williams Baker (1821-77)*

# 312

1. The Lord's my shepherd, I'll not
                                 want,
   he makes me down to lie
   in pastures green. He leadeth me
   the quiet waters by.

2. My soul he doth restore again,
   and me to walk doth make
   within the paths of righteousness,
   e'en for his own name's sake.

3. Yea, though I walk in death's dark vale,
yet will I fear none ill.
For thou art with me, and thy rod
and staff me comfort still.

4. My table thou hast furnished
in presence of my foes,
my head thou dost with oil anoint,
and my cup overflows.

5. Goodness and mercy all my life
shall surely follow me.
And in God's house for evermore
my dwelling-place shall be.

*Paraphrased from Ps. 22(23)
in the "Scottish Psalter" 1650*

# 313

1. The Mass is ended, all go in peace.
We must diminish,
and Christ increase.
We take him with us
where'er we go
that through our actions
his life may show.

2. We witness his love to ev'ryone
by our communion
with Christ the Son.
We take the Mass to
where men may be,
so Christ may shine forth
for all to see.

3. Thanks to the Father
who shows the way.
His life within us
throughout each day.
Let all our living
and loving be
to praise and honour
the Trinity.

4. The Mass is ended, all go in peace.
We must diminish
and Christ increase.
We take him with us
where'er we go
that through our actions
his life may show.

*Sebastian Temple*

# 314

1. The prophet in his hunger
asked for bread.
He asked the poor
and famine was their guest.
They saw starvation
walking in the street,
the doomed who thought
to eat their last and die.

2. It is the Lord
who lights the blinded eye,
who lends the poor his wealth,
the weak his strength,
who feeds us with
his everlasting love,
and pours for men
his justice like strong wine.

3. Because the widow
offered of her last,
and opened to his need
her empty hand,
Elijah promised her:
"You shall not want.
Your larder never shall
be clean of food."

4. The widow and the orphan
are his care;
whom none will else defend,
he will defend:
he puts the strutting pride
of tyrants down,
and raises up the lowly
from the dust.

5. See, in the temple,
how with gestures wide,
the rich men cast
their casual gold to God,
the widow offers
all her dwindling purse,
the pence of poverty —
a richer gift.

*Luke Connaughton (1919–79)*

# 315

1. The race that long in darkness pined
   has seen a glorious light:
   the people dwell in day, who dwelt
   in death's surrounding night.

2. To hail thy rise, thou better sun,
   the gathering nations come,
   joyous as when the reapers bear
   the harvest treasures home.·

3. To us a child of hope is born,
   to us a Son is given;
   him shall the tribes of earth obey,
   him all the hosts of heaven.

4. His name shall be the Prince of Peace
   for evermore adored,
   the Wonderful, the Counsellor,
   the great and mighty Lord.

5. His power increasing still shall
                              spread,
   his reign no end shall know;
   justice shall guard his throne above,
   and peace abound below.

   *John Morison (1749-98)*

# 316

1. There is a green hill far away,
   without a city wall,
   where the dear Lord was crucified
   who died to save us all.

2. We may not know, we cannot tell,
   what pains he had to bear,
   but we believe it was for us
   he hung and suffered there.

3. He died that we might be forgiven,
   he died to make us good;
   that we might go at last to heaven,
   saved by his precious blood.

4. There was no other good enough
   to pay the price of sin;
   he only could unlock the gate
   of heaven, and let us in.

5. O, dearly, dearly has he loved,
   and we must love him too,
   and trust in his redeeming blood,
   and try his works to do.

   *Cecil Frances Alexander (1818–95)*

# 317

1. There is a world
       where people come and go
   about their ways and
       never care to know
   that ev'ry step
       they take is placed on roads
   made out of men
       who had to carry loads too hard
       to bear.

   *"That world's not ours,"*
       *that's what we always say.*
   *"We'll build a new one*
       *but some other day."*
   *When will we wake*
       *from comfort and from ease,*
   *and strive together*
       *to create a world of love and peace?*

2. There is a world
       where people walk alone,
   and have around them
       men with hearts of stone,
   who would not spare
       one second of their day,
   or spend their breath
       in order just to say: "Your pain
       is mine."

3. There is a world
       where brothers cannot meet
   with one another
       where the tramp of feet
   brings men of ice,
       men who would force apart
   friends of all races
       having but one heart, a heart of
       love.

   *Estelle White*

## 318

1. The royal banners forward go,
   the cross shines forth in mystic glow,
   where he in flesh, our flesh who
                              made,
   our sentence bore, our ransom paid.

2. There whilst he hung, his sacred side
   by soldier's spear was open'd wide,
   to cleanse us in the precious flood
   of water mingled with his blood.

3. Fulfill'd is now what David told
   in true prophetic song of old,
   how God the heathen's king should
                              be;
   for God is reigning from the tree.

4. O tree of glory, tree most fair,
   ordain'd those holy limbs to bear,
   how bright in purple robe it stood,
   the purple of a saviour's blood!

5. Upon its arms, like balance true,
   he weigh'd the price for sinners due,
   the price which none but he could
                              pay:
   and spoil'd the spoiler of his prey.

6. To thee, eternal Three in One,
   let homage meet by all be done,
   as by the cross thou dost restore,
   so rule and guide us evermore.

*Venantius Fortunatus (530-609),*
*tr. J. M. Neale and others*

## 319

1. The Spirit of the Lord
       is now upon me
   to heal the broken heart
       and set the captives free,
   to open prison doors
       and make the blind to see.
   The Spirit of the Lord
       is now on me.

*Anonymous*

## 320    THE BEATITUDES

**The Kingdom** (the Kingdom)
**of Heaven,** (of Heaven)
**the Kingdom of Heaven is**
  **yours.**
**A new world** (a new world)
**in Jesus,** (in Jesus)
**a new world in Jesus is yours.**

1. Blessed are you in sorrow and
       grief:
   for you shall be consoled.
   Blessed are you the gentle in
       heart:
   you shall inherit the earth.

2. Blessed are you who hunger
       for right:
   for you shall be satisfied.
   Blessed are you the merciful
       ones:
   for you shall be pardoned too.

3. Blessed are you who hearts
       are pure:
   your eyes shall gaze on the Lord.
   Blessed are you who strive after
       peace:
   the Lord will call you His own.

4. Blessed are you who suffer for
       right:
   the Heavenly Kingdom is yours.
   Blessed are you who suffer for
       me:
   for you shall reap your reward.

*Mike Anderson*

# 321

1. The Virgin Mary had a baby boy,
   the Virgin Mary had a baby boy,
   the Virgin Mary had a baby boy,
   and they said that his name was
   
   Jesus

*He came from the glory,*
*he came from the glorious kingdom.*
*He came from the glory,*
*he came from the glorious kingdom.*
*Oh yes, believer,*
*Oh yes, believer.*
*He came from the glory,*
*he came from the glorious kingdom.*

2. The angels sang
   when the baby was born . . .
   and proclaimed him
   the Saviour Jesus.

3. The wise men saw
   where the baby was born . . .
   and they saw
   that his name was Jesus.

*Traditional West Indian*

# 322

1. The wandering flock of Israel
   is scattered and far
   from home and hope;
   the Shepherd alone,
   with crook and staff,
   can find them and lead
   and keep them safe.

*He made and upheld us,*
*granted grace;*
*his smile is our peace,*
*his word our hope.*

2. I walk on the heights,
   I climb and cling,
   the terror beneath,
   the ice aloft.
   I look for his tracks,
   await his hand
   to help and to hold,
   to guide and save.

3. I thirst for his word
   as grass in drought,
   dry, brittle and barren,
   parched and brown;
   no shower can fall,
   no sap rise green
   no hope, if the Lord
   should send no rain.

4. Creator of all,
   your craftman's care
   with fashioning hand
   caressed our clay:
   this vine is the work
   your hands have wrought,
   your love is the sun,
   our soil of growth.

*J. Smith*

# 323

1. They hung him on a cross,
   they hung him on a cross,
   they hung him on a cross for me.
   One day when I was lost,
   they hung him on a cross,
   they hung him on a cross for me.

2. They whipped him up the hill, . . .

3. They speared him in the side, . . .

4. The blood came streaming down . . .

5. He hung his head and died, . . .

6. He's coming back again, . . .

*Spiritual*

# 324

1. They say I am wise
    and they say I am King.
   I'm a carpenter's son
    and I don't own a thing.
   They say I am rich
    and they say I am poor,
   and when I came knocking
    they bolted the door.

2. They asked me for bread
    and they asked for a sign.
   I gave them some bread
    and I gave them some wine.
   The bread was my body,
    the wine was my blood.
   They still turned away from me
    looking for food.

3. They shouted with joy.
    They laid palms on the road,
   but into the town
    on a donkey I rode.
   They said: "Do not go
    for we can't stand the loss."
   The very next morning
    they gave me a cross.

4. They brought me down low
    though they hung me up high.
   They brought me to life
    though they left me to die.
   They buried me deep
    with a stone at my head,
   but I am the living
    and they are the dead.

*Michael Cockett*

# 325

1. This day God gives me
   strength of high heaven,
   sun and moon shining,
    flame in my hearth,
   flashing of lightning,
   wind in its swiftness,
   deeps of the ocean,
    firmness of earth.

2. This day God sends me
   strength as my steersman,
   might to uphold me,
    wisdom as guide.
   Your eyes are watchful,
   your ears are listening,
   your lips are speaking,
    friend at my side.

3. God's way is my way,
   God's shield is round me,
   God's host defends me,
    saving from ill.
   Angels of heaven,
   drive from me always
   all that would harm me,
    stand by me still.

4. Rising, I thank you,
   mighty and strong One,
   King of creation,
    giver of rest,
   firmly confessing
   Threeness of Persons,
   Oneness of Godhead,
    Trinity blest.

*Adapted from St. Patrick's Breastplate*

*James Quinn, S.J.*

# 326

1. This is the image of the queen
who reigns in bliss above;
of her who is the hope of men,
whom men and angels love.
Most holy Mary, at thy feet
I bend a suppliant knee;
in this thy own sweet month of May,
do thou remember me.

2. The homage offered at the feet
of Mary's image here
to Mary's self at once ascends
above the starry sphere.
Most holy Mary, at thy feet
I bend a suppliant knee;
in all my joy, in all my pain,
do thou remember me.

3. How fair soever be the form
which here your eyes behold,
its beauty is by Mary's self
excell'd a thousandfold.
Most holy Mary, at thy feet,
I bend a suppliant knee;
in my temptations each and all,
do thou remember me.

4. Sweet are the flow'rets we have
culled,
this image to adorn;
but sweeter far is Mary's self,
that rose without a thorn.
Most holy Mary, at thy feet
I bend a suppliant knee;
when on the bed of death I lie,
do thou remember me.

5. O lady, by the stars that make
a glory round thy head;
and by the pure uplifted hands,
that for thy children plead;
when at the judgment-seat I stand,
and my dread saviour see;
when waves of night around me roll
O then remember me.

*Edward Caswall (1814-78)*

# 327

1. This is my will,
my one command,
that love should dwell
among you all.
This my will
that you should love
as I have shown
that I love you.

2. No greater love
a man can have
than that he die
to save his friends.
You are my friends
if you obey
all I command
that you should do.

3. I call you now
no longer slaves;
no slave knows all
his master does.
I call you friends,
for all I hear
my Father say
you hear from me.

4. You chose not me,
but I chose you,
that you should go
and bear much fruit.
I called you out
that you in me
should bear much fruit
that will abide.

5. All that you ask
my Father dear
for my name's sake
you shall receive.
This is my will,
my one command,
that love should dwell
in each, in all.

*James Quinn S.J.*

## 328

1. This joyful Eastertide,
   away with sin and sorrow,
   my love, the Crucified,
   hath sprung to life this morrow:

   *Had Christ, that once was slain,*
   *ne'er burst his three-day prison,*
   *our faith had been in vain:*
   *but now hath Christ arisen.*

2. My flesh in hope shall rest,
   and for a season slumber:
   till trump from east to west
   shall wake the dead in number:

3. Death's flood hath lost his chill,
   since Jesus crossed the river:
   lover of souls, from ill
   my passing soul deliver:

   *George Ratclife Woodward*
   *(1849-1934)*

## 329

*This little light of mine,*
   *I'm gonna let it shine.*
*This little light of mine,*
   *I'm gonna let it shine.*
*This little light of mine,*
   *I'm gonna let it shine,*
*let it shine, let it shine, let it shine.*

1. The light that shines
      is the light of love,
   lights the darkness from above.
   It shines on me
      and it shines on you,
   and shows what the
      power of love can do.
   I'm gonna shine my light
      both far and near,
   I'm gonna shine my light
      both bright and clear.
   Where there's a dark corner
      in this land
   I'm gonna let my little light shine.

2. On Monday he
      gave me the gift of love,
   Tuesday peace came from above.
   On Wednesday he
      told me to have more faith,
   on Thursday he
      gave me a little more grace.
   Friday he told me just to
      watch and pray,
   Saturday he told me just
      what to say.
   On Sunday he gave me
      the power divine
   to let my little light shine.

   *Traditional*

## 330

1. Thou wilt keep him in perfect peace,
   thou wilt keep him in perfect peace,
   thou wilt keep him in perfect peace
   whose mind is stayed on thee.

2. Marvel not, I say unto you,
   marvel not, I say unto you,
   marvel not, I say unto you,
   you must be born again.

3. Though your sins as scarlet be,
   though your sins as scarlet be,
   though your sins as scarlet be,
   they shall be white as snow.

4. If the Son shall set you free,
   if the Son shall set you free,
   if the Son shall set you free,
   you shall be free indeed.

   *Anonymous*

# 331

1. Thy hand, O God, has guided
   thy flock from age to age;
   the wondrous tale is written,
   full clear, on ev'ry page;
   our fathers owned thy goodness,
   and we their deeds record;
   and both of this bear witness:
   one Church, one Faith, one Lord.

2. Thy heralds brought glad tidings
   to greatest, as to least;
   they bade men rise, and hasten
   to share the great king's feast;
   and this was all their teaching,
   in every deed and word,
   to all alike proclaiming
   one Church, one Faith, one Lord.

3. When shadows thick were falling,
   and all seemed sunk in night,
   thou, Lord, didst send thy servants,
   thy chosen sons of light.
   On them and on thy people
   thy plenteous grace was poured,
   and this was still their message:
   one Church, one Faith, one Lord.

4. Through many a day of darkness,
   through many a scene of strife,
   the faithful few fought bravely,
   to guard the nation's life.
   Their gospel of redemption,
   sin pardoned, man restored,
   was all in this enfolded:
   one Church, one Faith, one Lord.

5. And we, shall we be faithless?
   Shall hearts fail, hands hang down?
   Shall we evade the conflict,
   and cast away our crown?
   Not so: in God's deep counsels
   some better thing is stored;
   we will maintain, unflinching,
   one Church, one Faith, one Lord.

6. Thy mercy will not fail us,
   nor leave thy work undone;
   with thy right hand to help us
   the vict'ry shall be won;
   and then, by men and angels
   thy name shall be adored.
   And this shall be their anthem:
   one Church, one Faith, one Lord.

   *E. H. Plumptre (1821-91)*

# 332

1. To Christ the Lord of worlds we
   sing,
   the nations' universal king.
   Hail, conqu'ring Christ, whose reign
   alone
   over our hearts and souls we own.

2. Christ, who art known the prince of
   peace,
   bid all rebellious tumults cease;
   call home thy straying sheep, and
   hold
   for ever in one faithful fold.

3. For this, thine arms, on Calvary,
   were stretched across th' empurpled
   tree,
   and the sharp spear that through
   thee ran
   laid bare the heart that burned for
   man.

4. For this, in forms of bread and wine
   lies hid the plenitude divine,
   and from thy wounded body runs
   the stream of life to all thy sons.

5. May those who rule o'er men below
   thee for their greater sovereign
   know,
   and human wisdom, arts, and laws,
   in thee repose as in their cause.

6. Let kingly signs of pomp and state
   unto thy name be dedicate,
   city and hearth and household be
   under thy gentle sceptre free.

7. Praise be to Christ, whose name and
                              throne
   o'er every throne and name we own;
   and equal praises still repeat
   the Father and the Paraclete.

   *Roman Breviary, tr. W. H. Shewring*

# 333

1. To Christ, the Prince of peace,
   and Son of God most high,
   the father of the world to come,
   sing we with holy joy.

2. Deep in his heart for us
   the wound of love he bore;
   that love wherewith he still inflames
   the hearts that him adore.

3. O Jesu, victim blest,
   what else but love divine
   could thee constrain to open thus
   that sacred heart of thine?

4. O fount of endless life,
   O spring of water clear,
   O flame celestial, cleansing all
   who unto thee draw near!

5. Hide us in thy dear heart,
   for thither we do fly;
   there seek thy grace through life, in
                                     death
   thine immortality.

6. Praise to the Father be,
   and sole-begotten Son;
   praise, holy Paraclete, to thee
   while endless ages run.

   *Catholicum Hymnologium*
   *Germanicum (1587) tr. E. Caswall*

# 334

1. To Jesus' Heart, all burning
   with fervent love for men,
   my heart with fondest yearning
   shall raise its joyful strain.

   *While ages course along,*
   *blest be with loudest song*
   *the sacred heart of Jesus*
   *by ev'ry heart and tongue.*
   *The sacred heart of Jesus*
   *by ev'ry heart and tongue.*

2. O Heart, for me on fire
   with love no man can speak,
   my yet untold desire
   God gives me for thy sake.

3. Too true, I have forsaken
   thy love for wilful sin;
   yet now let me be taken
   back by thy grace again.

4. As thou art meek and lowly,
   and ever pure of heart,
   so may my heart be wholly
   of thine the counterpart.

5. When life away is flying,
   and earth's false glare is done;
   still, sacred Heart, in dying
   I'll say I'm all thine own.

   *Aloys Schlor (1805-52),*
   *tr. A. J. Christie*

# 335

1. To the name that brings salvation
   honour, worship, laud we pay:
   that for many a generation
   hid in God's foreknowledge lay;
   but to ev'ry tongue and nation
   Holy Church proclaims today.

2. Name of gladness, name of pleasure,
   by the tongue ineffable,
   name of sweetness passing measure,
   to the ear delectable;
   'tis our safeguard and our treasure,
   'tis our help 'gainst sin and hell.

3. 'Tis the name of adoration,
   'tis the name of victory;
   'tis the name for meditation
   in the vale of misery;
   'tis the name for veneration
   by the citizens on high.

4. 'Tis the name by right exalted
   over every other name:
   that when we are sore assaulted
   puts our enemies to shame:
   strength to them that else had
                              halted,
   eyes to blind, and feet to lame.

5. Jesu, we thy name adoring,
   long to see thee as thou art:
   of thy clemency imploring
   so to write it in our heart,
   that hereafter, upward soaring,
   we with angels may have part.

   *15th c., tr. J. M. Neale*

# 336

1. Trust is in the eyes
      of a tiny babe
   leaning on his mother's breast.
   In the eager beat
      of a young bird's wings
   on the day it leaves the nest.

   *It is the living Spirit*
   *filling the earth, bringing to birth*
   *a world of love and laughter,*
   *joy in the light of the Lord.*

2. Hope is in the rain
      that makes crystal streams
   tumble down a mountain side,
   and in every man
      who repairs his nets,
   waiting for the rising tide.

3. Love is in the hearts
      of all those who seek
   freedom for the human race.
   Love is in the touch
      of the hand that heals,
   and the smile that lights a face.

4. Strength is in the wind
      as it bends the trees,
   warmth is in the bright red flame,
   light is in the sun
      and the candle-glow,
   cleansing are the ocean's waves.

# 337
*Estelle White*

1. Unto us is born a Son,
   King of quires supernal;
   see on earth his life begun,
   of lords the Lord eternal,
   of lords the Lord eternal.

2. Christ, from heav'n descending low,
   comes on earth a stranger:
   ox and ass their owner know
   becradled in a manger,
   becradled in a manger.

3. This did Herod sore affray,
   and grievously bewilder:
   so he gave the word to slay,
   and slew the little childer,
   and slew the little childer.

4. Of his love and mercy mild
   this the Christmas story,
   and O that Mary's gentle Child
   might lead us up to glory!
   Might lead us up to glory!

5. O and A and A and O
   cum cantibus in choro,
   let the merry organ go,
   Benedicamus Domino,
   Benedicamus Domino.

   *15th c., tr. G. R. Woodward*

# 338

1. Vaster far than any ocean,
   deeper than the deepest sea
   is the love of Christ my Saviour,
   reaching through eternity.

2. But my sins are truly many,
   is God's grace so vast, so deep?
   Yes, there's grace o'er sin
   abounding,
   grace to pardon, grace to keep.

3. Can he quench my thirst for ever?
   Will his Spirit strength impart?
   Yes, he gives me living water
   springing up within my heart.

   *Author unknown*

# 339

1. Virgin, wholly marvellous,
   who didst bear God's Son for us,
   worthless is my tongue and weak
   of thy purity to speak.

2. Who can praise thee as he ought?
   Gifts, with every blessing fraught,
   gifts that bring the gifted life,
   thou didst grant us, Maiden-Wife.

3. God became thy lowly Son,
   made himself thy little one,
   raising men to tell thy worth
   high in heav'n as here on earth.

4. Heav'n and earth, and all that is
   thrill today with ecstasies,
   chanting glory unto thee,
   singing praise with festal glee.

5. Cherubim with fourfold face,
   are no peers of thine in grace;
   and the six-wing'd seraphim
   shine, amid thy splendour, dim.

6. Purer art thou than are all
   heav'nly hosts angelical,
   who delight with pomp and state
   on thy beauteous Child to wait.

   *St. Ephrem Syrus (c. 307-373),*
   *tr. J. W. Atkinson*

# 340

*Walk with me, oh my Lord,*
*through the darkest night*
*and brightest day.*
*Be at my side, oh Lord,*
*hold my hand*
*and guide me on my way.*

1. Sometimes the road seems long,
   my energy is spent.
   Then, Lord, I think of you
   and I am given strength.

2. Stones often bar my path
   and there are times I fall,
   but you are always there
   to help me when I call.

3. Just as you calmed the wind
   and walked upon the sea,
   conquer, my living Lord,
   the storms that threaten me.

4. Help me to pierce the mists
   that cloud my heart and mind
   so that I shall not fear
   the steepest mountain-side.

5. As once you healed the lame
   and gave sight to the blind,
   help me when I'm downcast
   to hold my head up high.

   *Estelle White*

# 341

1. We are gathering together unto him.
   We are gathering together unto him.
   Unto him shall the gath'ring
      of the people be.
   We are gathering together unto him.

2. We are offering together unto him.
   We are offering together unto him.
   Unto him shall the offering
      of the people be.
   We are offering together unto him.

3. We are singing together unto him.
   We are singing together unto him.
   Unto him shall the singing
      of the people be.
   We are singing together unto him.

4. We are praying together unto him.
   We are praying together unto him.
   Unto him shall the praying
      of the people be.
   We are praying together unto him.

*Anonymous*

# 342

1. We are one in the Spirit,
   we are one in the Lord,
   we are one in the Spirit
   we are one in the Lord,
   and we pray that all unity
   may one day be restored.

   *And they'll know we are Christians
   by our love, by our love,
   yes, they'll know we are Christians
   by our love.*

2. We will walk with each other,
   we will walk hand in hand.
   We will walk with each other,
   we will walk hand in hand.
   And together we'll spread the news
   that God is in our land.

3. We will work with each other,
   we will work side by side.
   We will work with each other,
   we will work side by side.
   And we'll guard each man's dignity
   and save each man's pride.

4. All praise to the Father
   from whom all things come,
   and all praise to Christ Jesus,
   his only Son,
   and all praise to the Spirit
   who makes us one.

*Peter Scholtes*
© *1966 F.E.L. Publications*

# 343

1. We bring our gifts to the Lord,
      our God.
   We bring our gifts to the Lord,
      our God.

2. We bring our love to the Lord,
      our God.
   We bring our love to the Lord,
      our God.

3. We bring ourselves to the Lord,
      our God.
   We bring ourselves to the Lord,
      our God.

*Estelle White*

# 344

1. We celebrate this festive day
   with pray'r and joyful song.
   Our Father's house is home to us,
   we know that we belong.

   *The bread is broken, wine is poured,
   a feast to lift us up!
   Then thank the Lord who gives
                              himself
   as food and saving cup!*

2. The door is open, enter in
   and take your place by right.
   For you've been chosen as his guest
   to share his love and light.

3. We come together as the twelve
   came to the Upper Room.
   Our host is Jesus Christ the Lord,
   now risen from the tomb.

4. Who travels needs both food and
   drink
   to help him on his way.
   Refreshed and strong we'll journey
   on
   and face another day.

5. Who shares this meal receives the
   Lord
   who lives, though he was dead.
   So death can hold no terrors now
   for those who eat this bread.

   *Willard F. Jabusch*

# 345

1. We gather together
   as brothers and sisters
   for Jesus our Lord truly lives.
   He's risen in glory;
   the full gospel story,
   what freedom and courage it gives.

   *He binds up the wounded*
   *and the broken.*
   *He gives the poor his chalice*
   *and his bread.*
   *The Father has raised him,*
   *together we'll praise him,*
   *and march with the Lord*
   *at our head.*

2. For mother and father,
   for sister and brother,
   for children and husband and wife,
   his Word spreads like flame,
   for all people came,
   bringing peace and the seeds of new
   life.

3. God takes what is foolish,
   he chooses the weakest
   to put wise and strong both to
   shame.
   Give thanks to the Father,
   we live in Christ Jesus,
   bow low and sing sweetly his name.

   *Willard F. Jabusch*

# 346

1. We plough the fields and scatter
   the good seed on the land,
   but it is fed and watered
   by God's almighty hand;
   he sends the snow in winter,
   the warmth to swell the grain,
   the breezes and the sunshine,
   and soft refreshing rain.

   *All good gifts around us*
   *are sent from heav'n above,*
   *then thank the Lord,*
   *O thank the Lord for all his love.*

2. He only is the maker
   of all things near and far;
   he paints the wayside flower,
   he lights the ev'ning star.
   The winds and waves obey him,
   by him the birds are fed:
   much more to us his children,
   he gives our daily bread.

3. We thank thee then, O Father,
   for all things bright and good:
   the seed-time and the harvest,
   our life, our health, our food.
   No gifts have we to offer
   for all thy love imparts,
   but that which thou desirest,
   our humble, thankful hearts.

   *M. Claudius (1740-1815),*
   *tr. J. M. Campbell*

# 347

1. Were you there
    when they crucified my Lord?
  Were you there
    when they crucified my Lord?
  Oh sometimes it causes me
    to tremble, tremble, tremble.
  Were you there
    when they crucified my Lord?

2. Were you there
    when they nailed him to a tree? . . .

3. Were you there
    when they pierced him in the side?

4. Were you there
    when the sun refused to shine? . . .

5. Were you there
    when they laid him in the tomb? . .

6. Were you there
    when he rose from out the tomb? .

*Negro Spiritual*

# 348

1. We shall overcome,
    we shall overcome,
    we shall overcome some day.
  Oh, deep in my heart I do believe
    that we shall overcome some day.

2. We'll walk hand in hand . . .

3. We shall live in peace . . .

4. We shall live with him . . .

*Traditional*

# 349

1. We three Kings of Orient are;
    bearing gifts we traverse afar,
  field and fountain, moor and
                                mountain,
  following yonder star.

  *O Star of wonder, star of night,*
  *star with royal beauty bright,*
  *westward leading, still proceeding,*
  *guide us to thy perfect light.*

2. Born a King on Bethlehem plain,
    gold I bring, to crown him again,
  King for ever, ceasing never,
    over us all to reign.

3. Frankincense to offer have I,
    Incense owns a Deity nigh.
  Prayer and praising, all men raising,
    worship him, God most high.

4. Myrrh is mine, its bitter perfume
    breathes a life of gathering gloom;
  sorrowing, sighing, bleeding, dying,
    sealed in the stone-cold tomb.

5. Glorious now behold him arise,
    King and God and sacrifice;
  alleluia, alleluia,
    earth to heaven replies.

*John Henry Hopkins (1822-1900)*

# 350

1. We will walk through the valley
    in the shadow of death.
  We will walk through the darkness
    without fear.
  Though the night may be long,
    the dark enclosing,
  we know Jesus,
    our morning light is near.

2. He has walked through the valley
    of the shadow of death,
  he has walked through the night of
    fear alone.
  Though the darkness had gathered
    to destroy him
  he was there at
    the rising of the sun.

3. We will walk in the glory
    of the bright morning sun,
  we will walk in the light that
    guides our way.
  For with Jesus the lord of
    light beside us
  we will walk in
    the glory of the day.

*Michael Cockett*

# 351

1. What can we offer you,
      Lord our God?
   How can we worship you
      as you deserve?
   We can only offer
      what our lips do proclaim.
   We can only offer you
      humble acts of praise.
   But we offer this with Jesus
      our brother, Jesus your Son.
   We join with him,
      glory to you, O God!
   We join with him,
      glory to you, O God!

2. What can we offer you,
      Lord our God?
   How can we thank you
      for all that you've done?
   We can only say it,
      Lord God, we thank you so.
   We can only try to live
      grateful lives, O Lord.
   But we offer this with Jesus,
      our brother, Jesus your Son.
   We join with him,
      our thanks to you, O God.
   We join with him,
      our thanks to you, O God.

3. What can we offer you,
      Lord our God?
   How do we prove we are
      truly sorry, Lord?
   We can say it often,
      God, sorry that we are.
   We can try to prove it,
      Lord, by the way we live.
   And we offer this with Jesus,
      our brother, Jesus, your Son.
   We join with him,
      forgive our sins, O God.
   We join with him,
      forgive our sins, O God.

4. What can we offer you,
      Lord our God?
   Dare we present you with
      another call for help?
   We just have to say it,
      Lord God, we need you so.
   We just have to beg you,
      Lord, take us by the hand.
   And we offer this with Jesus,
      our brother, Jesus, your Son.
   We join with him,
      Lord, we need you so.
   We join with him,
      Lord, we need you so.

*Tom Shelley*

# 352

*Whatsoever you do*
*to the least of my brothers,*
*that you do unto me.*

1. When I was hungry
   you gave me to eat.
   When I was thirsty
   you gave me to drink.
   Now enter into the
   home of my Father.

2. When I was homeless
   you opened your door.
   When I was naked
   you gave me your coat.
   Now enter into the
   home of my Father.

3. When I was weary
   you helped me find rest.
   When I was anxious
   you calmed all my fears.
   Now enter into the
   home of my Father.

4. When in a prison
   you came to my cell.
   When on a sick bed
   you cared for my needs.
   Now enter into the
   home of my Father.

5. Hurt in a battle
   you bound up my wounds.
   Searching for kindness
   you held out your hands.
   Now enter into the
   home of my Father.

6. When I was Negro
   or Chinese or White,
   mocked and insulted,
   you carried my cross.
   Now enter into the
   home of my Father.

7. When I was aged
   you bothered to smile.
   When I was restless
   you listened and cared.
   Now enter into the
   home of my Father.

8. When I was laughed at
   you stood by my side.
   When I was happy
   you shared in my joy.
   Now enter into the
   home of my Father.

*W. F. Jabusch*

# 353

1. When I needed a neighbour
      were you there were you there?
   When I needed a neighbour
      were you there?
   And the creed and the colour
      and the name won't matter
      were you there?

2. I was hungry and thirsty, . . .

3. I was cold, I was naked, . . .

4. When I needed a shelter, . . .

5. When I needed a healer, . . .

6. Wherever you travel,
      I'll be there I'll be there.
   Wherever you travel, I'll be there.
   And the creed and the colour
      and the name won't matter,
      I'll be there.

*Sydney Carter*

# 354

1. When Israel was in Egypt's land,
   let my people go,
   oppressed so hard they could not
                                stand,
   let my people go.

   *Go down, Moses,*
   *way down in Egypt's land.*
   *Tell old Pharoah*
   *to let my people go.*

2. The Lord told Moses what to do,
   let my people go,
   to lead the children of Israel
                             through,
   let my people go.

3. Your foes shall not before you stand,
   let my people go,
   and you'll possess fair Canaan's land,
   let my people go.

4. O let us all from bondage flee,
   let my people go,
   and let us all in Christ be free,
   let my people go.

5. I do believe without a doubt,
   let my people go,
   a Christian has a right to shout,
   let my people go.

*Traditional Spiritual*

# 355

1. When I survey the wondrous cross
   on which the Prince of Glory died,
   my richest gain I count but loss,
   and pour contempt on all my pride.

2. Forbid it, Lord, that I should boast,
   save in the death of Christ, my God:
   all the vain things that charm me
                                   most,
   I sacrifice them to his blood.

3. See from his head, his hands, his
feet,
sorrow and love flow mingled down:
did e'er such love and sorrow meet,
or thorns compose so rich a crown?

4. Were the whole realm of nature
mine,
that were an offering far too small;
love so amazing, so divine,
demands my soul, my life, my all.

*Isaac Watts (1674-1748)*

# 356

*Where are you bound, Mary, Mary?*
*Where are you bound,*
*Mother of God?*

1. Beauty is a dove
sitting on a sunlit bough,
beauty is a pray'r
without the need of words.
Words are more than sounds
falling off an empty tongue:
Let it be according to his word.

2. Mary heard the word
spoken in her inmost heart;
Mary bore the Word
and held him in her arms.
Sorrow she has known,
seeing him upon the cross
— greater joy to see him rise again.

3. Where are we all bound,
carrying the Word of God?
Time and place are ours
to make his glory known.
Mary bore him first,
we will tell the whole wide world:
Let it be according to his word.

*John Glynn*

# 357

1. Where does the wind come from?
Where is it going?
You see the swaying tree,
and all the grasses blowing.

You know the wind is there,
but where?
There is no knowing.

2. Whence does the Spirit come?
Where is his dwelling?
You see the weary world
so wilful, so rebelling.
But still the Spirit breathes,
and where,
there is no telling.

*Sister Mary Oswin*

# 358

1. Where is love and loving-kindness,
God is fain to dwell.
Flock of Christ, who loved us,
in one fold containèd,
joy and mirth be ours, for mirth
and joy he giveth,
fear we still and love the God who
ever liveth,
each to other joined by charity
unfeignèd.

2. Where is love and loving-kindness,
God is fain to dwell.
Therefore, when we meet, the
flock of Christ, so loving,
take we heed lest bitterness be
there engendered,
all our spiteful thoughts and
quarrels be surrendered,
seeing Christ is there, divine
among us moving.

3. Where is love and loving-kindness,
God is fain to dwell.
So may we be gathered once
again, beholding
glorified the glory, Christ, of
thy unveiling,
there, where never ending joy,
and never failing
age succeeds to age eternally
unfolding.

*From the Office of the Mandatum,*
*tr. R. A. Knox*

# 359

1. Where would we be
     without Christ our Lord?
   We would be lost
     and walking in darkness
   He is the lantern
     that lights up that darkness
   and he is the shepherd
     who finds the right path.

   *So let the trumpet sound to the
     glory of God.
   He is our Lord, loving and wise.*

2. Where would we be
     without Christ our Lord?
   We would be left
     to wander the desert.
   He is the beacon
     that leads us to safety,
   and he is the water
     that brings us new life.

3. Where would we be
     without Christ our Lord?
   We would be cold
     and starving and thirsty.
   He is the bread
     that is food for the spirit,
   and he is the wine of
     the new covenant.

4. Where would we be
     without Christ our Lord?
   He is the Son
     who saves all the nations.
   Through Christ the Son
     we are given the Spirit,
   and this is the Spirit
     who brings us new life.

   *Michael Cockett*

# 360

1. While shepherds watched their
     flocks by night,
   all seated on the ground,
   the Angel of the Lord came down,
   and glory shone around.

2. "Fear not," said he, (for mighty
     dread
   had seized their troubled mind)
   "Glad tidings of great joy I bring
   to you and all mankind.

3. "To you in David's town this day
   is born of David's line
   a Saviour, who is Christ the Lord;
   and this shall be the sign:

4. "The heavenly Babe you there shall
     find
   to human view displayed,
   all meanly wrapped in swathing
     bands,
   and in a manger laid."

5. Thus spake the Seraph; and
     forthwith
   appeared a shining throng
   of Angels praising God, who thus
   addressed their joyful song:

6. "All glory be to God on high,
   and on the earth be peace,
   goodwill henceforth from heaven
     to men
   begin and never cease".

   *Nahum Tate (1652–1715)*

# 361

*With a song in our hearts*
*we shall go on our way,*
*to bring God's love to ev'ryone*
*we meet today.*

Love, love, love is his name.
Love, love, love is his name.
Great, great, great is his name.
Great, great, great is his name.

*With a . . .*

*Estelle White*

# 362

*Yahweh,*
*you are my strength and salvation.*
*Yahweh,*
*you are my rock and my shield.*

1. When foes inside my soul
   assailed me,
   he heard my cry for help
   and came to my aid.

2. He bent the heav'ns and came
   in thunder.
   He flew to me and soared
   on wings of the wind.

3. The depths within my mind
   he showed me,
   the hidden thoughts that I
   did not know were there.

4. His arm stretched from on high
   and held me.
   He drew me from the deep,
   wild waters of self.

5. He is the lamp who lights
   the darkness.
   He guides me as I leap
   the ramparts of life.

6. I raise my voice and sing
   his glory.
   With all my heart I praise
   the God of my joy.

*Estelle White*

# 363

1. Ye choirs of new Jerusalem,
   your sweetest notes employ,
   the Paschal victory to hymn
   in strains of holy joy.

2. How Judah's Lion burst his chains,
   and crushed the serpent's head;
   and brought with him, from death's
                                domain,
   the long-imprisoned dead.

3. From hell's devouring jaws the prey
   alone our leader bore;
   his ransomed hosts pursue their way
   where he hath gone before.

4. Triumphant in his glory now
   his sceptre ruleth all:
   earth, heaven, and hell before him
                                bow
   and at his footstool fall.

5. While joyful thus his praise we sing,
   his mercy we implore,
   into his palace bright to bring,
   and keep us evermore.

6. All glory to the Father be,
   all glory to the Son,
   all glory, Holy Ghost, to thee,
   while endless ages run.

*St. Fulbert of Chartres (c.1000),*
*tr. R. Campbell*

# 364

1. Ye sons and daughters of the Lord!
   the king of glory, king adored,
   this day himself from death
   restored.

*Alleluia!*

2. All in the early morning grey
   went holy women on their way
   to see the tomb where Jesus lay.

3. Of spices pure a precious store
   in their pure hands these women
   bore
   to anoint the sacred body o'er

4. Then straightaway one
     in white they see,
   who saith, "Ye seek
     the Lord; but he
   is risen, and gone to Galilee".

5. This told they Peter,
     told they John;
   who forthwith to
     to the tomb are gone,
   but Peter is by John outrun.

6. That self-same night,
     while out of fear
   the doors were shut,
     their Lord most dear
   to his apostles did appear.

7. But Thomas, when
     of this he heard,
   was doubtful of
     his brethren's word;
   wherefore again
     there comes the Lord.

8. "Thomas, behold my side,"
     saith he;
   "My hands, my feet,
     my body see,
   and doubt not, but believe in me".

9. When Thomas saw
     that wounded side,
   the truth no longer
     he denied;
   "Thou art my Lord
     and God!" he cried.

10. Now let us praise
     the Lord most high,
   and strive his name
     to magnify
   on this great day,
     through earth and sky.

11. Whose mercy ever
     runneth o'er,
   whom men and angel
     hosts adore;
   to him be glory evermore.

*17th c., tr. E. Caswall*

# 365

1. Ye who own the faith of Jesus
   sing the wonders that were done,
   when the love of God the Father
   o'er our sin the victory won,
   when he made the Virgin Mary
   Mother of his only Son.

   *Hail, Mary, full of grace.*

2. Blessed were the chosen people
   out of whom the Lord did come,
   blessed was the land of promise
   fashioned for his earthly home;
   but more blessed far the mother
   she who bore him in her womb.

3. Wherefore let all faithful people
   tell the honour of her name,
   let the Church in her foreshadowed
   part in her thanksgiving claim;
   what Christ's mother sang in
                          gladness
   let Christ's people sing the same

4. May the Mother's intercessions
   on our homes a blessing win,
   that the children all be prospered
   strong and fair and pure within,
   following our Lord's own footsteps,
   firm in faith and free from sin.

5. For the sick and for the aged,
   for our dear ones far away,
   for the hearts that mourn in secret,
   all who need our prayers today,
   for the faithful gone before us,
   may the holy Virgin pray.

6. Praise, O Mary, praise the Father,
   praise thy Saviour and thy Son,
   praise the everlasting Spirit,
   who hath made thee ark and throne.
   O'er all creatures high exalted,
   lowly praise the three in one.

*V. S. S. Coles (1845-1929)*

## 366 AMERICAN EUCHARIST

*Lord, have mercy*

Lord, have mercy.
   Lord, have mercy,
on your servants, Lord, have mercy.
God Almighty, just and faithful,
Lord have mercy.
   Lord, have mercy.

Christ, have mercy.
   Christ, have mercy,
gift from heaven, Christ have mercy.
Light of truth, and light of justice,
Christ, have mercy.
   Christ have mercy.

Lord, have mercy.
   Lord, have mercy,
on your servants, Lord, have mercy.
God almighty, just and faithful,
Lord, have mercy.
   Lord, have mercy.

*Holy, holy, holy*

Holy, holy, holy, holy,
Lord of hosts. You fill with glory
all the earth and all the heavens.
Sing hosanna, sing hosanna.

Blest and holy, blest and holy
he who comes now in the Lord's
                                    name.

In the highest sing hosanna,
in the highest sing hosanna.

*Lamb of God*

Jesus, Lamb of God, have mercy,
bearer of our sins, have mercy.
Jesus, Lamb of God, have mercy,
bearer of our sins, have mercy.

Saviour of the world, Lord Jesus,
may your peace be with us always.
Saviour of the world, Lord Jesus,
may your peace be with us always.

*Sandra Joan Billington*

## 367 ISRAELI MASS

*Lord, have mercy*

Lord, have mercy.
   Lord, have mercy.
Lord, have mercy on us all.
Lord, have mercy.
   Lord, have mercy
Lord, have mercy on us all.

Christ, have mercy.
   Christ, have mercy.
Christ, have mercy on us all.
Christ, have mercy.
   Christ, have mercy.
Christ, have mercy on us all.

Lord, have mercy.
   Lord, have mercy.
Lord, have mercy on us all.
Lord, have mercy.
   Lord, have mercy.
Lord, have mercy on us all.

*Holy, holy, holy*

Holy, holy, holy, holy
Lord of power, Lord of might.
Heav'n and earth are filled with
                                    glory.
Sing hosanna evermore.

Blest and holy, blest and holy
he who comes from God on high.
Raise your voices, sing his glory,
praise his name for evermore.

*Lamb of God*

Lamb of God,
   you take away the sin,
the sin of all the world.
Give us mercy,
   give us mercy,
give us mercy, Lamb of God.

Lamb of God,                *(Repeat)*
   you take away the sin,
the sin of all the world.
Grant us peace, Lord,
   grant us peace, Lord,
grant us peace, O Lamb of God.

*Anthony Hamson*

## 368 GEORDIE MASS

*Lord have mercy*

Lord, have mercy on us all.
Lord, have mercy on us.
Lord, have mercy on us all.
Lord, have mercy on us.

Christ, have mercy on us all.
Christ, have mercy on us.
Christ, have mercy on us all.
Christ, have mercy on us.

Lord, have mercy on us all.
Lord, have mercy on us.
Lord, have mercy on us all.
Lord, have mercy on us.

*Holy, holy, holy*

Holy, holy, holy Lord
God of might and God of pow'r.
Glory fills all heav'n and earth.
Sing to him hosanna!

Blessed is the one who comes
in the name of Christ our Lord.
Holy, holy, holy Lord.
Sing to him hosanna!

*Lamb of God*

Lamb of God, you take our sins,
take away our sins, Lord.
So have mercy on us all,
so have mercy on us. *(Repeat)*

Lamb of God, you take our sins,
take away our sins, Lord.
Grant us peace, O grant us peace,
grant us peace for ever.

*Anthony Hamson*

## 369 MONMOUTHSHIRE MASS

*Lord, have mercy*

Lord, have mercy on us all.
Lord, have mercy on us.
Lord, have mercy on us all.
Lord, have mercy on us.

Christ, have mercy on us all.
Christ have mercy on us.
Christ, have mercy on us all
Christ have mercy on us.

Lord, have mercy on us all.
Lord, have mercy on us.
Lord, have mercy on us all.
Lord, have mercy on us.

*Holy, holy, holy*

Holy, holy, holy Lord,
God of might and power.
Glory fills all heav'n and earth.
Sing to him hosanna!

Blessed is the one who comes
bringing this great glory.
Praise and honour be to God.
Sing to him hosanna!

*Lamb of God*

Lamb of God, you take away
the sin of all the world.
Lamb of God, you take away
the sin of all the world.

Lamb of God, you take away
the sin of all the world.
Grant us peace, O Lamb of God,
grant us peace for ever.

*Anthony Hamson*

## 370 SWEDISH MASS

*Lord, have mercy*

Lord, have mercy on us all.
Lord, have mercy on us.
Lord, have mercy on us all.
Lord, have mercy on us.

Christ, have mercy on us all.
Christ, have mercy on us.
Christ, have mercy on us all.
Christ, have mercy on us.

Lord, have mercy on us all.
Lord, have mercy on us.
Lord, have mercy on us all.
Lord, have mercy on us.

*Holy, holy, holy*

Holy, holy, holy Lord,
earth is full of your glory.
Glory fills the heavens too.
Sing to him hosanna!

Blessed is the one who comes
bringing this great glory.
Holy, holy, holy Lord.
Sing to him hosanna!

*Lamb of God*

Lamb of God, O Jesus Christ,
take away our sins,
and have mercy on us all,
and have mercy on us.     *(Repeat)*
Lamb of God, O Jesus Christ,
take away our sins.
Grant us peace, O grant us peace,
grant us peace for ever.

*Anthony Hamson*

# 371 PILGRIM'S MASS

*Lord have mercy*

1. Lord, have mercy on my soul.
   Lord, have mercy on my soul.
   Lord, have mercy, Lord have mercy,
   Lord, have mercy on my soul.

2. Christ, have mercy on my soul,
   Christ have mercy on my soul.
   Christ, have mercy, Christ have
                                   mercy,
   Christ, have mercy on my soul.

3. Pray for me, pray for me,
   brothers and sisters, pray for me.
   Lord, have mercy on my soul.
   Lord, have mercy on my soul.

4. I confess that I have sinned,
   sinned in thought and word and
                                   deed
   done the things I should not do,
   left undone what I should do.

*Repeat Verse 1*

*Gloria*

1. Glory be to God in heaven,
   glory be to God on high,
   glory be, we give you thanks
   for the glory of the universe.

2. Peace on earth to all creation,
   peace on earth to all God's friends,

peace on earth to everyone
through the mercy of our Lord
                           Jesus Christ.

3. Jesus Christ, the Son of the Father,
   Jesus Christ, the Son of Man,
   Jesus Christ, the Lamb of God
   who takes away the sins of the
                                   world.

4. Lamb of God, right hand of the
                                   Father,
   Lamb of God the sacrifice,
   Lamb of God who bore our sins,
   have mercy on us, receive our pray'r.

5. You alone are the Lord of creation,
   you alone are the Holy One,
   you alone are the three in one,
   the Father, the Son and the Spirit.

6. Glory be, glory be,
   glory be, glory be.     Amen.

*Creed*

1. I believe.
   I believe that God almighty
   made the world for us to use.
   I believe in good and evil
   and that we've the power to choose.

2. I believe.
   I believe in God the Father.
   I believe in God the Son.
   I believe that he was born
   on earth to save us every one.

3. I believe.
   I believe he loved and suffered,
   taught us how to live and die,
   showed us all the way to heaven
   in our hearts, not in the sky.

4. I believe.
   I believe that God the Spirit
   ever was since time began.
   I believe that he will judge our
   actions when we've lived our span.

5. I believe.
   I believe the church is holy,
   I believe the church is true.
   I believe the church was made for
   all men, not just me and you.

6. I believe.
   Doubts and fears will fall upon us;
   we must trust that God will guide.
   Faith and hope and love will help us,
   and in joy we will abide.

*Sanctus*

Holy, holy, holy Lord God of hosts.
Your glory fills all heaven and earth.
Hosanna in the highest.
Holy, holy, holy Lord God of hosts.
Blessed is he who comes in your name.
Hosanna in the highest.

*Lord's Prayer*

*Our Father, king of heav'n and earth
we praise thy sacred name.*

1. Thy kingdom come, thy will be done
   in thought and deed not in words
                                    alone.

2. Give us this day our daily bread,
   our spirits and our bodies fed.

3. And forgive us all our trespasses,
   while we in turn will do no less.

4. And keep us from temptation's way,
   and help us when we go astray.

*Lamb of God*
Lamb of God,
you take away the sins of the world,
have mercy on us.
Lamb of God,
you take away the sins of the world,
have mercy on us.
Lamb of God,
you take away the sins of the world,
have mercy on us, and grant us peace.

*Gordon Rock*

# 372

1. O salutaris hostia,
   Quae caeli pandis ostium,
   Bella premunt hostilia,
   Da robur, fer auxilium.

2. Uni trinoque Domino
   Sit sempiterna gloria,
   Qui vitam sine termino
   Nobis donet in patria. Amen.

# 373

*English version*   *(see also nos. 245,309)*

1. O saving victim, opening wide
   The gate of heav'n to man below;
   Our foes press on from ev'ry side;
   Thine aid supply, thy strength bestow.

2. To thy great name be endless praise,
   Immortal Godhead, one in three;
   O grant us endless length of days
   In our true native land with thee.
                                    Amen.

*St. Thomas Aquinas (1227-74),
tr. J.M. Neale, E. Caswall and others*

# 374   *(see also no. 716)*

1. Tantum ergo Sacramentum
   Veneremur cernui:
   Et antiquum documentum
   Novo cedat ritui;
   Praestet fides supplementum
   Sensuum defectui.

2. Genitori, genitoque
   Laus et jubilatio,
   Salus, honor, virtus quoque
   Sit et benedictio;
   Procedenti ab utroque
   Compar sit laudatio.   Amen.

# 375

*English version*   *(see also nos. 46,219)*

1. Therefore we, before him bending,
   This great sacrament revere;
   Types and shadows have their ending,
   For the newer rite is here;
   Faith, our outward sense befriending,
   Makes the inward vision clear.

2. Glory let us give, and blessing
   To the Father and the Son,
   Honour, might, and praise addressing,
   While eternal ages run;
   Ever too his love confessing
   Who from both, with both is one.
                                    Amen.

*St. Thomas Aquinas (1227-74),
tr. J.M. Neale, E. Caswall and others*

# 376

1. A certain traveller on his way
was robbed and left to die;
helpless by the road he lay
and no one heard his cry.
A certain priest came down that
way,
a man most dignified;
'I will not get involved' said he,
and passed on the other side.

**Don't pass your neighbour by, my
friend,
don't pass your neighbour by.
Love your neighbour as yourself,
don't pass your neighbour by.**

2. A certain Levite came that way
a man of wealth and pride,
'I'm much too busy to stop'
said he,
and passed on the other side.
But a certain man from Samaria,
a stranger in the land,
took pity on the injured man
and lent a helping hand.

*Mary Lu Walker
Based on Luke 10:25–37*

# 377

**A child is born for us today,
alleluia.
He is our saviour and our God,
alleluia.**

1. Let our hearts resound with joy
and sing a song of gladness
for the Lord, our brother,
is come and we are redeemed.

2. Tell the world of our good news:
Jesus the Christ is among us,
and his presence we celebrate
offering peace and our joy to all.

3. Christ is born, the Christ has
come!
Sing everyone 'Alleluia!'
Caught in wonder at this birth
we worship God become man for
us.

4. Glory to God, born today
of the Virgin Mary,
in a cave at Bethlehem:
is there room in our lives for him?

5. His name shall be 'Emmanuel':
'God-who-lives-among-us',
Angels sing and shepherds cry:
'Born is the saviour, our Lord!'

6. The magi went and worshipped
him
with gifts so precious and costly.
In the fervour of their faith
they sought the child who is Lord
and King.

7. The Lord will make integrity
and peace to grow in our times.
A covenant he offers us:
lasting joy will be ours to share.

8. Arise! Shine out, Jerusalem!
The glory of Yahweh* has come
to you.
Lift up your eyes and look around!
Radiant is your salvation!

*Instead of 'Yahweh' you may
prefer to substitute 'God'*

*Final Refrain*
A child is born for us today,
alleluia.
He is our saviour and our God,
alleluia.
Alleluia, Alleluia.

*Gregory Norbet*

# 378

1. A child is born in Bethlehem,
alleluia;
so leap with joy Jerusalem,
alleluia, alleluia.

A new song let us sing
for Christ is born
let us adore
and let our gladness ring.

2. Through Gabriel the word has
come,
alleluia:
The Virgin will conceive a son,
alleluia, alleluia.

3. Within a manger now he lies,
alleluia:
Who reigns on high beyond the
skies,
alleluia, alleluia.

4. The shepherds hear the angel's
word,
alleluia:
This child is truly Christ the Lord,
alleluia, alleluia.

5. From Saba, from the rising sun,
alleluia:
With incense, gold, and myrrh
they come,
alleluia, alleluia.

6. Till with their gifts they enter in,
alleluia:
and kings adore the new-born
King,
alleluia, alleluia.

7. From virgin's womb this child is
born,
alleluia:
the Light from Light who brings
the dawn,
alleluia, alleluia.

8. He comes to free us from our
strife,
alleluia;
and share with us the Father's life,
alleluia, alleluia.

9. At this the coming of the Word,
alleluia;
o come, let us adore the Lord,
alleluia, alleluia.

10. To Father, Son, and Spirit praise,
alleluia:
from all his creatures all their
days,
alleluia, alleluia.

*Latin, 14th Century, tr. Ralph Wright,*
*OSB*

# 379

1. A mighty stronghold is our God,
   a sure defence and weapon.
   He'll help us out of every need
   whatever now may happen.
   The ancient evil fiend
   has deadly ill in mind;
   great power and craft are his,
   his armour gruesome is
   on earth is not his equal.

2. With our own strength is nothing
   done
   soon we are lost, dejected;
   but for us fights the rightful Man
   whom God himself elected.
   You ask: Who may this be?
   Christ Jesus it is he,
   the Lord Sabaoth's Son,
   our God, and he alone
   shall hold the field victorious.

3. And though the world were full
   of fiends
   all lurking to devour us,
   we tremble not nor fear their
   bands,
   they shall not overpower us.
   The prince of this world's ill
   may scowl upon us still,
   he cannot do us harm,
   to judgement he has come;
   one word can swiftly fell him.

4. The Word they must allow
   to stand –
   for this they win no merit;
   upon the field, so near at hand,
   he gives to us his Spirit.
   And though they take our life,
   goods, honour, child, and wife,
   though we must let all go,
   they will not profit so:
   to us remains the Kingdom.

*Martin Luther (1483–1546) tr. by*
*Honor Mary Thwaites*

# 380

A new Commandment I give unto you,
that you love one another as I have
   loved you,
that you love one another as I have
   loved you.

By this shall all men know that you
   are my disciples,
if you have love one for another.
By this shall all men know that you
   are my disciples,
if you have love for one another.

*Source unknown*
*Based on John 13:34–35*

# 381

1. A noble flow'r of Juda
   from tender roots has sprung,
   a rose from stem of Jesse,
   as prophets long had sung;
   a blossom fair and bright,
   that in the midst of winter
   will change to dawn our night.

2. The rose of grace and beauty
   of which Isaiah sings
   is Mary, virgin mother,
   and Christ the flow'r she brings.
   By God's divine decree
   she bore our loving Saviour
   who died to set us free.

3. To Mary, dearest mother,
   with fervent hearts we pray:
   grant that your tender infant
   will cast our sins away,
   and guide us with his love
   that we shall ever serve him
   and live with him above.

*German, 15th Century, paraphrased by*
*Anthony G. Petti*

# 382

1. A sign is seen in heaven,
   a maiden-mother fair;
   her mantle is the sunlight,
   and stars adorn her hair.
   The maiden's name is Mary;
   in love she brings to birth
   the Lord of all the ages,
   the King of all the earth.

2. Like moonlight on the hilltops
   she shines on all below,
   like sunlight on the mountains
   her Child outshines the snow.
   O Mary, Queen of mothers,
   still smile on young and old;
   bless hearth and home and
     harvest,
   bless farm and field and fold.

3. Pray, Mother, Queen in glory,
   before the Father's throne;
   praise God's eternal Wisdom,
   the Child who is your own;
   rejoice in God the Spirit,
   whose power let you conceive
   the Child of Eden's promise,
   O new and sinless Eve.

*James Quinn, SJ.*

# 383

**Abba, Abba, Father,**
**you are the potter,**
**we are the clay,**
**the work of your hands.**

1. Mould us,
   mould us and fashion us
   into the image
   of Jesus, your Son.
   of Jesus, your Son.

2. Father,
   may we be one in you
   as he is in you
   and you are in him,
   and you are in him.

3. Glory,
   glory and praise to you,
   glory and praise to you
   for ever. Amen.
   For ever. Amen.

*Carey Landry*

# 384

1. Abba, Father, send your Spirit ...

   **Glory hallelujah, glory, Jesus**
   **Christ.**
   **Glory hallelujah, glory, Jesus**
   **Christ.**

2. I will give you living water ...

3. If you seek me you will find me ...

4. If you listen you will hear me ...

5. Come, my children, I will teach
   you ...

6. I'm your shepherd, I will lead
   you ...

7. Peace I leave you, peace I give
   you ...

8. I'm your life and resurrection ...

9. Glory Father, glory Spirit ...

*Other words from Scripture may be*
*substituted according to the occasion*
*or the season. For example, in Advent:*

1. Come, Lord Jesus, Light of
   nations ...

2. Come, Lord Jesus, born of
   Mary . . .

3. Come, and show the Father's
   glory . . .

*Ginny Vissing*

# 385

1. Across the years there echoes still
   the Baptist's bold assertion:
   the call of God to change of heart,
   repentance and conversion.

2. The word that John more boldly
      spoke
   in dying than in living
   now Christ takes up as he
      proclaims
   a Father all-forgiving.

3. The erring son he welcomes home
   when all is spent and squandered.
   He lovingly pursues the sheep
   that from the flock has wandered.

4. Forgive us, Lord, all we have done
   to you and one another.
   So often we have gone our way,
   forgetful of each other.

5. Forgetful of the cross they bear
   of hunger, want, oppression –
   grant, Lord, that we may make
      amends
   who humbly make confession.

*Denis E. Hurley*

# 386

1. Again the Lord's own day is here,
   the day to Christian people dear,
   as week by week it bids them tell
   how Jesus rose from death and
      hell.

2. For by his flock the Lord declared
   his resurrection should be shared;
   and we who trust in him to save
   with him are risen from the grave.

3. We, one and all, of him possessed,
   are with exceeding treasures blest;
   for all he did and all he bore
   is shared by us for evermore.

4. Eternal glory, rest on high,
   a blesséd immortality,
   true peace and gladness, and a
      throne,
   are all his gifts and all our own.

5. And therefore unto thee we sing,
   O Lord of peace, eternal King;
   thy love we praise, thy name
      adore,
   both on this day and evermore.

*Attributed to Thomas a Kempis*
*(1380–1471)*
*tr by J.M. Neale (1818–66) and others*

# 387

**Alabaré, alabaré, alabaré a mi
Señor. (2)**

1. John saw the number of all those
      redeemed,
   and all were singing praises to the
      Lord.
   Thousands were praying, ten
      thousands rejoicing,
   and all were singing praises to the
      Lord.

2. There is no god as great as you,
   O Lord,
   there is none, there is none. (2)
   There is no god who does the
   mighty wonders
   that the Lord our God has
   done. (2)
   Neither with an army, nor with
   their weapons,
   but by the Holy Spirit's power. (2)
   And even mountains shall be
   moved, (3)
   by the Holy Spirit's power.

3. And even England * shall be
   saved (3)
   by the Holy Spirit's power.

   *or Scotland, Ireland, Wales, or
   wherever your live, or even a
   friend's name!*

   ('*Alabaré a mi Señor is Spanish
   for 'I will praise my Lord*')

   *Author unknown*

# 388

1. All for Jesus, all for Jesus,
   this our song shall ever be;
   for we have no hope, nor Saviour,
   if we have not hope in Thee.

2. All for Jesus, thou wilt give us
   strength to serve thee, hour by
   hour;
   none can move us from thy
   presence,
   while we trust thy love and power.

3. All for Jesus, at thine altar
   thou wilt give us sweet content;
   there, dear Lord, we shall receive
   thee
   in the solemn sacrament.

4. All for Jesus, thou hast loved us;
   all for Jesus, thou hast died;
   all for Jesus, thou art with us;
   all for Jesus crucified.

5. All for Jesus, all for Jesus,
   this the Church's song must be;
   till, at last, her sons are gathered
   one in love and one in thee.

   *J. Sparrow-Simpson (1859–1952)*

# 389

1. All my hope on God is founded;
   he doth still my trust renew.
   Me through change and chance he
   guideth,
   only good and only true.
   God unknown, he alone
   calls my heart to be his own.

2. Pride of man and earthly glory,
   sword and crown betray God's
   trust;
   what with lavish care man
   buildeth,
   tower and temple, fall to dust.
   But God's power, hour by hour,
   is my temple and my tower.

3. God's great goodness ay endureth,
   deep his wisdom, passing thought:
   splendour, light and life attend
   him,
   beauty springeth out of nought.
   Evermore, from his store
   new-born worlds rise and adore.

4. Still from man to God eternal
   sacrifice of praise be done,
   high above all praises praising
   for the gift of Christ his Son.
   Christ doth call one and all;
   Ye who follow shall not fall.

   *J Neander (1650–80), paraphrased by
   R.S. Bridges (1844–1930)*

# 390

**All the earth proclaim the Lord,
sing your praise to God.**

1. Serve you the Lord, hearts filled
   with gladness.
   Come into his presence, singing
   for joy!

2. Know that the Lord is our creator.
   Yes, he is our Father; we are his
   sons.

3. We are the sheep of his green
   pasture,
   for we are his people; he is our
   God.

4. Enter his gates bringing
   thanksgiving,
   O enter his courts while singing
   his praise.

5. Our Lord is good, his love
   enduring,
   his word is abiding now with all
   men.

6. Honour and praise be to the
   Father,
   the Son, and the Spirit, world
   without end.

*Lucien Deiss
Based on Psalm 99(100)*

# 391

**All you nations,
sing out your joy in the Lord:
Alleluia, alleluia!**

1. Joyfully shout, all you on earth,
   give praise to the glory of God;
   and with a hymn,
   sing out his glorious praise:
   **Alleluia!**

2. Lift up your hearts, sing to your
   God:
   tremendous his deeds among men!
   Vanquished your foes,
   struck down by power and might:
   **Alleluia!**

3. Let all the earth kneel in his sight,
   extolling his marvellous fame;
   honour his name,
   in highest heaven give praise:
   **Alleluia!**

4. Come forth and see all the great
   works
   that God has brought forth by his
   might;
   fall on your knees
   before his glorious throne:
   **Alleluia!**

5. Parting the seas with might and
   pow'r,
   he rescued his people from shame;
   let us give thanks
   for all his merciful deeds:
   **Alleluia!**

6. His eyes keep watch on all the
   earth,
   his strength is forever renewed;
   and let no man
   rebel against his commands:
   **Alleluia!**

7. Tested are we by God the Lord,
   as silver is tested by fire;
   burdened with pain,
   we fall ensnared in our sins:
   **Alleluia!**

8. Over our heads wicked men rode,
   we passed through the fire and the
   flood;
   then, Lord, you brought
   your people into your peace:
   **Alleluia!**

9. Glory and thanks be to the Father;
   honour and praise to the Son;
   and to the Spirit,
   source of life and of love:
   **Alleluia!**

*Lucien Deiss*
*Based on Psalm 65(66)*

# 392

**Alleluia, alleluia, alleluia, Jesus
is alive!**

1. Praise the Lord
   for he is good eternally,
   and his loving kindness for us
   never fails.

2. His strong right hand
   overcomes and lifts us up;
   I'll never die, but live
   to praise his power to save.

3. For the stone rejected
   by the builder's sin
   has become the cornerstone
   of God's new House.

4. And he gives us the light
   wherewith to see;
   his intention is
   that we should live with him.

*Bonaventure Hinwood*
*Based on Psalm 117(118)*

# 393

**Alleluia, alleluia, alleluia, may
God's Spirit come!**

1. Bless the Lord, my soul,
   for he is great and good:
   earth he has enriched
   with all his mighty works.

2. You send forth your Spirit,
   then creation starts,
   and you still renew
   all things upon the earth.

3. May the Lord find joy
   in all that he creates;
   and my thoughts about him
   fill my heart with joy.

*Bonaventure Hinwood*
*Based on Psalm 103(104)*

# 394

**Alleluia! Alleluia! Alleluia,
Sons of God arise and follow
Alleluia! Alleluia!
sons of God arise and follow
the Lord.**

1. Come and be clothed in his
   righteousness;
   come join the band who are
   called by his name.

2. Look at the world which is bound
   by sin;
   walk into the midst of it
   proclaiming my life.

*Mimi Farra*

# 395

**Alleluia, alleluia,
give thanks to the risen Lord.
Alleluia, alleluia,
give praise to his name.**

1. Jesus is Lord of all the earth.
   He is the King of creation.

2. Spread the good news o'er all the
   earth.
   Jesus has died and has risen.

3. We have been crucified with
      Christ.
   Now we shall live for ever.

4. God has proclaimed the just
      reward.
   Life for all men, alleluia.

5. Come, let us praise the living God,
   joyfully sing to our Saviour.

*Don Fishel*

# 396

**Alleluia, alleluia!**
1. Salvation and glory and pow'r
      belong to our God,
   **allelluia!**
   His judgements are true and just.

2. Praise our God, all you his
      servants,
   **alleluia!**
   You, who fear him, great and
      small.

3. The Lord, our God, the almighty,
      reigns,
   **alleluia!**
   Let us rejoice and exult and give
      him the glory.

4. The marriage of the Lamb has
      come,
   **alleluia!**
   And his Bride has made herself
      ready.

*Based on Revelation 19:1–2,5–7, from
The Divine Office*

# 397

1. Almighty Father, who for us thy
      Son didst give,
   that men and nations through his
      precious death might live,
   in mercy guard us, lest by sloth
      and selfish pride
   we cause to stumble those for
      whom the Saviour died.

2. We are thy stewards; thine our
      talents, wisdom, skill;
   our only glory that we may thy
      trust fulfill;
   that we thy pleasure in our
      neighbours' good pursue,
   if thou but workest in us both to
      will and do.

3. On just and unjust thou thy
      care dost freely shower;
   make us, thy children, free from
      greed and lust for power,
   lest human justice, yoked with
      man's unequal laws,
   oppress the needy and neglect
      the humble cause.

4. Let not thy worship blind us to
      the claims of love;
   but let thy manna lead us to the
      feast above,
   to seek the country which by faith
      we now possess,
   where Christ, our treasure, reigns
      in peace and righteousness.

*George B. Caird*

# 398

1. Angel-voices ever singing
   round thy throne of light,
   angel-harps for ever ringing,
   rest not day nor night;
   thousands only live to bless thee
   and confess thee Lord of might.

2. Thou who art beyond the farthest
   mortal eye can scan,
   can it be that thou regardest
   songs of sinful man?
   Can we know that thou art near
   us,
   and wilt hear us? Yes, we can.

3. Yes, we know that thou rejoicest
   o'er each work of thine;
   thou didst ears and hands and
   voices
   for thy praise design;
   craftsman's art and music's
   measure
   for thy pleasure all combine.

4. In thy house, great God, we offer
   of thine own to thee;
   and for thine acceptance proffer
   all unworthily;
   hearts and minds and hands and
   voices
   in our choicest psalmody.

5. Honour, glory, might and merit
   thine shall ever be,
   Father, Son, and Holy Spirit,
   Blessed Trinity!
   Of the best that thou hast given
   earth and heaven render thee.

   *Francis Pott (1832–1909)*

# 399

1. An upper room did our Lord
   prepare
   for those he loved until the end:
   and his disciples still gather there,
   to celebrate their Risen Friend.

2. A lasting gift Jesus gave his own:
   to share his bread, his loving cup.
   Whatever burdens may bow us
   down,
   he by his cross shall lift us up.

3. And after Supper he washed their
   feet,
   for service, too, is sacrament.
   In him our joy shall be made
   complete –
   sent out to serve, as he was sent.

4. No end there is! We depart in
   peace.
   He loves beyond our uttermost:
   in every room in our Father's
   house
   he will be there, as Lord and Host.

   *F. Pratt Green*

# 400

1. As earth that is dry and parched
   in the sun
   lies waiting for rain,
   my soul is a desert, arid and waste;
   it longs for your Word, O Lord.

   **Come to the waters, all you
   who thirst;
   come now, and eat my bread.**

2. Though you have no money,
      come, buy my corn
   and drink my red wine.
   Why spend precious gold on
      what will not last?
   Hear me, and your soul will live.

3. As one on a journey strays
      from the road
   and falls in the dark,
   my mind is a wanderer,
      choosing wrong paths
   and longing to find a star.

4. The Lord is your light,
      the Lord is your strength;
   turn back to him now.
   For his ways are not the ways
      you would choose,
   and his thoughts are always new.

5. As rain from the mountains
      falls on the land
   and brings forth the seed,
   the word of the Lord sinks deep
      in our hearts,
   creating the flower of truth.

*Isaiah 55:1,2,6,9 & 12, paraphrased*
*by Anne Conway*

# 401

1. As I kneel before you,
   as I bow my head in pray'r,
   take this day, make it yours
   and fill me with your love.

   **Ave Maria, gratia plena,**
   **Dominus tecum, benedicta tu.**

2. All I have I give you,
   ev'ry dream and wish are yours.
   Mother of Christ, Mother of mine,
   present them to my Lord.

3. As I kneel before you,
   and I see your smiling face,
   ev'ry thought, ev'ry word
   is lost in your embrace.

*Maria Parkinson*

# 402

1. As long as men on earth are
      living,
   and trees are yielding fruits on
      earth,
   you are our Father. Thanks we
      give you,
   for all that owes to you its birth.

2. You are our light and life and
      Saviour,
   you rescue us when we are dead.
   You gave your Son to be our
      neighbour.
   He feeds us with his living bread.

3. As long as human words are
      spoken
   and for each other we exist,
   your steadfastness remains
      unbroken;
   for Jesus' sake, your name be
      blessed.

4. You are the one who clothes the
      flowers,
   you feed the birds in all the land.
   You are our shelter: all my hours
   and all my days are in your hand.

5. Therefore, let all the world adore
      you.
   It is your love that brought it
      forth.
   You live among us, we before you.
   Your offspring are we, Praise the
      Lord!

*Huub Oosterhuis and C.M. De Vries*

# 403

As one body we are wed
by partaking of the self-same Bread;
and Jesus Christ of that body is the
  head:
the holy Church of God.

1.    I am the living bread which has
      come down from heaven.
      Anyone who eats this bread will
      live for ever,
      and the bread that I shall give
      is my flesh for that life of the
      world. *(John 6:51)*

2.    On the same night that he was
      betrayed, the Lord Jesus took
      some bread
      thanked God for it, and broke
      it, and said:
      'This is my body, which is given
      up for you. *(1 Cor.11:23b-24)*

3.    In the same way, after supper,
      he took the cup and said:
      'This cup is the new covenant in
      my blood.
      Do this in memory of me.'
      So doing, we proclaim his
      death, until he comes again.
      *(1 Cor.11:25-26)*

4.    Just as a human body, though it
      is made up of many parts
      these parts, though many, make
      one body.
      In the one Spirit we were all
      baptised,
      one Spirit given to us all to
      drink. *(1 Cor.11:12-13)*

5.    There is one body, there is one
      Spirit
just as we were called into one
and the same hope.
There is one Lord, one faith,
  one baptism
and one God, who is Father
  over all. *(Ephesians 4:4-6)*

*Words from Scripture:*
*Jean-Paul Lecot, W.R. Lawrence,*
*R.B. Kelly*

# 404

1. As the bridegroom to his chosen,
  as the king unto his realm,
  as the keep unto the castle,
  as the pilot to the helm,
  so, Lord, art thou to me.

2. As the fountain in the garden,
  as the candle in the dark,
  as the treasure in the coffer,
  as the manna in the ark,
  so, Lord, art thou to me.

3. As the music at the banquet,
  as the stamp unto the seal,
  as the medicine to the fainting,
  as the wine-cup at the meal,
  so, Lord, art thou to me.

4. As the ruby in the setting,
  as the honey in the comb,
  as the light within the lantern,
  as the father in the home,
  so, Lord, art thou to me.

5. As the sunshine in the heavens,
  as the image in the glass,
  as the fruit unto the fig-tree,
  as the dew unto the grass,
  so, Lord, art thou to me.

*Paraphrased from John Tauler*
*(1330–61)*
*by Emma Frances Bevan (1827–1909)*

# 405

1. Awake, awake: fling off the night!
   For God has sent his glorious
      light;
   and we who live in Christ's new
      day
   must works of darkness put away.

2. Awake and rise, like men renewed,
   men with the Spirit's power
      endued.
   The light of life in us must glow,
   and fruits of truth and goodness
      show.

3. Let in the light; all sin expose
   to Christ, whose life no darkness
      knows.
   Before his cross for guidance
      kneel;
   his light will judge and, judging,
      heal.

4. Awake, and rise up from the dead,
   and Christ his light on you will
      shed.
   Its power will wrong desires
      destroy,
   and your whole nature fill with
      joy.

5. Then sing for joy, and use each
      day;
   give thanks for everything alway.
   Lift up your hearts; with one
      accord
   praise God through Jesus Christ
      our Lord.

*J.R. Peacey (1896–1971)*
*Based on Ephesians 5:6–20*

# 406

1. 'Bartimaeus, Bartimaeus,
   do you hear them, do you know?
   They have seen the prophet Jesus
   in the streets of Jericho.
   Bartimaeus, it is he!
   What a shame you cannot see.'

2. 'Son of David, Son of David
   walking in the blessed light,
   I a beggar ask no money.
   Lord, may I receive my sight?
   Son of David, pity me.
   You have power to make me see.'

3. 'Bartimaeus, Bartimaeus,
   you have eyes to know your need;
   you have eyes to know the Giver;
   surely this is sight indeed!
   Bartimaeus, come to me.
   Bartimaeus, you shall see.'

4. Son of David, Son of David
   kindle in the human soul.
   One blind faith like Bartimaeus;
   call us out, and make us whole.
   Son of David, source of light,
   Lord, may we receive our sight?

*Michael Hewlett*

# 407

1. Be still, my soul: the Lord
      is on your side;
   bear patiently the cross
      of grief and pain;
   leave to your God
      to order and provide;
   in every change he faithful will
      remain.

Be still, my soul: your best,
  your heavenly friend
through thorny ways lead to a
  joyful end.

2 Be still, my soul: your God
    will undertake
  to guide the future as he has
    the past.
  Your hope, your confidence let
    nothing shake,
  all now mysterious shall be clear
    at last.
  Be still, my soul: the tempests
    still obey
  his voice, who ruled them once
    on Galilee.

3. Be still, my soul: the hour is
     hastening on
   when we shall be for ever with
     the Lord,
   when disappointment, grief and
     fear are gone,
   sorrow forgotten, love's pure
     joy restored.
   Be still, my soul: when change
     and tears are past,
   all safe and blessed we shall meet
     at last.

*Katharina von Schegel,*
*tr. Jane L. Borthwick (1813–1897)*

# 408

1. Before Christ died
     he took some bread,
   and then he took some wine.
   'My body and my blood,' he said,
   'a sacrificial sign.'

2. 'Now eat and drink, I am your
     food.
   I promise you will see
   your lives transformed, your
     hearts renewed;
   you'll die and live with me.'

3. We drink this wine,
     we eat this bread,
   as Jesus bade us do.
   The covenant for which he bled
   today we must renew.

4. By faith, in broken bread we see
   the body of our Lord.
   By faith, we know the wine to be
   his holy blood outpoured.

5. Each time the church,
     for memory's sake,
   repeats Christ's holy act,
   each time we of that meal partake,
   Christ's death we re-enact.

6. From sunrise to the setting sun
   this death we will proclaim.
   Each day Christ promises to come
   until he comes again.

*Peter de Rosa*

# 409

Bind us together, Lord,
bind us together
with cords that cannot be broken.
Bind us together, Lord,
bind us together,
bind us together with love.

1. There is only one God,
   there is only one King,
   there is only one Body,
   that is why we sing:

2. Made for the glory of God,
purchased by His precious Son,
born with the right to be clean,
for Jesus the victory has won.

3. You are the family of God,
you are the promise divine,
you are God's chosen desire,
you are the glorious new wine.

*Bob Gillman*

# 410

1. Blest are you, Lord, God of all
creation,
   thanks to your goodness this
   bread we offer:
   fruit of the earth, work of our
   hands,
   it will become the bread of life.

**Blessed be God! Blessed be God!**
**Blessed be God forever! Amen!**
**Blessed be God! Blessed be God!**
**Blessed be God forever! Amen!**

2. Blest are you, Lord, God of all
creation,
   thanks to your goodness this
   wine we offer:
   fruit of the earth, work of our
   hands,
   it will become the cup of life.

*Aniceto Nazareth*

# 411

**Blest be the Lord; blest be the Lord,**
**the God of mercy, the God who**
**saves.**
**I shall not fear the dark of night,**
**nor the arrow that flies by day.**

1. He will release me from the nets
of all my foes;
   He will protect me from their
   wicked hands.
   Beneath the shadow of His wings
   I will rejoice
   To find a dwelling place secure.

2. I need not shrink before the terrors
of the night,
   Nor stand alone before the light
   of day.
   No harm shall come to me, no
   arrow strike me down,
   No evil settle in my soul.

3. Although a thousand strong have
fallen at my side,
   I'll not be shaken with the Lord
   at hand.
   His faithful love is all the armour
   that I need
   To wage my battle with the foe.

*Based on Psalm 90(91)*
*by Daniel L. Schutte, SJ.*

# 412

1. Bread of the world, in mercy
broken,
   wine of the soul, in mercy shed,
   by whom the words of life were
   spoken,
   and in whose death our sins are
   dead.

2. Look on the heart by sorrow
      broken,
   look on the tears by sinners shed;
   and be your feast to us the token
   that by your grace our souls are
      fed.

*Reginald Heber (1783–1826)*

# 413

1. Break not the circle of enabling
      love,
   where people grow, forgiven
      and forgiving;
   break not that circle, make it
      wider still,
   till it includes, embraces all the
      living.

2. Come, wonder at this love
      that comes to life,
   where words of freedom are
      with humour spoken
   and people keep no score of
      wrong and guilt,
   but will that human bonds
      remain unbroken.

3. Come, wonder at the Lord
      who came and comes
   to teach the world the craft
      of hopeful craving
   for peace and wholeness that
      will fill the earth:
   he calls his people to creative
      living.

4. Join then the movement of
      the love that frees,
   till people of whatever race
      or nation,
   will truly be themselves,
      stand on their feet,
   see eye to eye with laughter
      and elation.

*Fred Kaan*

# 414

MAGNIFICAT

**Breathing the words of humble
   obedience true,
let it be so, and let it be done
   for you,
I am the handmaid of the Lord.**

1. My soul magnifies the Lord
      and my spirit rejoices in God my
      king.
   Henceforth all men will call me
      blessed
   because God has done great
      things for me.

2. His mercy spans each generation
      on those who fear him, holy is his
      name,
   he has shown the might of his
      arm,
   the proud he scattered with all
      their plans.

3. Mighty kings have been tumbled
      from their thrones,
   and exalted have been the lowly.
   He has filled the hungry with
      good things,
   the rich sent empty-handed away.

4. He has helped his servant Israel,
   to keep the promise made in time
       long past:
   his mercy shown to Abraham,
   and to all his descendants for ever.

*Liz Powell and Jean Henriot*
*Based on Luke 1:46–56*

# 415

1. Bright star of morning, dawn on
       our darkness,
   Jesus our Master, our Lord and
       King,
   our hearts we give you now and
       forever,
   all that we care for to you we
       bring.

2. All of life's troubles, each daily
       burden
   are eased and lightened when you
       are near.
   Help us to stay close, trusting
       and child-like,
   calmed by your presence and free
       from fear.

3. Immortal Saviour, forgive our
       weakness,
   for you have known, Lord, our
       frailty.
   May we walk with you, safe in
       your love-light,
   each day and until eternity.

*Estelle White*

# 416

1. Brother Sun and Sister Moon,
   I seldom hear you,
   seldom hear your tune.
   Preoccupied with selfish misery.

2. Brother Wind and Sister Air,
   open my eyes to visions pure and
       fair
   that I may see the glory around
       me.

   **I am God's creature,**
   **of him I am part.**
   **I feel his love**
   **awakening my heart.**

3. Brother Sun and Sister Moon,
   I now do see you,
   I can hear your tune,
   so much in love with all I survey.

*St. Francis of Assisi, adapted by*
*Donovan*

# 417

1. But I say unto you,
   love your enemies
   and pray for those who hurt you.
   Give to those who ask, don't turn
       away.

   **And be like your Father in heaven**
   **above**
   **who causes his sun to shine on evil**
   **and good,**
   **and sends down his rain to quench**
   **all our thirst.**
   **In him we live and move and have**
   **our being.**

2. If you forgive each other,
   so will God forgive you.
   Do not judge lest
   you be judg'd yourselves.

3. When you see the hungry,
   feed them from your table.
   For the poor and weary,
   be their wat'ring place.

*Beverlee Paine*
*Based on Luke 6:27ff.*


# 418

**By his wounds we have been healed.**

1. Christ suffered for you,
   leaving you an example
   that you should follow
   in his steps.

2. He committed no sin;
   no guile was found on his lips.
   When he was reviled,
   he did not revile in return.

3. When he suffered,
   he did not threaten;
   but he trusted in him
   who judges justly.

4. He himself bore our sins
   in his body on the tree,
   that we might die to sin
   and live to righteousness.

5. For you were straying like sheep,
   but now have returned
   to the shepherd
   and guardian of your souls.

*From 1 Peter 2:21,24*


# 419

1. By the Cross which did to death
   our only Saviour,
   this blessed vine from which
   grapes are gathered in:
   **Jesus Christ, we thank and bless
   you.**
   By the Cross which casts down fire
   upon our planet,
   this burning bush in which
   love is plainly shown:
   **Jesus Christ, we glorify you.**
   By the Cross on Calv'ry's hill
   securely planted,
   this living branch
   which can heal our ev'ry sin:
   **conquering God,
   we your Church proclaim you!**

2. By the Blood with which we
   marked
   the wooden lintels
   for our protection the night
   when God passed by:
   **Jesus Christ, we thank and bless
   you.**
   By the Blood which in our Exodus
   once saved us,
   when hell was sealed up
   by God's engulfing sea:
   **Jesus Christ, we glorify you.**
   By the Blood which kills the
   poison
   in bad fruitage,
   and gives new life
   to the dead sap in the tree:
   **conquering God,
   we your Church proclaim you!**

3. By the Death on Calv'ry's hill
   of him the First-born,

who bears the wood and the
flame for his own pyre:
**Jesus Christ, we thank and bless
you.**
By the Death, amid the thorns,
of God's own Shepherd,
the Paschal Lamb who was
pierced
by our despair:
**Jesus Christ, we glorify you.**
By the Death of God's belov'd
outside his vineyard,
that he might change us
from murd'rer into heir:
**conquering God,
we your Church proclaim you!**

4. By the Wood which sings a song
of nuptial gladness,
of God who takes for bride
our human race:
**Jesus Christ, we thank and bless
you.**
By the Wood which raises up
in his full vigour
the Son of Man who draws
all men by his grace:
**Jesus Christ, we glorify you.**
By the Wood where he perfects
his royal Priesthood
in one High Priest
who for sin is sacrifice:
**conquering God,
we your Church proclaim you!**

5. Holy Tree which reaches up
from earth to heaven
that all the world may
exult in Jacob's God:
**Jesus Christ, we thank and bless
you.**

Mighty Ship which snatches us
from God's deep anger,
saves us, with Noah,
from drowning in the Flood:
**Jesus Christ, we glorify you.**
Tender Wood which gives to
brackish water sweetness,
and from the Rock shall strike
fountains for our food:
**conquering God,
we your  Church proclaim you!**

*Didier Rimaud, tr. F. Pratt Green*

# 420

**Called to be servants,
called to be sons,
called to be daughters,
we're called to be one.
Called into service,
called to be free;
you are called to be you,
and I'm called to be me.**

1. Children, come, with wide open
eyes.
Look at the water; you have been
baptised.
You're free from the slav'ry that
bound you to sin,
so live now as children in the
kingdom of heav'n.

2. We are saints! Forgiveness is sure
not of ourselves, but the cross
Christ endured.
We're free from the Law that said
'You must provide!'
We're free to be servants; we're
called; we're baptised.

3. Jesus closed the dark pit of death.
   He has breathed on us with his
   holy breath.
   He gives us the faith to respond to
   his News.
   We're free to show mercy, to love,
   to be bruised.

*James G. Johnson*

# 421

1. Child in the manger, infant of
   Mary;
   outcast and stranger, Lord of all;
   child who inherits all our
   transgressions,
   all our demerits on him fall.

2. Once the most holy child of
   salvation
   gently and lowly lived below;
   now as our glorious mighty
   Redeemer,
   see him victorious o'er each foe.

3. Prophets foretold him, infant of
   wonder;
   angels behold him on his throne:
   worthy our Saviour of all their
   praises;
   happy for ever are his own.

*Lachlan Macbean (1853–1931),
after Mary Macdonald (1789–1872)*

# 422

1. Christ be my way, my path to find
   the Father,
   my guide when there's no trusting
   sound or sight;
   Christ fill my mind to cleanse
   the understanding,

to be my truth, a beacon blazing
bright;
Christ all I hope for,
strengthening, upholding,
my breath of life, my pride and
my delight.

**Truth on my tongue, his way
to guide my walking
and I shall live, not I but
Christ in me!**

2. No way but Christ, his cross
   the only signpost
   and he our road through death
   to blessedness;
   no safety else, no footing
   for the pilgrim,
   without his leading there's no
   guide nor guess:
   our way to where the Father
   waits in welcome
   to greet us home from night and
   wilderness.

3. We name him Lord, Truth rising
   like a tower
   above the world his coming shook
   and stirred:
   truth born in time, a child, and
   shown to shepherds
   when God's great glory on the
   hills was heard;
   truth born beyond all time, when
   first the Father
   pronounced his mighty
   all-creating Word.

4. Christ, Life of man, creation's
   mind and maker,
   hid deep in God before the
   world began,
   God born of God, the
   everlasting mercy,
   the Father's love, who stopped

and put on man:
man's life that ebbed beneath
the nails, the crowning,
then burst in one white dawn
death's narrow span.

*Luke Connaughton (1919–79)*

# 423

1. Christ has arisen, Alleluia!
Rejoice and praise him; Alleluia!
For our Redeemer burst from
the tomb,
even from death, dispelling its
gloom.

**Let us sing praise to him with
endless joy.**
**Death's fearful sting he has come
to destroy.**
**Our sins forgiving, Alleluia!**
**Jesus is living, Alleluia!**

2. For three long days the grave did
its worst,
until its strength by God was
dispersed
He who gives life did death
undergo,
and in its conquest his might
did show.

3. The angel said to them, 'Do not
fear,
you look for Jesus who is not here.
See for yourselves, the tomb is
all bare:
only the grave-clothes are lying
there.'

4. Go spread the news, he's not in
the grave.
He has arisen, mankind to save.
Jesus' redeeming labours are
done.
Even the battle with sin is won.

*Tr. from Swahili by Howard S. Olsen*

# 424

1. Christ is alive, with joy we sing;
we celebrate our risen Lord,
praising the glory of his name.
**Alleluia, alleluia, alleluia.**

2. He is the grain of wheat that died;
sown in distress and reaped in joy,
yielding a harvest of new life.
**Alleluia, alleluia, alleluia.**

3. He is the sun which brings the
dawn:
he is the light of all the world,
setting us free from death and sin.
**Alleluia, alleluia, alleluia.**

4. He is the vine set in the earth,
sharing our life, becoming man,
that man might share in God's
own life.
**Alleluia, alleluia, alleluia.**

5. Christ is alive, with joy we sing;
we celebrate our risen Lord,
praising the glory of his name.
**Alleluia, alleluia, alleluia.**

*Pamela Stotter*

# 425

1. Christ is arisen from the grave's
     dark prison.
   We now rejoice with gladness;
   Christ will end all sadness.
   Lord, have mercy.

2. All our hopes were ended had
     Jesus not ascended
   from the grave triumphantly.
   For this, Lord Christ, we worship
     Thee.
   Lord, have mercy.

3. Alleluia! Alleluia! Alleluia!
   We now rejoice with gladness;
   Christ will end all sadness.
   Lord, have mercy.

*Anon (11th Century), tr. Gustave*
*Polack*

# 426

1. Christ is coming
   to set the captives free,
   He is coming
   to rescue you and me.

   **Christ is coming from above**
   **bringing joy and bringing love.**
   **He is coming for you and me.**

2. Christ has come
   to a stable cold and bare;
   He is coming
   to a world where no one cares.

3. Christ is coming,
   bringing light where darkness
     reigned;
   He is coming
   where we gather in his name.

4. Christ is coming
   to this altar in our Mass;
   He is coming
   to a new home in our hearts.

5. Christ is coming,
   the Father's only Son;
   He is coming
   – his spirit makes us one.

*N. & K. Donnelly*

# 427

1. Christ is made the sure
     foundation,
   Christ the head and corner stone,
   chosen of the Lord, and precious,
   binding all the Church in one,
   holy Sion's help for ever,
   and her confidence alone.

2. All that dedicated city,
   dearly loved of God on high,
   in exultant jubilation
   pours perpetual melody,
   God the One in Three adoring
   in glad hymns eternally.

3. To this temple where we call you
   come, O Lord of Hosts, today;
   with your wonted loving kindness
   hear your people as they pray,
   and your fullest benediction
   shed within its walls alway.

4. Here vouchsafe to all your
     servants
   what they ask of you to gain,
   what they gain of you forever
   with the blessed to retain,
   and hereafter in your glory
   evermore with you to reign.

5. Praise and honour to the Father,
   praise and honour to the Son,
   praise and honour to the Spirit,
   ever Three and ever One,
   consubstantial, co-eternal,
   while unending ages run.

*Latin 7th or 8th Century*
*tr. J.M. Neale (1818–66), alt.*

# 428

1. Christ is the world's light,
   he and no other;
   born in our darkness,
   he became our brother.
   If we have seen him,
   we have seen the Father:
   **glory to God on high.**

2. Christ is the world's peace,
   he and no other;
   no man can serve him
   and despise his brother.
   Who else unites us,
   one in God the Father?
   **Glory to God on high.**

3. Christ is the world's life,
   he and no other,
   sold once for silver,
   murdered here, our brother
   he who redeems us,
   reigns with God the Father:
   **glory to God on high.**

4. Give God the glory,
   God and no other;
   give God the glory,
   Spirit, Son and Father;
   give God the glory,
   God in man, my brother:
   **glory to God on high.**

*F. Pratt Green*

# 429

1. Christ is the world's redeemer,
   the lover of the pure,
   the fount of heavenly wisdom,
   our trust and hope secure,
   the armour of his soldiers,
   the lord of earth and sky,
   our health while we are living,
   our life when we shall die.

2. Christ has our host surrounded
   with clouds of martyrs bright
   who wave their palms in triumph
   and fire us for the fight.
   For Christ the cross ascended
   to save a world undone
   and suffering for the sinful
   and full redemption won.

3. Down in the realm of darkness
   he lay a captive bound,
   but at the hour appointed
   he rose, a victor crowned,
   and now, to heaven ascended,
   he sits upon the throne
   in glorious dominion,
   his Father's and his own.

*St. Columba (521–97)*
*tr. Duncan McGregor*

# 430

**Christ our Lord has come to save his people!**
**Alleluia! Alleluia! Alleluia!**

1. Baptized in Christ our Lord,
   reborn to new life in our Saviour
   and Lord, alleluia!
   For we are the people whom God
   made his own
   through the blood of his own Son,
   our Lord Jesus Christ.

2. O come then, bless the Lord,
   the Father of all, who is love
      without end, alleluia!
   Before he created the world with
      great pow'r,
   we were chosen then in Christ,
      God made us his own.

3. Since time itself began
   God loved us and planned to
      adopt us in Christ, alleluia!
   He chose us to live in his glorious
      name,
   as his children and his friends, a
      people redeemed.

4. Be joyful in the Lord,
   rejoice and give thanks to the
      Father of all, alleluia!
   For Christ is alive and we live now
      in him;
   we are filled now with his life.
      Rejoice, praise his name!

5. With Christ we are made heirs
   and called to belong to the fam'ly
      of God, alleluia!
   Christ freed us from sin by his
      death on the cross,
   and has raised us up to life, a life
      without end.

6. Give glory to our God, the Father
      of all;
   to his Son, Jesus Christ, alleluia!
   And praise to the Spirit, the gift of
      his love.
   Let us sing out to the Lord for
      ever. Amen.

*Paul Décha, tr. Sr Mary Lucia and
Robert B. Kelly*

# 431

**Christ our Pasch has been slain,
   alleluia!
Sing with joy, alleluia, alleluia,
   alleluia!**

1. Pasch of the New Law,
   the Spirit's holy feast;
   O Pasch of Christ the Lord,
   who for us has come to earth!

2. Pasch of the New Law,
   O joy of all mankind;
   the doors of life are wide,
   giving life to us once more.

3. Pasch of the New Law,
   the banquet hall is full
   of guests the Lord has called,
   that all men may share his feast.

4. Pasch of the New Law,
   behold your baptized saints
   in robes of purest white
   for the marriage of the Lamb.

5. Pasch of the New Law,
   our souls' immortal flame
   shines forth in splendor bright,
   nevermore to cease its light.

6. Pasch of the New Law,
   O Christ who lives again:
   the pow'r of death you crushed,
   you have given us your life.

7. Pasch of the New Law,
   we pray to you, O Lord:
   stretch forth your blessed hands
   on the people you have saved.

8. Pasch of the New Law,
   O Christ, receive our songs;
   to you be glory, Lord,
   with all joy and praise. Amen!

*Lucien Deiss*

# 432

1. City of God, how broad and far
   outspread thy walls sublime!
   The true thy chartered freeman
   are,
   of every age and clime.

2. One holy Church, one army
   strong,
   one steadfast, high intent;
   one working band, one harvest
   song
   one King omnipotent.

3. How purely hath thy speech come
   down
   from man's primeval youth!
   How grandly hath thine empire
   grown,
   of freedom, love and truth!

4. How gleam thy watch-fires
   through the night
   with never-fainting ray!
   How rise thy towers, serene and
   bright,
   to meet the dawning day!

5. In vain the surge's angry shock,
   in vain the drifting sands:
   unharmed upon the eternal Rock
   the eternal City stands.

*Samuel Johnson (1822–82)*

# 433

1. Come, God's people, sing for joy,
   shout your songs of gladness;
   for the hope of Easter day
   overcomes our sadness.
   Come with all his people here,
   who with true affection,
   join again to celebrate
   Jesus' resurrection.

2. Years before, as Moses led
   Israel's sons and daughters
   from their bonds to Exodus
   through the Red Sea waters:
   so the living Lord of life
   speaks through our baptism
   of the new life that we share
   with him who is risen.

3. That first Easter he arose,
   his disciples greeting;
   Christians now throughout the
   world,
   still their Lord are meeting.
   Christ, who dies for all mankind,
   in his death brings healing;
   and his rising from the grave,
   God's power is revealing.

*St. John Damascene (d 7540),*
*freely paraphrased by Keith D. Pearson*

# 434

1. Come, holy Lord, our faith renew,
   our little praise enough for you.

   We ask your mercy, Lord,
   who bear your sacred name;
   your healing touch
   the glorious blessing we can claim.

2. O Jesus, come, our hope on earth,
   from heaven you came to share
   our birth.

3. Come, Spirit blest, our love revive;
   our failing prayer is made alive.

*John Glynn*

# 435

**Come let us sing out our joy to
the Lord!
Hail the rock of salvation,
come into his presence to give
thanks,
singing psalms of triumph.**

1. In his hands are the depths of the
   earth,
   the mountain peaks belong to him.
   His is the sea, he created it,
   His is the dry land, formed by his
   hands.

2. Bow down before him in prayer,
   kneel before the Lord and adore.
   He is the Lord our shepherd,
   we his people, the flock that he
   feeds.

3. Listen to the voice of the Lord,
   do not grow stubborn nor harden
   your hearts.
   Put not your God to the test,
   well you know how he cares for us.

4. Praise the Father who made all
   things,
   praise the Son who died for us.
   Praise the Spirit who gladdens
   our hearts,
   praise unceasing fill heaven and
   earth.

*Stephen Dean
Based on Psalm 94(95)*

# 436

**Come, Lord Jesus,
   come Lord, come!
Come, Lord Jesus,
   come Lord, come!
Open my eyes,
   open my mind,
open my heart to peace
   and love.**

1. Like rain falling on the thirsty
   ground,
   like grass springing from the
   barren earth,
   like the sun rising over the land,
   heralds new life and a new rebirth.

2. So he comes bringing
   righteousness,
   bringing justice to all the land;
   so he comes as a man among men,
   Saviour and Lord of all mankind.

3. Wonder Counsellor and Prince
   of Peace,
   a man of such integrity!
   Come Lord Jesus, we plead to
   you,
   come and give us liberty.

*Psalm 71(72) and Isaiah 9:6,
adapted by Garfield Rochard*

# 437

1. Come, O divine Messiah!
   The world in silence waits the day
   when hope shall sing its triumph,
   and sadness flee away.

   **Sweet Saviour, haste; come,
      come to earth:**

dispel the night, and show Thy
      face,
and bid us hail the dawn of grace.
Come, O divine Messiah!
The world in silence waits the day
when hope shall sing its triumph,
and sadness flee away.

2. O Thou, whom nations sighed for,
   whom priests and prophets long
      foretold,
   wilt break the captive fetters,
   redeem the long-lost fold.

3. Shalt come in peace and meekness,
   and lowly will thy cradle be:
   all clothed in human weakness
   shall we thy Godhead see.

*French 18th Century,*
*tr. Sr. Mary of St. Phillip (1887)*

# 438

Come, O Lord, to my heart today
and stay with me all the day.
Come, O Lord, to my heart today
and stay with me all the day.

1. Your flesh is food and your
      blood is drink,
   and these you give to me your life.

2. This is the bread
      come down from heaven
   which, if a man eats, he'll live
      for ever.

3. He who takes my flesh and blood
   lives in me and I in him.

4. When you give your self to us,
   you bind us to yourself and each
   other.

*Douglas Rowe*
*Based on John 6:50,55,56*

# 439

1. Come, thou long-expected Jesus,
   born to set thy people free,
   from our fears and sins release us,
   let us find our rest in thee.

2. Israel's strength and consolation,
   hope of all the earth thou art;
   dear desire of every nation,
   joy of every longing heart.

3. Born thy people to deliver,
   born a child and yet a king,
   born to reign in us for ever,
   now thy gracious kingdom bring.

4. By thine own eternal Spirit
   rule in all our hearts alone;
   by thine all-sufficient merit
   raise us to thy glorious throne.

*Charles Wesley (1707–88)*

# 440

1. Day and night the heav'ns are
      telling
   the glory which with us is dwelling,
   the works of God to us made
      known.
   Dawn and dusk are still with
      wonder.
   The wind cries out, the waters
      thunder,
   displaying his almighty power.
   Our God is great indeed.
   He knows our constant need, our
      creator.
   So with creation we proclaim
   his goodness as we praise his
      name.

2. Lord, we stand in awe before you,
   your people coming to adore you,
   so cleanse our hearts, renew our
      minds.
   See us now in shadows dwelling,
   and come like sun, the clouds
      dispelling,
   enlighten, heal us, Lord of love.
   Your Spirit in us prays.
   He teaches us your ways,
   as we listen.
   Touch once again with living
      flame
   your people gathered in your
      name.

   *Pamela Stotter*

# 441

Day by day, dear Lord,
of thee three things I pray;
to see thee more clearly,
to love thee more dearly,
to follow thee more nearly,
day by day.

   *St. Richard of Chichester,*
   *arr by D. Austin*

# 442

1. Dear love of my heart,
      O heart of Christ, my Lord,
   what treasure you leave
      within my heart, O Guest!
   You come to my heart
      O heart on fire with love,
   and leave me your heart:
      O how my heart is blest!

2. My heart cannot tell,
      O King of angel hosts,
   how great was that pain
      you bore upon the cross:
   so small is my heart,
      so deep your wounds of love,
   so precious the crown
      of those you save from loss!

3. Your death has restored
      your likeness in my heart,
   your cross in my shield,
      your loving heart my gain!
   How sad is my heart
      when I recall my sins!
   How could I have loved
      what gave your heart such pain?

4. O King of all bliss,
      all glory set aside,
   what heart could have known
      the pain within your breast?
   The wound in your side
      laid bare your burning love,
   and opened for all
      the heart where all find rest!

   *James Quinn, SJ.*
   *Based on the Irish of Tadhg Gaelach O*
   *Suilleabhain*

# 443

**Divided our pathways,**
**and heavy our guilt;**
**burden'd, unseeing,**
**we grope for the one way.**
**Far from our home,**
**O Father, we call out –**
**'Heal us, forgive us**
**bring us together in Jesus your**
   **Son!**

1. Holy Father, keep those
   you have given me
   true to your name,
   so that they may all
   be as we are one.

2. Father, may they be one in us,
   as you are in me and I am in you,
   so that the world may come to
      believe
   it was you who sent me.

3. I have given them the glory
   that you gave to me,
   that they may all be one
   as we are one.

4. With me in them and you in me
   may they be so completely united,
   that the world may know
   that it was you who sent me,
   and that you love them
   as much as you love me.

*Christopher Coelho,*
*from John 17:11,21,23*

# 444

Do not be afraid, for I have
redeemed you.
I have called you by your name;
you are mine.

1. When you walk through the
      waters I'll be with you.
   You will never sink beneath the
      waves.

2. When the fire is burning all
      around you,
   you will never be consumed by
   the flames.

3. When the fear of loneliness is
      looming,
   then remember I am at your side.

4. When you dwell in the exile of the
      stranger,
   remember you are precious in my
   eyes.

5. You are mine, O my child, I am
      your Father,
   and I love you with a perfect love.

*Gerald Markland*
*Based on Isaiah 43:1–4*

# 445

1. 'Do you really love me?'
   Jesus said to Peter.
   'Do you really love me?'
   Jesus said again.
   'Lord, you know I love you!'
   Peter said with joy.
   'Then feed my lambs', he said,
   'Peter, feed my lambs.'

2. 'Do you really love me?'
   Jesus said to Peter.
   'Do you really love me?'
   Jesus said again.
   'Lord, you know I love you!'
   Peter said with joy.
   'Then feed my sheep,' he said,
   'Peter, feed my sheep.'

3. 'Do you really love me?'
   Jesus says to me.
   'Do you really love me?'
   Jesus says to you.
   'Yes, we really love you,
   we will follow you!'
   'Then feed my lambs,' he says,
   'people, feed my sheep.'

*Carey Landry*

# 446

1. Each morning with its new born
   light
   proclaims the Lord of life is great!
   His faithfulness will have no end;
   to him our songs of praise ascend.

2. The gift of light that fills the sky
   helps us to see and choose our
   way;
   then let us order our affairs
   in praise of him who for us cares.

3. Lord, let our eyes, the body's light,
   be drawn to what is good and right
   and to yourself, the source of life,
   our hope in fear, our peace in
   strife.

4. You, Lord of all creation, are
   as brilliant as the morning star;
   light in our hearts your holy flame
   and make us fit to bear your name.

5. Dispel the darkness from our days
   and free us from all bitterness,
   from haughty mind and blinded
   sight,
   and lead us forward day and night.

6. To walk as in the light of day,
   be steadfast always, come what
   may,
   we turn in faith to you, our Friend,
   and pray: sustain us to the end.

*Johannes Zwick (1496–1542),*
*tr. by Fred Kaan*

# 447

**Faith in God**
   **can move the mountains;**
**trust in him can calm the sea.**
**He's my fortress,**
   **he's my stronghold;**
**he's the rock who rescues me.**

1. Lord, you are my refuge;
   never let me be ashamed.
   In your justice rescue me;
   turn to me and hear my prayer.

2. You are my salvation:
   from oppression set me free.
   Ever since my childhood
   you have been my only hope.

3. Bitter troubles burden me,
   but you fill me with new life.
   From the grave you raise me up,
   so my tongue will sing your praise.

*Words paraphrased from Scripture by*
*Aniceto Nazareth*

# 448

1. Fashion me a people,
   a people set apart;
   that I may be your God,
   and you will give me your heart.

2. Come together in community,
   a sign of my love here on earth,
   to share the life of Nazareth,
   and incarnate the myst'ry of my
   birth.

3. Be a fam'ly, humble and forgiving,
   who listen to my voice,
   who call upon my mercy,
   and at my coming rejoice.

4. Fashion me a people,
   a people set apart;
   that I may be your God,
   and I will give you my heart.

   *Carol Gordon*

# 449

1. Father, hear the prayer we offer:
   not for ease that prayer shall be,
   but for strength that we may ever
   live our lives courageously.

2. Not for ever in green pastures
   do we ask our way to be;
   but the steep and rugged pathway
   may we tread rejoicingly.

3. Not for ever by still waters
   would we idly rest and stay;
   but would smite the living
      fountains
   from the rocks along the way.

4. Be our strength in hours of
      weakness,
   in our wanderings be our guide;
   through endeavour, failure,
      danger,
   Father, be there at our side.

   *Love Maria Willis (1824–1908)*
   *and others*

# 450

1. Father, I place into your hands
   the things I cannot do.
   Father, I place into your hands
   the things that I've been through.
   Father, I place into your hands
   the way that I should go,
   For I know I always can trust you.

2. Father, I place into your hands
   my friends and family.
   Father, I place into your hands
   the things that trouble me.
   Father, I place into your hands
   the person I would be,
   for I know I always can trust you.

3. Father, we love to see your face,
   we love to hear your voice,
   Father, we love to sing your praise
   and in your name rejoice,
   Father, we love to walk with you
   and in your presence rest,
   for we know we always can trust
      you.

4. Father, I want to be with you
   and do the things you do.
   Father, I want to speak the words
   that you are speaking too.
   Father, I want to love the ones
   that you will draw to you,
   for I know that I am one with you.

   *J. Hewer*

# 451

1. Father in heaven,
   grant to your children
   mercy and blessing,
   songs never ceasing,
   love to unite us,
   grace to redeem us,
   Father in heaven,
   Father our God.

2. Jesus, Redeemer,
   may we remember
   your gracious Passion,
   your resurrection.
   Worship we bring you,
   praise we shall sing you
   Jesus, Redeemer,
   Jesus our God.

3. Spirit descending
   whose is the blessing –
   strength for the weary,
   help for the needy,
   sealed in our sonship
   yours be our worship –
   Spirit unending,
   Spirit adored.

   *D.T. Niles*

# 452

1. Father, in my life I see,
   you are God, who walks with me.
   You hold my life in your hands:
   close beside you I will stand.
   I give all my life to you:
   help me, Father, to be true.

2. Jesus, in my life I see . . .

3. Spirit, in my life I see . . .

   *Frank Anderson, MSC*

# 453

1. Father, Lord of all creation,
   ground of being, life and love;
   height and depth beyond
      description
   only life in you can prove:

you are mortal life's dependence:
thought, speech, sight are ours by
   grace;
yours is every hour's existence,
Sovereign Lord of time and space.

2. Jesus Christ, the man for others,
   we, you people, make our prayer:
   give us grace to love as brothers
   all whose burdens we can share.
   Where your name binds us
      together
   you, Lord, Christ, will surely be;
   where no selfishness can sever
   there your love may all men see.

3. Holy Spirit, rushing, burning
   wind and flame of Pentecost,
   fire our hearts afresh with
      yearning
   to regain what we have lost.
   May your love unite our action,
   nevermore to speak alone:
   God, in us abolish faction,
   God, through us your love make
      known.

   *Stewart Cross*

# 454

1. Father of heaven, whose love
      profound
   a ransom for our souls hath found,
   before thy throne we sinners bend,
   to us thy pardoning love extend.

2. Almighty Son, incarnate Word,
   our prophet, priest, Redeemer,
      Lord,
   before thy throne we sinners bend,
   to us thy saving grace extend.

3. Eternal Spirit, by whose breath
   the soul is raised from sin and
      death,
   before thy throne we sinners bend,
   to us thy quickening power
      extend.

4. Thrice Holy Father, Spirit, Son;
   mysterious Godhead, Three in
      One,
   before thy throne we sinners bend,
   grace, pardon, life to us extend.

*E. Cooper (1770–1833)*

# 455

1. Father, we praise you,
      now the night is over;
   active and watchful,
      stand we all before you;
   singing, we offer pray'r
      and meditation:
      thus we adore you.

2. Monarch of all things,
      fit us for your kingdom;
   banish our weakness,
      health and wholeness sending;
   bring us to heaven,
      where your saints united
      joy without ending.

3. All holy Father, Son,
      and equal Spirit,
   Trinity blessed,
      send us your salvation;
   yours is the glory,
      gleaming and resounding
      through all creation.

*St. Gregory the Great (540–604) tr. by*
*Percy Dearmer (1867–1936),*
*slightly altered*

# 456

Fear not, for I have redeemed you:
I have called you by name;
I have called you by name;
you are mine.

1. When you pass through the waters
   I will be with you;
   and through rivers,
   they will not overwhelm you.
   When you walk through the fire
   you will not be burned,
   the flames shall not consume you.

2. Because you are precious,
   and I love you;
   you whom I formed
   for my glory;
   you whom I called
   by my name,
   I will gather together.

3. You are my witness;
   I have chosen you
   that you may know
   and believe me.
   You are my servants
   for the world to see
   I am the Lord, I'm among you.

4. It's time now to lay aside
   the former things;
   a new day has dawned,
   do you see it
   I'm making a way
   in the wilderness
   and rivers to flow in the desert.

5. The rivers that flow
   in the desert
   give drink
   to my chosen people;
   to quench their thirst
   and to strengthen them,
   that they might show forth
   my praise.

*Jodi Page*
*Based on Isaiah 43:2,4,10,18–20*

# 457

**Fear not, rejoice and be glad,**
**the Lord hath done a great thing;**
**hath poured out his Spirit on all**
   **mankind,**
**on those who confess his name.**

1. The fig tree is budding, the vine
   beareth fruit,
   the wheat fields are golden with
   grain.
   Thrust in the sickle, the harvest
   is ripe,
   the Lord has given us rain.

2. Ye shall eat in plenty and be
   satisfied,
   the mountains will drip with sweet
   wine.
   My children shall drink of the
   fountain of life,
   my children will know they are
   mine.

3. My people shall know that I am
   the Lord,
   their shame I have taken away.
   My Spirit will lead them together
   again,
   my Spirit will show them the way.

4. My children shall dwell in a body
   of love,
   a light to the world they will be.
   Life shall come forth from the
   Father above,
   my body will set mankind free.

*Priscilla Wright*

# 458

1. 'Feed my lambs, my son, feed
   my sheep;
   if you love me, do not sleep.
   In the fields, my son, work and
   weep;
   feed my lambs, my son, feed
   my sheep.'

2. To the servant girl first he lied:
   'You were with him!' this she
   cried.
   But the Master he denied;
   on the following day, Jesus died.

3. Someone questioned him quietly,
   'Aren't you Peter of Galilee?
   I can tell you by your speech,
   you see.'
   Peter swore and said, 'It's not me!'

4. Peter heard the cock when it crew;
   as he left, he wept – and he knew!
   Ev'ry one of us is guilty too;
   yet Christ died for us, me and you.

5. Feed my lambs, my son, feed
   my sheep;
   if you love me, do not sleep.
   In the fields, my son, work and
   weep;
   feed my lambs, my son, feed
   my sheep.

*Charles A. Buffham (altered)*

# 459

1. Firm is our faith in one true God,
   loving Father and King supreme,
   mighty creator, Lord of all,
   visible world and world unseen.

2. And we believe in God's own Son,
   one with him from eternal dawn,
   who by the Spirit was conceived,
   and of his Virgin Mother born.

3. Man he was made and man he
      lived,
   man he suffered in cruel strife
   when on the Cross he fought
      with death,
   conquered and rose to deathless
      life.

4. This is our faith in the Spirit too:
   Lord and giver of life is he,
   one with the Father and the Son,
   spirit of love and unity.

5. Faith we profess in one true
      Church,
   sin forgiven and grace restored,
   hope for the vict'ry over death,
   life without end in Christ the Lord.

*Denis E. Hurley*

# 460

**Follow me, follow me,**
**leave your home and family,**
**leave your fishing nets and boats**
**upon the shore.**
**Leave the seed that you have sown,**
**leave the crops that you've grown,**
**leave the people you have known**
**and follow me.**

1. The foxes have their holes
   and the swallows have their nests,
   but the Son of man has no place to
      lay down.
   I do not offer comfort,
   I do not offer wealth,
   but in me will all happiness be
      found.

2. If you would follow me,
   you must leave old ways behind.
   You must take my cross
   and follow on my path.
   You may be far from loved ones,
   you may be far from home
   but my Father will welcome you
      at last.

3. Although I go away
   you will never be alone,
   for the Spirit will be
   there to comfort you.
   Though all of you may scatter,
   each follow his own path,
   still the Spirit of love will lead
      you home.

*Michael Cockett*

# 461

1. For the fruits of his creation,
   thanks be to God;
   for his gifts to every nation,
   thanks be to God;
   for the ploughing, sowing,
      reaping,
   silent growth while men are
      sleeping,
   future needs in earth's safe
      keeping,
   thanks be to God.

2. In the just reward of labour,
   God's will is done;
   in the help we give our neighbour,
   God's will is done;
   in our world-wide task of caring
   for the hungry and despairing
   in the harvests men are sharing,
   God's will is done.

3. For the harvests of his Spirit,
   thanks be to God;
   for the good all men inherit,
   thanks be to God;
   for the wonders that astound us,
   for the truths that still confound
   us,
   most of all, that love has found us,
   thanks be to God.

*F. Pratt Green*

# 462

1. For the healing of the nations,
   Lord, we pray with one accord,
   for a just and equal sharing
   of the things that earth affords.
   To a life of love in action
   help us rise and pledge our word.

2. Lead us, father, into freedom,
   from despair your world release,
   that, redeemed from war and
   hatred,
   men may come and go in peace.
   Show us how through care and
   goodness
   fear will die and hope increase.

3. All that kills abundant living,
   let it from the earth be banned;
   pride of status, race or schooling,
   dogmas keeping man from man.
   In our common quest for justice
   may we hallow life's brief span.

4. You, creator-God, have written
   your great name on all mankind;
   for our growing in your likeness
   bring the life of Christ to mind;
   that by our response and service
   earth its destiny may find.

*Fred Kaan*

# 463

For to those who love God,
who are called in his plan,
ev'rything works out for good.
And God himself chose them
to bear the likeness of his Son,
that he might be the first
of many, many brothers.

1. Who is able to condemn?
   Only Christ who died for us;
   Christ who rose for us;
   Christ who prays for us.

2. In the face of all this
   what is there left to say?
   For if God is with us,
   who can be against us?

3. What can separate us
   from the love of Christ?
   Neither trouble, nor pain,
   nor persecution.

4. What can separate us
   from the love of Christ?
   Not the past, the present,
   nor the future.

*Enrico Garzilli*
*Based on Romans 8:29,31–35*

# 464

For unto us a child is born,
unto us a son is given;
and the government
shall be upon his shoulder
and his name shall be called
'wonderful-counsellor',
'the Mighty-God',
'the everlasting Father',
and 'the Prince of Peace' is he.

*Based on Isaiah 9:6*

# 465

**Freely I give to you the gift of
a child my own
in hope that you will receive the
life that he gives for your own ...**

1. Call him Emmanuel for your God
   is with you this day
   he'll be by your side sharing your
   joy and pain . . .

2. Call him Jesus, for Yahweh gives
   his own
   for he is the shepherd who will
   guide his flock safely home . . .

3. Call him Lamb of God for he has
   died for your sins
   and all will be saved and truly
   belong to him . . .

*J. Garrity*

# 466

1. From the depths of sin and
   sadness
   I have called unto the Lord;
   be not deaf to my poor pleading,
   in your mercy, hear my voice.
   Be not deaf to my poor pleading,
   in your mercy, hear my voice.

2. If you, Lord, record our sinning
   who could then before you stand?
   But with you there is forgiveness;
   you shall ever be revered.
   But with you there is forgiveness;
   you shall ever be revered.

3. For the Lord my heart is waiting,
   for his word I hope and wait.
   More than watchmen wait for
   sunrise
   I am waiting for the Lord.
   More than watchmen wait for
   sunrise
   I am waiting for the Lord.

4. Hope, O people, in your Saviour,
   he will save you from your sin.
   Jesus from his cross is praying,
   'Father, forgive them,
   they know not what they do.'
   Jesus from his cross is praying,
   'Father, forgive them,
   they know not what they do.'

*Willard F. Jabusch*
*Based on Psalm 129(130)*

# 467

**Gather Christians, let's now
celebrate;
gather Christians, the Lord we
now await;
gather Christians, behold he comes;
rejoice and sing, for the Lord is
King!**

1. To God the Father, let's give
      him praise;
   to God the Father, our voice we
      raise;
   to God the Father, who reigns
      above;
   praise the Lord for his mercy
      and his love.

2. As we stand here before our God,
   with Christ Jesus, our saving
      Lord,
   we'll hear his word now, and
      break the bread,
   as we proclaim: he's risen from
      the dead!

3. Let us all now, as one community,
   praise and honour the Trinity.
   Let us all now with one accord
   sing out our praise to the living
      Lord!

*Garfield Rochard*

# 468

1. Gathered here from many
      churches,*
   one in worship and intent,
   let us for the days that face us
   all our hopes to God present,
   that our life and work may be
   symbols of our unity.

2. May the spring of all our actions
   be, O Lord, your love for man;
   may your word be seen and
      spoken
   and your will be clearly done.
   Help us, who your image bear,
   for the good of each to care.

3. Give us grace to match our calling,
   faith to overcome the past;
   show us how to meet the future,

planning boldly, acting fast.
Let the servant-mind of Christ
in our life be manifest.

4. Now ourselves anew committing
   to each other and to you,
   Lord, we ask that you will train us
   for the truth we have to do;
   that the world may soon become
   your great city of shalom.

   * or Gathered here from many
      nations,

*Fred Kaan*

# 469

1. Gifts of bread and wine, gifts
      we've offered,
   fruits of labour, fruits of love:
   taken, offered, sanctified,
   blessed and broken; words of one
      who died:
   'Take my body; take my saving
      blood.'
   Gifts of bread and wine: Christ
      our Lord.

2. Christ our Saviour, living presence
      here,
   as he promised while on earth:
   'I am with you for all time,
   I am with you in this bread and
      wine.
   Take my body, take my saving
      blood.'
   Gifts of bread and wine: Christ
      our Lord.

3. Through the Father, with the
   Spirit,
   one in union with the Son,
   for God's people, joined in prayer
   faith is strengthened by the food
   we share.
   'Take my body, take my saving
   blood.'
   Gifts of bread and wine: Christ
   our Lord.

*Christine McCann*

# 470

1. Give praise to the Lord, all you
   men, **alleluia!**
   O praise the name of the Lord,
   **alleluia!**
   Bless'd be the name of the Lord,
   **alleluia, alleluia!**

2. Now and evermore,
   from dawn to the close of the day,
   bless'd be the name of the Lord.

3. On high, above the earth is the
   Lord,
   his glory above the sky;
   there is none like the Lord our
   God.

4. Enthroned in heaven on high,
   he views the earth and the sky;
   to those in need he gives his help.

5. From the dust he raises the poor,
   he makes them sit among kings,
   among the kings of the earth.

6. Behold the barren wife,
   now abides in her home
   as the happy mother of sons.

7. Let us sing to the Lord,
   singing glory and praise,
   both now and evermore. Amen.

*Lucien Deis*
*Based on Psalm 112(113*

# 471

1. Give us the will to listen
   to the message you impart:
   we thank you, Lord,
   for showing us your heart!

2. Give us the will to persevere
   though meaning disappears:
   we thank you, Lord,
   for calming all our fears.

3. Give us the will to work on
   at what we may like the least:
   we thank you, Lord,
   for ev'ry bird and beast.

4. Give us the will to work and serve
   where we are needed most:
   we thank you, Lord,
   for staying with us close.

5. Give us the will to seek you
   in the quiet and the calm:
   we thank you, Lord,
   for keeping us from harm.

6. Give us the will to see you
   as our God, as man, as friend:
   we thank you, Lord,
   for your love has no end.

*Kurt Rommel,*
*tr. by Eileen M. Burzynska*

# 472

1. Glorious things of you are spoken,
   Sion, city of our God:
   he whose word cannot be broken
   formed you for his own abode.
   On the Rock of Ages founded,
   what can shake your sure repose?
   With salvation's walls
      surrounded,
   you may smile at all your foes.

2. See, the streams of living waters,
   springing from eternal love,
   well supply your sons and
      daughters
   and all fear of want remove:
   who can faint while such a river
   ever flows their thirst to assuage –
   grace, which like the Lord the
      giver
   never fails from age to age?

3. Blest inhabitants of Sion,
   washed in their Redeemer's blood:
   Jesus, whom their souls rely on,
   makes them Kings and priests to
      God.
   'Tis his love his people raises
   over self to reign as kings,
   and as priests, his solemn praises
   each for a thank-offering brings.

4. Saviour, since of Sion's city
   I, through grace, a member am,
   let the world deride or pity,
   I will glory in your name:
   fading is the worldling's pleasure,
   all his boasted pomp and show;
   solid joys and lasting treasure
   none but Sion's children know.

   *John Newton (1725–1807)*

# 473

**Glory and praise to our God,**
**who alone gives light to our days.**
**Many are the blessings He bears**
**to those who trust in his ways.**

1. We, the daughters and sons of
      Him
   who built the valleys and plains,
   praise the wonders our God has
      done
   in ev'ry heart that sings.

2. In His wisdom He strengthens us,
   like gold that's tested in fire,
   though the power of sin prevails,
   our God is there to save.

3. Ev'ry moment of ev'ry day
   our God is waiting to save,
   always ready to seek the lost,
   to answer those who pray.

4. God has watered our barren land
   and spent His merciful rain.
   Now the rivers of life run full
   for anyone to drink.

   *Dan Schutte SJ.*

# 474

**Glory to God! Peace to all men,**
**joy to earth comes from heaven.**

1. For all your wonders, O Lord
      God,
   your people come to thank you.
   Our gracious friend, we bless
      your name,

for your Kingdom which comes!
To you we bring our praises
through the love of the Son and
of the Spirit.

2. The world's redeemer, Jesus
Christ,
receive the pray'r we bring you.
O Lamb of God, you conquered
death;
now have mercy on us.
Most holy Jesus, Son of God:
living Lord of all worlds,
our Lord God!

*José Weber,*
*tr. Erik Routley (1917–1982)*

# 475

1. God, at creation's dawn,
over a world unborn,
your Spirit soared.
By word and water deign
that this same Spirit reign
in those now born again,
through Christ our Lord.

2. We, who in Adam fell,
are, as the Scriptures tell,
saved and restored.
For, when these rites are done,
dying we are made one,
rising we overcome,
with Christ our Lord.

3. Hear us, your Church, rejoice,
singing with grateful voice,
Father adored;
telling our faith anew,
greeting with welcome true
children new born to you,
in Christ our Lord.

*Denis E. Hurley*

# 476

1. God be with you till we meet
again;
by his counsels guide, uphold you,
with his sheep securely fold you:
God be with you till we meet
again.

2. God be with you till we meet
again;
'neath his wings protecting hide
you,
daily manna still provide you:
God be with you till we meet
again.

3. God be with you till we meet
again;
when life's perils thick confound
you,
put his arm unfailing round you:
God be with you till we meet
again.

4. God be with you till we meet
again;
keep love's banner floating o'er
you,
smite death's threatening wave
before you:
God be with you till we meet
again.

*J.E. Rankin (1828–1904)*

# 477

1. God forgave my sin in Jesus'
name;
I've been born again, in Jesus'
name;
and in Jesus' name I come to you
to share his love as he told me to.

He said:
'Freely, freely, you have received;
freely, freely give.
Go, in my name,
and because you believe,
others will know that I live.'

2. All pow'r is giv'n in Jesus' name,
in earth and heav'n in Jesus' name;
and in Jesus' name I come to you
to share his pow'r as he told me to.

3. God gives us life in Jesus' name,
he lives in us in Jesus' name;
and in Jesus' name I come to you
to share his peace as he told me to.

*Carol Owens*

# 478

1. God gives us harvest from fields
we have sown,
bread that we bake has been
earned by our toil,
bread of our sadness we bring to
the Lord.

**Praise to the Lord of the harvest.**
**Praise to the Lord of the harvest.**
**Lord of the vineyard be blest.**
**Lord of the vineyard be blest.**

2. God has made fruitful the vines
we have grown,
wine that we make has been
pressed for our joy.
wine of our gladness we bring to
the Lord.

*Patrick Lee*

# 479

**God has gladdened my heart with**
**joy, alleluia!**
**He has vested me with holiness,**
**alleluia!**

1. Sing my soul of the glory of the
Lord;
with God's Spirit I'm full to
overflowing!

2. See the love that God showers on
the poor;
see the Lord overshadow those
who fear him.

3. All the world will join in this song
of praise,
for through me they now know the
Lord is with them.

4. To fulfill what he promised from
of old
God has chosen me! Bless his
name for ever.

5. Day by day, year by year, God's
love is sure;
Those who listen and keep his
word will know it.

6. See the pow'r of the Lord destroy
the strong!
Those who think themselves
strong, the Lord will humble.

7. Empty pride, self conceit, the Lord
ignores;
but he raises the poor who call
upon him.

8. No more thirst, no more hunger
with the Lord;
unsurpassed in his goodness to his
people.

9. See the care that the Lord shows to us all.
   Day by day, year by year, God's love's unending.

10. Praise the Father, the Son, the Spirit, praise!
    May the glory of God be sung for ever.

*Jean Paul Lecot, W.R. Lawrence and*
*R.B. Kelly*
*Based on Luke 1:46–55*

# 480

1. God is working his purpose out as year succeeds to year,
   God is working his purpose out and the time is drawing near;
   nearer and nearer draws the time, the time that shall surely be,
   when the earth shall be filled with the glory of God as the waters cover the sea.

2. From utmost east to utmost west where-e'er man's foot hath trod,
   by the mouth of many messengers goes forth the voice of God.
   'Give ear to me, ye continents, ye isles give ear to me,
   that the earth may be filled with the glory of God as the waters cover the sea.'

3. What can we do to work God's work, to prosper and increase
   the brotherhood of all mankind, the reign of the Prince of Peace?
   What can we do to hasten the time, the time that shall surely be,
   when the earth shall be filled with the glory of God as the waters cover the sea?

4. March we forth in the strength of God with the banner of Christ unfurled,
   that the light of the glorious Gospel of truth may shine throughout the world.
   Fight we the fight with sorrow and sin, to set their captives free,
   that the earth may be filled with the glory of God as the waters cover the sea.

5. All we can do is nothing worth unless God blesses the deed;
   vainly we hope for the harvest-tide till God gives life to the seed;
   yet nearer and nearer draws the time, the time that shall surely be,
   when the earth shall be filled with the glory of God as the waters cover the sea.

*A.C. Ainger (1841–1919)*

# 481

1. God made the birds, their home is the air;
   God made the beasts, each in its lair;
   God made the fish, their home is the sea;
   but God himself is home for me.

2. Birds find their food in their home of air;
   beasts find theirs too, 'most everywhere;
   the fish find theirs in the paths of the sea;
   but God himself is food for me.

3. God loves the birds, they answer
   in song;
   God loves the beasts, so
   pow'rfully strong;
   God loves the fish as they swim
   in the sea;
   but God himself is love for me.

   *Magnus Wenninger*


# 482

1. God most high of all creation,
   glory be to you!
   **Living God, we come before you,**
   **glory be to you!**
   Hosts of Heav'n, your praises
   are singing.
   Shouts of joy and thanks are
   ringing.
   **We on earth re-echo their praises;**
   **glory be to you!**

2. God of light, our darkness ending,
   glory be to you!
   **God of truth, our doubts dispelling,**
   **glory be to you!**
   Light of God on all men dawning,
   Christ the rising sun brings
   morning.
   **You have shed your light on our**
   **pathway;**
   **glory be to you!**

3. Mighty God, who brings us
   freedom,
   glory be to you!
   **Faithful God who keeps his**
   **promise,**
   **glory be to you!**
   As your Church we gather before
   you,

and with thanks, we sing and
adore you.
**Now made one in Christ, let us**
**praise you;**
**glory be to you!**

4. God of love, your ways are gentle,
   glory be to you!
   **God of peace, you heal our sadness,**
   **glory be to you!**
   Called by you, we hasten to meet
   you,
   and together pray as we greet you.
   **With your loving kindness surround**
   **us,**
   **glory be to you!**

5. Sing your praise to God our
   Father,
   glory be to you!
   **Praise the Son and Holy Spirit,**
   **glory be to you!**
   Abba, Father, Lord of creation,
   Jesus Lord, who brought
   salvation.
   **Holy Spirit, dwelling within us,**
   **glory be to you!**

   *French, tr. and adapted by Pamela*
   *Stotter*


# 483

1. God, our maker, mighty Father,
   all creation sings your praise,
   sun and stars in all their
   splendour,
   moon in ev'ry changing phase,
   earth with all its trees and grasses,
   sparkling rivers, ocean blue,
   all unite to pay you homage,
   singing joyously to you.

2. Provident and wise creator,
as your mighty plan unfurled,
man you made to share your
    labour
in the building of the world.
Man and woman you created,
that united, heart and home,
they might work and strive
    together
till your endless kingdom come.

3. God of truth and love unbounded,
further still your mercy went,
when uniting earth with heaven,
your incarnate Son you sent:
first-born of your vast creation,
holding all in unity,
leading all in power and wisdom
to a glorious destiny.

*Denis E. Hurley*

# 484

1. God rest you merry, gentlemen,
let nothing you dismay,
remember Christ our Saviour
was born on Christmas Day,
to save us all from Satan's pow'r
when we were gone astray;
**O tidings of comfort and joy,
    comfort and joy,
O tidings of comfort and joy.**

2. In Bethelehem, in Jewry,
this blessed Babe was born,
and laid within a manger,
upon this blessed morn;
the which His Mother Mary,
did nothing take in scorn.

3. From God our heavenly Father,
a blessed Angel came;
and unto certain Shepherds
brought tidings of the same;
how that in Bethlehem was born
the Son of God by Name.

4. "Fear not then," said the Angel,
"Let nothing you affright,
this day is born a Saviour
of a pure Virgin bright,
to free all those who trust in Him
from Satan's power and might."

5. The shepherds at those tidings
rejoicéd much in mind,
and left their flocks a-feeding,
in tempest, storm, and wind;
and went to Bethlehem
    straightway,
the Son of God to find.

6. And when they came to Bethlehem
where our dear Saviour lay,
they found Him in a manger,
where oxen feed on hay;
His Mother Mary kneeling down,
unto the Lord did pray.

7. Now to the Lord sing praises,
all you within this place,
and with true love and
    brotherhood
each other now embrace;
this holy tide of Christmas
all other doth deface.

*English Traditional Carol*

# 485

God's Spirit precedes us,
guides and gently leads us.
Alleluia, alleluia!
God's Spirit precedes us,
guides and gently leads us.
Alleluia, alleluia!

1. Through mountains and valleys
he journeys with us,
all his work
entrusts to our control;
and those who know not
what God wants from them
must silently wait
on the voice of our God.

2. In sorrow and gladness,
he's always near us,
and his love,
he gives to everyone;
and those who know not
God's presence with them
must just take a look
at the life all around.

*Bonaventure Hinwood*
*Based on Psalms 65(66) and 66(67)*

# 486

1. Good Christian men, rejoice
and sing!
Now is the triumph of our King!
To all the world glad news we
bring:
Alleluia!

2. The Lord of Life is risen for ay:
bring flowers of song to strew his
way;
let all mankind rejoice and say
Alleluia!

3. Praise we in songs of victory
that Love, that Life, which cannot
die,
and sing with hearts uplifted high
Alleluia!

4. Thy name we bless, O risen Lord,
and sing today with one accord
the life laid down, the life restored:
Alleluia!

*C.A. Alington (1872–1955)*

# 487

1. Good Lady Poverty,
come be my bride;
forever you and me,
walk side by side.
Teach me your wisdom,
lead me your way.
Show me the path you take
and walk with Christ each day.

2. Good Lady Poverty,
so filled with grace;
such sweet humility
shines from your face.
You have no pride
or vanity.
Great daughter of the Lord,
his love has made you free.

3. Good Lady Poverty,
I sing your praise.
St. Francis, blessed one,
has walked your ways.
He sang your virtues;
you were his prize.
Good Lady Poverty,
an angel in disguise.

*Sebastian Temple*

# 488

1. Grant us thy peace; for thou alone
   canst bend
   our faltering purpose to a nobler
   end;
   thy love alone can teach our hearts
   to see
   the fellowship that binds all lives
   in thee.

2. Grant us thy peace; for men have
   filled the years
   with greed and envy and with
   foolish fears,
   with squandered treasures and
   ignoble gain,
   and fruitless harvests that we
   reap in vain.

3. Grant us thy peace; till all our
   strife shall seem
   the hateful memory of some evil
   dream;
   till that new song ring out that
   shall not cease,
   'In heaven thy glory and on earth
   thy peace'.

*J.H.B. Masterman (1867–1933)*

# 489

**Greater love has no man than this:
that he give his life for his friends.**

1. Now I give you
   my new commandment:
   Love one another
   as I myself have loved you.

2. You will be my friends
   if you follow my precept:
   Love one another
   as I myself have loved you.

3. As the Father loves me always,
   so also have I loved you:
   Love one another
   as I myself have loved you.

4. Be constant in my love
   and follow my commandment.
   Love one another
   as I myself have loved you.

5. And approaching my Passover
   I have loved you to the end.
   Love one another
   as I myself have loved you.

6. By this shall men know
   that you are my disciples.
   Love one another
   as I myself have loved you.

*Helena Scott,
from John 13, 14 & 15*

# 490

Hail Mary, full of grace,
the Lord is with you.
Blessed are you among women,
and blest is the fruit of your
womb, Jesus.
Holy Mary, Mother of God,
pray for us sinners
now and at the hour of death.
Amen.

**Gentle woman, quiet light,
morning star, so strong and bright,
gentle mother, peaceful dove,
teach us wisdom; teach us love.**

1. You were chosen by the Father;
   you were chosen for the Son.
   You were chosen from all women,
   and for women, shining one.

2. Blessed are you, among women.
   Blest in turn all women too.
   Blessed they with gentle spirits.
   Blessed they with gentle hearts.

*Carey Landry*
*Based on Luke 1:28ff*

# 491

1. Hail Mary, full of grace.
   The Lord is with thee.
   Blessed art thou among women,
   and blessed is the fruit of thy
      womb, Jesus.

2. Holy Mary, Mother of God,
   pray for us, sinners,
   now and at the hour of death;
   pray for us sinners now. Amen.

*Mary Lu Walker*
*Based on Luke 1:28ff*

# 492

1. Hail Mary, mother of our God,
   a lamp that always burns;
   for you the angels keep a feast,
   from you all evil turns,
   from you all evil turns.

2. It's thanks to you God's only Son
   in darkness shed his light;
   it's thanks to you that sinful man

rejoiced to know what's right,
rejoiced to know what's right.

3. You gave a place within your
      womb
   to him who knows no bound;
   a virgin yet a mother too,
   in you his home he found,
   in you his home he found.

4. It's thanks to you creation came
   to know what's good and true;
   God calls his servant 'mother'
      now –
   no other maid but you,
   no other maid but you!

*Willard F. Jabusch*

# 493

1. He is Lord, he is Lord.
   He is risen from the dead and he is
      Lord.
   Ev'ry knee shall bow, ev'ry tongue
      confess
   that Jesus Christ is Lord.

2. He is King, he is King.
   He is risen from the dead and he
      is King.
   Ev'ry knee shall bow, ev'ry tongue
      confess
   that Jesus Christ is King.

3. He is love, he is love.
   He is risen from the dead and he
      is love.
   Ev'ry knee shall bow, ev'ry tongue
      confess
   that Jesus Christ is love.

*Anonymous*

# 494

**He is risen, alleluia, alleluia!**
**He is risen, alleluia, alleluia!**

1. Cry out with joy the Lord, all the
   earth, **alleluia.**
   Serve the Lord with gladness,
   **alleluia.**
   Come before him, singing for joy,
   **alleluia!**

2. Know that he, the Lord, is God,
   **alleluia.**
   He made us, we belong to him,
   **alleluia.**
   We are his people, the sheep of his
   flock, **alleluia.**

3. Go within his gates giving
   thanks, **alleluia.**
   Enter his courts with songs of
   praise, **alleluia.**
   Give thanks to him and bless his
   name, **alleluia.**

4. Indeed, how good is the Lord,
   **alleluia.**
   Eternal his merciful love, **alleluia.**
   He is faithful from age to age,
   **alleluia.**

5. Glory to the Father and Son,
   **alleluia.**
   And to the Spirit with them one,
   **alleluia.**
   As it was and ever shall be one
   God for eternity.

*Psalm 99(100) (The Grail)*

# 495

1. He is risen, tell the story
   to the nations of the night;
   from their sin and from their
   blindness,
   let them walk in Easter light.
   Now begins a new creation,
   now has come our true salvation.
   Jesus Christ, the Son of God!

2. Mary goes to tell the others
   of the wonders she has seen;
   John and Peter come a running
   what can all this truly mean?
   O Rabboni, Master holy,
   to appear to one so lowly!
   Jesus Christ, the Son of God!

3. He has cut down death and evil,
   he has conquered all despair;
   he has lifted from our shoulders,
   all the weight of anxious care.
   Risen Brother, now before you,
   we will worship and adore you.
   Jesus Christ, the Son of God!

4. Now get busy, bring the message,
   so that all may come to know
   there is hope for saint and sinner,
   for our God has loved us so.
   Ev'ry church bell is a'ringing,
   ev'ry Christian now is singing.
   Jesus Christ, the Son of God!

*Willard F. Jabusch*

# 496

1. He's a most unusual man,
   he makes the crowds all stop and
       stare,
   he teaches people how to care,
   he teaches people how to share.
   He has no place to lay his head,
   his home is everywhere.
   **Follow if you can,**
   **this most unusual man,**
   **follow if you can,**
   **this most unusual man.**

2. He's a most unusual man,
   he makes the stormy days turn
       fine,
   he changes water into wine,
   he gives his body as a sign.
   And he died that we might live,
   his life is yours and mine.

3. He's a most unusual man,
   as rich and poor as a man can be,
   he came to set the prisoners free,
   he came to make the blind men
       see.
   And he gave the world this
       message,
   'Come and follow me.'

*Wendy Poussard*

# 497

1. Help us accept each other
   as Christ accepted us;
   teach us as sister, brother,
   each person to embrace.
   Be present, Lord among us
   and bring us to believe
   we are ourselves accepted
   and meant to love and live.

2. Teach us, O Lord, your lessons,
   as in our daily life
   we struggle to be human
   and search for hope and faith.
   Teach us to care for people,
   for all not just for some,
   to love them as we find them
   or as they may become.

3. Let your acceptance change us,
   so that we may be moved
   in living situations
   to do the truth in love;
   to practise your acceptance
   until we know by heart
   the table of forgiveness
   and laughter's healing art.

4. Lord, for today's encounters
   with all who are in need,
   who hunger for acceptance,
   for righteousness and bread,
   we need new eyes for seeing,
   new hands for holding on:
   renew us with your Spirit;
   Lord, free us, make us one!

*Fred Kaan*

# 498

1. Hills of the north, rejoice;
   river and mountain-spring,
   hark to the advent voice;
   valley and lowland, sing:
   though absent long, your Lord is
       nigh;
   he judgement brings and victory.

2. Isles of the southern seas,
   deep in your coral caves
   pent be each warring breeze,
   lulled be your restless waves:
   he comes to reign with boundless
       sway,

and makes your wastes his great
highway.

3. Lands of the east, awake,
soon shall your sons be free;
the sleep of ages break,
and rise to liberty.
On your far hills, long cold and
grey,
has dawned the everlasting day.

4. Shores of the utmost west,
ye that have waited long,
unvisited, unblest,
break forth to swelling song;
high raise the note, that Jesus died,
yet lives and reigns, the Crucified.

5. Shout, while ye journey home;
songs be in every mouth;
lo, from the north we come,
from east and west and south.
City of God, the bond are free,
we come to live and reign in thee!

*C.E. Oakley (1832–65)*

# 499

1. His light now shines in the
darkness about us,
his light now shines and the
darkness has gone.

   **His name is love and he gives**
   **himself to us;**
   **his name is love, and he makes**
   **us his own.**

2. His love is warm like the sun
of the morning,
his love is warm like the promise
of dawn.

3. His love surrounds like a
mother's devotion,
he meets our needs when awake
and asleep.

4. How can we answer the love that
he shows us,
what can we do to respond to
his care?

5. Receive his love and reflect it
to others,
do all for them as he does all for
you.

6. For when we know him, we give
ourselves to them,
and when we love him, we give
them out all.

*Tom Colvin*

# 500

1. How lovely on the mountains
are the feet of him
who brings good news, good news,
announcing peace, proclaiming
news of happiness:
Our God reigns . . .

2. You watchmen, lift your voices
joyfully as one,
shout for your king, your king!
See eye to eye, the Lord restoring
Sion:
Our God reigns . . .

3. Wasteplaces of Jerusalem, break
forth with joy!
We are redeemed, redeemed,
the Lord has saved and comforted
his people.
Our God reigns . . .

4. Ends of the earth, see the salvation
of our God!
Jesus, is Lord, is Lord!
Before the nations, he has bared
his holy arm.
Our God reigns . . .

*Leonard J. Smith*
*Based on Isaiah 52*

# 501

1. I am the Bread of life.
He who comes to me shall not
hunger;
he who believes in me shall not
thirst.
No one can come to me
unless the Father draw him.
*(Jn 6:35, 37)*

**And I will raise him up,**
**and I will raise him up,**
**and I will raise him up**
**on the last day.**

2. The bread that I will give
is my flesh for the life of the world,
and he who eats of this bread,
he shall live for ever,
he shall live for ever.
*(Jn 6: 50-51)*

3. Unless you eat
of the flesh of the Son of Man,
and drink of his blood,
and drink of his blood,
you shall not have life within you.
*(Jn 6:53)*

4. For my flesh is food indeed,
and my blood is drink indeed.
He who eats of my flesh
and drinks of my blood
abides in me.
*(Jn 6: 55-56)*

5. Yes, Lord, I/we believe,
that you are the Christ,
the Son of God,
who have come
into the world.
*(Jn 11:27)*

*Suzanne Toolan*

# 502

1. I am the vine, you are the
branches:
no one can live apart from me.
Cut off from me you can do
nothing:
yet joined with me, all things are
yours.

2. You are the fruit borne by my
Father,
who tends and cares for every
limb.
Be not afraid: he will not harm
you.
Your fear he'll prune, and set you
free.

3. Remain in me: keep my
commandments.
My love for you led me to die.
Hold fast to me: I'll never leave
you.
in life, in death, I'll love you still.

*John Glynn,*
*paraphrased from John 15*

# 503

1. I heard the Lord call my name;
   listen close, you'll hear the
      same! (3)
   Take his hand, we are glory
      bound!

2. His Word is love, love's his word,
   that's the message that I heard! (3)
   Take his hand; we are glory
      bound!
   Place your hand in his and you will
      know;
   he will show you where to go.

3. I felt his love from above
   settle on me like a dove. (3)
   Take his hand; we are glory
      bound!

4. And to the Father all your days
   with the Son and Spirit praise! (3)
   Take his hand, we are glory
      bound!
   Place your hand in his and you will
      know;
   he will show you where to go.

5. *Repeat verse 1.*

*Jacob Krieger*

# 504

1. I lift my eyes to the mountains;
   from where shall come my help?
   My help shall come from the Lord,
      Yahweh;
   it is he who made heaven and
      earth.

2. May he never allow you to
      stumble,
   let him sleep not, your guard.
   No, he sleeps not, nor slumbers,
   the Lord, Israel's guard.

3. The Lord is your guard and your
      shade,
   at your right hand he stands.
   By day the sun shall not smite you,
   nor the moon in the night.

4. The Lord will guard you from evil,
   he will guard your soul.
   The Lord will guard your coming
      and going,
   both now and for evermore.
   The Lord will guard your going
      and coming,
   both now and for evermore.

*Gregory Norbet*
*Based on Psalm 120(121)*

# 505

*Antiphon:*

> I lift up my eyes to the
>    mountain,
> is anyone there to help me?
> **Yes, my God comes to help me,**
> **the Lord who made both heaven**
> **and earth.**

1. He will not allow you to stumble,
   he never sleeps but stands watch
      over you.
   **The Lord who made both heaven**
   **and earth.**
   No, he will not sleep nor slumber,
   he stands watch over all his people.
   **Yes, my God comes to help me,**
   **the Lord who made both heaven and**
   **earth.**

2. Our God keeps watch;
   like a shadow he covers you.
   **The Lord who made both heaven
   and earth.**
   In the daytime the sun shall not
   strike you;
   by night the moon shall not harm
   you.
   **Yes, my God comes to help me,
   The Lord who made both heaven
   and earth.**

3. He keeps all evil away from you;
   he takes you under his protection.
   **The Lord who made both heaven
   and earth.**
   Whether you are coming or going,
   God looks after you for ever.
   **Yes, my God comes to help me,
   The Lord who made both heaven
   and earth.**

   *Repeat antiphon*

   *Ps 120(121) arr. by Huub Oosterhuis,
   tr. Tony Barr*

# 506

1. I met you at the cross,
   Jesus my Lord;
   I heard you from that cross:
   my name you called –
   Asked me to follow you all of my
   days,
   asked me for evermore your name
   to praise.

2. I saw you on the cross
   dying for me;
   I put you on that cross:

but your one plea –
Would I now follow you all of my
days,
and would I evermore your great
name praise?

3. Jesus, my Lord and King,
   Saviour of all,
   Jesus the King of kings,
   you heard my call –
   That I would follow you all of my
   days,
   and that for evermore your name
   I'd praise.

   *Eric A. Thorn*

# 507

1. I saw a star up high above the
   heavens.
   I heard the angels singing in the
   sky.
   I watched the shepherds coming
   from the sheepfold:
   I even thought I heard a baby cry.

   **No one there would listen to my
   story,
   and no one seemed to care about
   the child;
   but he was beautiful,
   the baby born to save us,
   as in his mother's arms he gently
   lay.**

2. I saw the star shine down upon
   the stable.
   I watched the kings with gifts go
   riding by.
   I crept up close and looked into
   the manger
   and it was then I heard a baby cry.
   **But . . .**

3. I hurried home and there I met
   the townsfolk.
   I wandered in the hills and all
   around.
   I tried to tell my friends about
   the story
   of angels, shepherds, kings and
   babe I'd found.

   But all alone I knelt before that
   manger,
   the sheeps and cows and oxen
   standing by;
   and he was beautiful —
   the baby born to save us,
   as in his mother's arms he gently
   lay.
   Yes, he was beautiful,
   the baby Jesus born on Christmas
   Day.

   *Joan McCrimmon*

2. I, the Lord of snow and rain,
   I have borne my people's pain.
   I have wept for love of them.
   They turn away.
   I will break their hearts of stone,
   give them hearts for love alone.
   I will speak my word to them.
   Whom shall I send?

3. I, the Lord of wind and flame,
   I will send the poor and lame.
   I will set a feast for them.
   My hand will save.
   Finest bread I will provide
   till their hearts be satisfied.
   I will give my life to them.
   Whom shall I send?

   *Dan Schutte SJ.*

# 508

1. I, the Lord of sea and sky,
   I have heard my people cry.
   All who dwell in dark and sin
   my hand will save.
   I who made the stars of night,
   I will make their darkness bright.
   Who will bear my light to them?
   Whom shall I send?

   Here I am, Lord. Is it I, Lord?
   I have heard You calling in the
   night.
   I will go, Lord, if You lead me.
   I will hold Your people in my heart.

# 509

1. I was born before creation,
   when the world was yet to be.
   From the dawn of time uncounted
   I have sung God's melody.

   I am Wisdom, his companion,
   ever at his side to be;
   I delight in his creating,
   never ending, ever free.

2. Ev'ry sea and ev'ry river
   I have seen them come to birth;
   for the hills and for the mountains
   seen him raise the virgin earth.

3. There were stars hung in the
   heavens,
   and the clouds were in his plan:
   but the time I'll ever cherish
   was the day he formed a man.

4. Never has he ceased creating,
   and I'm with him to this day;
   so I'm glad to see his image
   in the people of today.

*John Glynn*
*Based on Proverbs 8: 22–31*

# 510

I will be with you wherever you go.
Go now throughout the world!
I will be with you in all that you say.
Go now and spread my word!

1. Come, walk with me on stormy
   waters.
   Why fear? Reach out, and I'll be
   there.

2. And you, my friend, will you now
   leave me,
   or do you know me as your Lord?

3. Your life will be transformed with
   power
   by living truly in my name.

4. And if you say: 'Yes, Lord I love
   you,'
   then feed my lambs and feed my
   sheep.

*Gerald Markland*

# 511

1. I will never forget you,
   my people,
   I have carved you
   on the palm of my hand.
   I will never forget you;
   I will not leave you orphaned.
   I will never forget my own.

2. Does a mother
   forget her baby?
   Or a woman the child
   within her womb?
   Yet, even if these forget,
   yes, even if these forget,
   I will never forget my own.

*Repeat Verse 1*

*Carey Landry*
*Based on Isaiah 49:15–16a*

# 512

1. I will sing, I will sing a song unto
   the Lord. (3)
   Alleluia, glory to the Lord.

   Allelu alleluia, glory to the
   Lord (3)
   alleluia, glory to the Lord.

2. We will come, we will come as one
   before the Lord. (3)
   Alleluia, glory to the Lord.

3. If the Son, if the Son shall make
   you free, (3)
   you shall be free indeed.

4. They that sow in tears shall reap
   in joy. (3)
   Alleluia, glory to the Lord.

5. Ev'ry knee shall bow and ev'ry
   tongue confess (3)
   that Jesus Christ is Lord.

6. In his name, in his name we have
   the victory. (3)
   Alleluia, glory to the Lord.

*Max Dyer*

# 513

**I will tell of your love**
**for me always, Lord;**
**I will tell of your goodness to me.**

1. Ev'ry morning the sun comes
   shining through
   to tell me a new day is born;
   and I feel a joy rising in my heart,
   the joy of life that comes from you.

2. Ev'ry mountain and hill that you
   have made
   tells me how strong you are;
   and I feel a pow'r rising in my
   heart,
   the pow'r of strength that comes
   from you.

3. Ev'ry flower that lifts its head to
   me
   tells me how gentle you are;
   and I feel a joy rising in my heart,
   the joy of love that comes from
   you.

4. As the darkness comes on at close
   of day
   it tells me you watch through the
   night;
   and I feel a longing rising in my
   heart,
   a longing to be one with you.

*Sister Marie Lydia Pereira*

# 514

**I'll sing God's praises,**
**now and evermore.**
**I'll sing God's praises,**
**now and evermore.**

1. He is my guide and my shepherd,
   **now and evermore.**
   He gives me rest in green pastures,
   **now and evermore.**

2. Near restful waters he leads me,
   **now and evermore.**
   Along the right path he keeps me,
   **now and evermore.**

3. His rod and crook are my comfort,
   **now and evermore.**
   With oil my head is anointed,
   **now and evermore.**

4. His loving favours pursue me,
   **now and evermore.**
   His house, my dwelling for ever,
   **now and evermore.**

*Aniceto Nazareth*
*Based on Psalm 22(23)*

# 515

**If God is for us, who can be against,**
**if the Spirit of God has set us free?**
**If God is for us, who can be against,**
**if the Spirit of God has set us free?**

1. I know that nothing in this world
   can ever take us from his love.

2. Nothing can take us from his love,
   poured out in Jesus, the Lord.

3. And nothing present or to come
   can ever take us from his love.

4. I know that neither death nor life
   can ever take us from his love.

*John Foley SJ.*
*Based on Romans 8:31–39*

# 516

1. If God is our defender,
   who will th' accuser be?
   His only Son he spared not,
   but gave him graciously.
   When God himself grants pardon,
   who ventures to condemn?
   Will Jesus Christ, the Saviour,
   who died and rose for men?

2. Can anything divide us
   from that most loving Lord?
   Can pain, or tribulation?
   Can famine, peril, sword?
   No, none of these can cause us
   from his great love to fall;
   for by the strength he gave us,
   we triumph over all.

3. Of this we can be certain,
   and sing with every breath:
   that nought that is, or will be,
   and neither life nor death,
   and nothing in creation,
   below us or above,
   can tear us from Christ Jesus,
   and from his Father's love.

*Denis E. Hurley*
*Based on Romans 8:31–39*

# 517

1. In God alone there is rest for
   my soul,
   from his care comes my safety
   in life.
   With him alone for my rock and
   my fortress,
   this I know I will never fall down.

So rest in God alone my soul,
he is the source of my hope.

2. In God I find my shelter, my
   strength
   all you people do rely on him.
   Unburden your hearts to the Lord
   your God,
   at all times he will listen to you.

3. Beware of those who will scoff
   at our God;
   their intent is to misguide your
   way.
   We trust alone in the rock of our
   safety
   and we know we will never lose
   hope.

*Douglas Rowe*
*Based on Psalm 70(71)*

# 518

In the beginning all was empty
and void;
God's spirit moved above the
water.
Our of the darkness came a word
that brought new life:
'This is so good, let there be light.'

1. Then in the stillness of the night
   your Word
   leapt into our city of turmoil;
   a man was born, a man of peace
   and not of war,
   revealing hopes yet unfulfilled.

2. Jesus, his name and what a gift
   he was,
   inspired to know the Father's
   vision.

And he so loved us more than his
own life.
What greater gift could he have
shared?

3. So we are called to give flesh to
our word
and be creators with the Spirit.
Wonder will be the sign that we
are on the way,
sharing our hope, alive our word.

*Gregory Norbet*

# 519

1. It's a long hard journey,
and the road keeps turning
and we just keep travelling on;
the signs aren't clear enough,
the ends aren't near enough,
and half our time is gone.

O, the Lord sends troubles,
the Lord sends trials,
the Lord sends a heavy load.
But he'll keep on leading us,
and keep on guiding us,
as long as we're trav'ling his road,
as long as we're trav'ling his road.

2. With so many days to live,
it's hard for life to give
a meaning mile after mile.
The roads keep crossing,
and the coins we're tossing
choose the path in a visionless
style.

3. Though we walk as brothers,
still we hurt each other,
and our love turns acid and stone.
Though we're hand in hand
we don't understand
that no one's walking alone.

4. Well, he never told us
that the road before us
would be smooth or simple or
clear.
But he set us singing
and our hope keeps springing
and we're raised from hating and
fear.

5. Well, the road is ours
with its rocks and flowers
and mica gleams in the stone.
Well, there's joy awaiting
in the celebrating
that we're never walking alone.

*Nick Hodson*

# 520

1. It's good to give thanks to the
Lord,
declare your love in the morning;
the lute will sound a new chord,
the melody adorning!

And you, O Lord, have made me
glad;
for all your works I'll be singing;
the righteous flourishing like the
grass
which from the earth keeps
springing.

2. They're planted in God's own
abode,
in God's own house they will
flourish;
they'll still bear fruit when they're
old,
for God will tend and nourish!

3. Sing glory to God up above,
the Son of God, our dear Saviour,
and to the Spirit of Love,
whose care will never waver!

*Psalm 91(92) paraphrased by John*
*Ylvisaker*

# 521

1. Jesus said: 'I am the bread.
Eat of my flesh, you will live for
ever.'
'How can this be?' the people said;
most of them went away.
So he said to the twelve, 'What of
you?'
And this is the answer they gave,
saying:

**'Lord, to whom shall we go?**
**You have the words of eternal life.**
**Lord, to whom shall we go?**
**You have the message of life.'**

2. Jesus said: 'I came from heaven.
I give my flesh for the life of the
world.'
'This man is mad!' the people said;
slowly, they went away.
So he said to the twelve, 'What of
you?'
And this is the answer they gave,
saying:

3. Jesus said: 'I have seen God.
Eat of my body and you too will
see him.'
'This is not true!' the people said;
angry, they went away.
So he said to the twelve, 'What of
you?'
And this is the answer they gave,
saying:

*Stephen Dean*

# 522

**Jesus, the holy Lamb of God**
**carried the cross for me;**
**Jesus, the holy lamb of God**
**died that I might be free.**

1. He who is God made himself low:
a servant, and humbler yet,
He bowed his head
as he was led
obedient unto his death

2. Therefore has God raised him
on high
and named him our Saviour
and Lord:
all knees will bend
in praise without end
to Jesus for ever adored.

*Briege O'Hare*
*Based on Philippians 2:6–11*

# 523

1. Jesus the Lord said, 'I am the
bread,
the bread of life for mankind
am I.' (3)
Jesus the Lord said, 'I am the
bread,
the bread of life for mankind
am I.'

2. Jesus the Lord said, 'I am the door,
   the way and the door for the poor am I.' (3)
   Jesus the Lord said, 'I am the door,
   the way and the door for the poor am I.'

3. Jesus the Lord said, 'I am the light,
   the one true light of the world am I.' (3)
   Jesus the Lord said, 'I am the light,
   the one true light of the world am I.'

4. Jesus the Lord said, 'I am the shepherd,
   the one good shepherd of the sheep am I.' (3)
   Jesus the Lord said, 'I am the shepherd,
   the one good shepherd of the sheep am I.'

5. Jesus the Lord said, 'I am the life,
   the resurrection and the life am I.' (3)
   Jesus said, 'I am the life,
   the resurrection and the life am I.'

*Anon, Urdu,*
*tr. Dermott Monahan (1906–57)*

# 524

1. Jesus the Word has lived among us,
   sharing his fullness, truth and grace,
   God's only Son, the Father's loved one
   reveals him to the human race.
   Jesus the Word has lived among us
   sharing his fullness, truth and grace.

2. He was with God from the beginning
   and through him all things came to be.
   He lightens darkness, conquers evil,
   gives life for living, glad and free.
   He was with God from the beginning
   and through him all things came to be.

3. Sing praise to God who sent Christ Jesus
   to be his sign of endless love;
   sent him to live his life among us,
   lifting our hearts to things above.
   Sing praise to God who sent Christ Jesus
   to be his sign of endless love!

*Keith D. Pearson*
*(from John chs 1, 3)*

# 525

**Jesus, you are Lord.**
**You are risen from the dead**
**and you are Lord.**
**Ev'ry knee shall bow,**
**and ev'ry tongue confess**
**that Jesus, you are Lord.**
**You are the way.**

1. I am the Way.
   No one knows the Father but it be through me.
   I am in my Father, and my Father is in me,
   and we come in love to live within your hearts.

2. I am the Truth.
   And I set my spirit deep within
      your hearts,
   and you will know me, and love
      me,
   and the truth I give to you will set
      you free.

3. I am the Life.
   The living waters I pour out for
      you.
   Anyone who drinks of the waters
      that I give
   will have eternal life.

4. I am the Word,
   the true light that shines brightly
      in the dark,
   a light that darkness could not
      overpower,
   the Word made flesh, risen among
      you.

*Mary Barrett*
*(from John 14:6)*

# 526

**Keep in mind that Jesus Christ has
   died for us
and is risen from the dead.
He is our saving Lord,
he is joy for all ages.**

1. If we die with the Lord,
   we shall live with the Lord.

2. If we endure with the Lord,
   we shall reign with the Lord.

3. In him all our sorrow,
   in him all our joy.

4. In him hope of glory,
   in him all our love.

5. In him our redemption,
   in him all our grace.

6. In him our salvation,
   in him all our grace.

*Lucien Deiss*

# 527

### Laudato sii, O mi Signore (4)

1. Yes, be praised in all your
      creatures,
   brother sun and sister moon;
   in the stars and in the wind,
   air and fire and flowing water.

2. For our sister, mother earth,
   she who feeds us and sustains us;
   for her fruits, her grass, her
      flowers,
   for the mountains and the oceans.

3. Praise for those who spread
      forgiveness,
   those who share your peace with
      others,
   bearing trials and sickness
      bravely!
   Even sister death won't harm
      them.

4. For our life is but a song,
   and the reason for our singing
   is to praise you for the music;
   join the dance of your creation.

5. Praise to you, Father most holy,
   praise and thanks to you, Lord
      Jesus,
   praise to you, most Holy Spirit,
   life and joy of all creation!

*Damien Lundy*
*Based on St. Francis of Assisi*

# 528

Lay your hands gently upon us,
let their touch render your peace;
let them bring your forgiveness
and healing,
lay your hands,
gently lay your hands.

1. You were sent to free
   the broken hearted.
   You were sent to give sight
   to the blind.
   You desire to heal
   all our illness.
   Lay your hands,
   gently lay your hands.

2. Lord, we come to you
   through one another.
   Lord, we come to you
   in all our need.
   Lord, we come to you
   seeking wholeness.
   Lay your hands,
   gently lay your hands.

*Carey Landry*

# 529

1. Lead me, guide me along life's
   way.
   If I should stumble, Lord, send a
   helping hand.
   Love me, lead me through the
   trials of life;
   and with my brothers, Lord,
   teach us to understand
   that you have all things in your
   mighty hands.

Take me and fold me in your
   loving arms,
on the day when I come home.
Take me and fold me in your
   loving arms
then I shall be yours for ever.

*Peter Skinner*

# 530

Leave your country and your
   people,
leave your fam'ly and your friends.
Travel to the land he'll show you;
God will bless the ones he sends.

1. Go like Abraham before you,
   when he heard the Father's call,
   walking forth in faith and trusting;
   God is master of us all.

2. Sometimes God's Word is
   demanding,
   leave security you know,
   breaking ties and bonds that
   hold you,
   when the voice of God says: "Go".

3. Take the path into the desert,
   barren seems the rock and sand.
   God will lead you through the
   desert
   when you follow his command.

4. Go with courage up the mountain,
   climb the narrow, rocky ledge,
   leave behind all things that hinder,
   go with only God as pledge.

*Willard F. Jabusch*
*Based on Genesis 12:1ff*

# 531

1. Lest he be too far from us, he
   prepared his coming.
   He who longed to share our fate
   made with us his dwelling.

   **There among you stands the one
   you do not know. (2)**

2. He is everywhere at hand, every
   detail human.
   Yet he is not recognised, silent,
   never spoken.

3. God from God and light from
   light, all creation's keeper,
   has a human face and talks, man
   to man as brother.

4. So with patience as your guide,
   show all kinds of goodness:
   owe each other, for his sake,
   only love and kindness.

5. Now be carefree, full of joy:
   God, whom we do worship,
   brushes past us day by day, shares
   our home and kinship.

   *Huub Oosterhuis, tr. Tony Barr*

# 532

1. Let all who share one bread and
   cup remember
   the oneness of that host of
   countless number
   of those who are, as children
   of one Father,
   part of each other.

2. If only we would live as sisters,
   brothers,

put faith to practice, truly care
for others,
then we would do the will of him
who sends us,
whose love attends us.

3. Use for yourself our highest and
   profoundest,
   so that, O Lord, with all men
   who surround us,
   we may enjoy a world in Christ
   united,
   so long awaited.

   *J.A. Cramer, tr. Fred Kaan*

# 533

Let it breathe on me, let it breathe
on me,
Let this breath of God now
breathe on me.
Let it breathe on me, let it breathe
on me.
Let this breath of God now breathe
on me.

   *William E. Booth-Clibborn*

# 534

1. Let us praise our sovereign
   Saviour,
   Christ, our shepherd, and our
   leader,
   Till the ending of our days.
   Though we praise him all we're
   able,
   All our praise is all too feeble,
   he is far beyond all praise.

2. He, before he gave to others,
   Gave his little band of brothers
   Both his body and his blood —
   Not a mere symbolic token,
   Blood outpoured and body
      broken —
   As an everlasting food.

3. What a theme to baffle study –
   That mere bread becomes his
      body,
   Wine his blood! The King of kings
   Comes down on this altar duly
   To repeat the wonder daily,
   Quite outside the run of things.

*Repeat verse 1*

*J. Gordon Nichols*

# 535

1. Let us talents and tongues employ,
   reaching out with a shout of joy:
   bread is broken, the wine is
      poured,
   Christ is spoken and seen and
      heard.

   **Jesus lives again,
   earth can breath again,
   pass the Word around:
   loaves abound!**

2. Christ is able to make us one,
   at his table he sets the tone,
   teaching people to live to bless,
   love in word and in deed express.

3. Jesus calls us in, sends us out
   bearing fruit in a world of doubt,
   gives us love to tell, bread to share:
   God-Immanuel everywhere!

*Fred Kaan
Mary Lu Walker*

# 536

1. Light the Advent candle one.
   Now the waiting has begun,
   we have started on our way:
   time to think of Christmas day.

   **Candle, candle, burning bright,
   shining in the cold winter night.
   Candle, candle, burning bright,
   fill our hearts with Christmas light.**

2. Light the Advent candle two.
   Think of humble shepherds who
   filled with wonder at the sight
   of the child on Christmas night.

3. Light the Advent candle three.
   Think of heav'nly harmony:
   angels singing 'Peace on earth'
   at the blessed Saviour's birth.

4. Light the Christmas candles now!
   Sing of donkey, sheep and cow.
   Birthday candles for the King –
   let the 'Alleluias' ring!

*Mary Lu Walker*

# 537

1. Like a sea without a shore
   love divine is boundless.
   Time is now and evermore
   and his love surrounds us.

   **Maranatha! Maranatha!
   Maranatha! Come, Lord Jesus,
      come!**

2. So that mankind could be free
   he appeared among us,
   blest are those who have not seen,
   yet believe his promise.

3. All our visions, all our dreams,
   are but ghostly shadows
   of the radiant clarity
   waiting at life's close.

4. Death where is your victory?
   Death where is your sting?
   Closer than the air we breathe
   is our risen King.

*Estelle White*

# 538

**Like the deer that thirsts for water,
O God I long for you.**

1. Like the deer that thirsts for water,
   O God, I long for you.
   Weeping, I have heard them taunt
     me:
   'What help is in your God?'

2. Gladly I would lead your people
   rejoicing to your house.
   Trust in God, my soul, and praise
     him,
   and he will dry your tears.

3. Grief and pain, like roaring
     torrents,
   had swept my soul away.
   But his mercy is my rescue,
   I will praise him all my days.

4. Weeping, I have heard them
     taunt me:
   'What help is your God?'
   Rock of strength, do not forget
     me;
   in you alone I trust.

(5. To the Father, praise and honour;
   all glory to the Son;

honour to the Holy Spirit;
let God be glorified.)

*Luke Connaughton (1919–79)
Paraphrased from Psalm 41(42)*

# 539

1. Look around, look around you
     and you will see,
   all the sunshine, the sky so blue
     and feel the breeze;
   they are saying: God's love is real.

2. Take a walk thru' the countryside
     and watch the trees,
   hear the birds singing sweetly
     and you will feel peace
   and joy you've never known.

   **If you doubt your Father loves you,
   stop and think for just a while:
   is it need or greed that drives you
   to be crying all the time?**

3. Cleanse your mind, open wide
     your heart,
   and call to him,
   and he'll fill you with wisdom
     so that you'll begin
   to realise God's love is real.

*Ronald Gokool*

# 540

1. 'Look around you, can you see?
   Times are troubled, people grieve.
   See the violence, feel the hardness;
   all my people, weep with me.'

   **Kyrie eleison,
   Christe eleison,
   Kyrie eleison.**

2. 'Walk among them, I'll go with
   you.
   Reach out to them with my hands.
   Suffer with me, and together we
   will serve them,
   help them stand.'

3. Forgive us, Father; hear our
   prayer.
   We would walk with you
   anywhere,
   through your suff'ring, with
   forgiveness;
   take your life into the world.

*Jodi Page Clark*

# 541

1. Looking at the sunrise
   heralding the dawn;
   list'ning to the birds sing
   hearing ev'ry sound.
   I'm at peace with nature,
   because, I suppose,
   all my cares and troubles
   are resting with the Lord.

2. Children playing round me,
   laughter's in my heart.
   People toiling sadly,
   comfort I impart.
   Joy is with me daily
   and it's all I know,
   because Jesus loves me,
   for he told me so.

3. Listen to me, brothers,
   heed to what I say;
   Place your trust in Jesus,
   let him guide your way.
   He will not forsake or
   from you turn away;

peace is yours, my brothers,
Jesus is the way.

*Ronald Gokool*

# 542

1. Lord, confronted with your might,
   with your purity and light
   we are made with shame to see
   all that we fail to be.

2. Conscious of our feeble will,
   wanting good, but choosing ill,
   we are sorry for our sin:
   Lord, make us clean within.

3. Steady, Lord, our stumbling feet,
   free our spirits from deceit.
   Give us openness for pride;
   we have no place to hide.

4. Lift us from despair and grief,
   help us in our unbelief.
   As we spread our hands to you,
   fill us with life anew.

5. For the sake of Christ, forgive,
   speak the Word, and we shall live.
   Send us forward on our way,
   Lord, with our heads held high.

*Fred Kaan*

# 543

1. Lord, enthroned in heavenly
   splendour,
   first begotten from the dead,
   thou alone, our strong defender,
   liftest up thy people's head.
   Alleluia, alleluia,
   Jesus, true and living bread!

2. Prince of life, for us thou livest,
   by thy body souls are healed;
   Prince of peace, thy peace thou
   givest,
   by thy blood is pardon sealed;
   alleluia, alleluia,
   Word of God, in flesh revealed.

3. Paschal Lamb! Thine offering
   finished,
   once for all, when thou wast slain,
   in its fullness undiminished
   shall for evermore remain,
   alleluia, alleluia,
   cleansing souls from every stain.

4. Great high priest of our
   profession,
   through the veil thou entered in;
   by thy mighty intercession
   grace and mercy thou canst win:
   alleluia, alleluia,
   only sacrifice for sin.

5. Life-imparting heavenly manna,
   stricken rock, with streaming side,
   heaven and earth, with loud
   hosanna,
   worship thee, the Lamb who died;
   alleluia, alleluia,
   risen, ascended, glorified!

   *G.H. Bourne (1840–1925)*

# 544

1. Lord, graciously hear us,
   hear us as we call on you,
   we tried to be faithful, Lord,
   but we have sinned against you.

2. You gave us your message,
   you showed us the way to live;
   we tried to be faithful, Lord,
   but we have not understood.

3. Lord, show us your mercy,
   heal those we have wounded here;
   we wanted to love like you,
   but we have forgotten the way.

4. Speak, Lord, to your people,
   speak, now, in a million ways;
   we want to be true to you,
   help, Lord, and forgive us, we
   pray.

   *Anne Conway*

# 545

1. Lord, in everything I do
   let me always follow you;
   let the moments of my days
   overflow with endless praise;
   take my hands and let them move
   at the impulse of your love;
   every move that I shall make
   Lord, direct the steps I take.

2. Lord, with all your people here
   you invite me to draw near;
   Lord, accept the gifts I bring,
   Lord, accept the praise I sing.
   Take my lips and let them speak
   of your goodness through the
   week;
   let me echo this refrain
   till I come to you again.

3. As I listen to your call,
   Lord, I want to give my all;
   take my heart and mind and use
   every power you shall choose;
   all I have has come from you
   and I offer back to you
   only what was yours before:
   take my life for evermore.

   *Patrick Appleford*

# 546

1. Lord Jesus Christ, be present now,
   and let your Holy Spirit bow
   all hearts in love and truth today
   to hear your Word and keep your
   way.

2. May your glad tidings always
   bring
   good news to men that they may
   sing
   of how you came to save all men.
   Instruct us till you come again.

3. To God the Father and the Son
   and Holy Spirit three in one,
   to you, O blessed Trinity,
   be praise throughout eternity.

*Author Unknown*

# 547

1. Lord of Creation, to you be all
   praise!
   Most mighty your working, most
   wondrous your ways.
   Your glory and might are beyond
   us to tell,
   and yet in the heart of the humble
   you dwell.

2. Lord of all power, I give you my
   will,
   in joyful obedience your tasks to
   fulfil.
   Your bondage is freedom, your
   service is song,
   and, held in your keeping, my
   weakness is strong.

3. Lord of all wisdom, I give you
   my mind,
   rich truth that surpasses man's
   knowledge to find.
   What eye has not seen and what
   ear has not heard
   is taught by your Spirit and shines
   from your Word.

4. Lord of all bounty, I give you my
   heart;
   I praise and adore you for all
   you impart:
   your love to inspire me, your
   counsel to guide,
   your presence to cheer me,
   whatever betide.

5. Lord of all being, I give you my all;
   if e'er I disown you I stumble and
   fall;
   but, sworn in glad service your
   word to obey,
   I walk in your freedom to the end
   of the way.

*This hymn may also start at Verse 2*

*Jack C. Winslow (1882–1974)*

# 548

1. Lord, this paschal time reminds us
   how you came back from the dead.
   Firm and true the faith that
   binds us
   to our glorious, risen Head.
   Alleluia, alleluia,
   you have risen as you said,
   alleluia, alleluia,
   you have risen as you said.

2. 'Neath the burden of our labour,
   mid our joy and pain and strife,
   in our trying to be neighbour,
   to be parent, husband, wife;
   alleluia, alleluia,
   be to us the source of life,
   alleluia, alleluia,
   be to us the source of life.

3. Make us true to our vocation
   with the strength that comes
        from you;
   make our life a dedication
   with the love that you imbue.
   Alleluia, alleluia,
   grace and peace in us renew,
   alleluia, alleluia,
   grace and peace in us renew.

4. Hold this vision, Lord, before us;
   in this hope our faith sustain:
   that to life you will restore us
   when at last you come again.
   Alleluia, alleluia,
   make us worthy of your reign,
   alleluia, alleluia,
   make us worthy of your reign.

   *Denis E. Hurley*

# 549

1. Lord, thy word abideth,
   and our footsteps guideth;
   who its truth believeth
   light and joy receiveth.

2. When our foes are near us,
   then thy word doth cheer us,
   word of consolation,
   message of salvation.

3. When the storms are o'er us,
   and dark clouds before us,
   then its light directeth,
   and our way protecteth.

4. Word of mercy, giving
   courage to the living;
   word of life, supplying
   comfort to the dying!

5. O that we discerning
   its most holy learning,
   Lord, may love and fear thee,
   evermore be near thee.

   *H.W. Baker (1875–1959)*

# 550

1. Lord, you have come to the
        lakeside
   seeking neither wealthy nor wise
        men.
   You, only ask, Lord, that I should
        love you.

   **With love you have looked in my
        eyes, Lord,
   smiling gently. You called my
        name;
   and I left my boat by the lakeside,
   now with you I will seek other
        shores.**

2. Lord, you well know that I carry
   in my boat no treasure nor
        weapon.
   I bring you only my willing labour.

3. Lord, you have need of my hands;
   I shall labour that others may rest;
   and from my love, Lord, may
        others love you.

4. Lord, other seas call me onward;
   hope eternal for hearts that are
        searching;
   and love will bind us as friends
        for ever.

   *C. Gabarain, tr. Fr. Edmund O'Shea*

# 551

1. Love came down at Christmas,
   love all lovely, love divine:
   love was born at Christmas,
   star and angels gave the sign.

2. Worship we the Godhead,
   love incarnate, love divine;
   worship we our Jesus:
   but wherewith for sacred sign?

3. Love shall be our token,
   love be yours and love be mine,
   love to God and all men,
   love for plea and gift and sign.

*Christina Rossetti (1830–94)*

# 552

**Lumen Christi! Alleluia! Amen!**

1. I am the light of the world
   he who follows me
   will not walk in darkness.

2. You are the light of the world
   let your light
   shine before men.

3. Tell the wonderful deeds of the
   Lord
   He called you
   from darkness to light.

*Jean Paul Lecot*

# 553

**May the peace of the Lord be with
you,
with your friends and your family
too.
Let it be, let it grow, and**
everywhere you go
may the peace of the Lord follow
you.

1. I leave you peace now, it's my
   peace I give to you:
   not as the world gives do I give
   to you.

2. Don't be afraid, let your hearts be
   untroubled:
   have faith in God and have faith
   in me.

*Gary Ault*

# 554

1. Modern man has the city for his
   home
   where his life is walled by want
   and dread,
   pained by nights without sleep
   and days of grinding work,
   in the struggle to earn his daily
   bread.

2. In our cities, immense and
   growing out,
   there are millions from faith and
   love estranged,
   who need to recapture hope of
   better things,
   and whose hearts, by the grace of
   Christ, can change.

3. In the dark of our noisy city life,
   men and women are groping for
   the light,
   human beings who hunger to see
   right prevail,
   unaware of the liberating Christ.

4. In the great giant cities of our
   globe,
   hollowed out by the ways of greed
   and crime,
   we are set to reflect the likeness
   of our God
   and to act out renewal's great
   design.

5. Grow, then, cities to house the
   world of man,
   with your skyscrapers blotting
   out the sun.
   Let Christ be the light to shine
   from human homes
   in the high-rising blocks of steel
   and stone.

   *Joao Dias de Araujo, tr. Fred Kaan*

# 555

**Mother of Jesus,**
**and mother of lowliness,**
**bearing the light of the world.**
**Radiant with glory,**
**the glory of Jesus,**
**conceived by the Spirit of God.**

1. In the beginning of time
   God's Holy Spirit did shine,
   breathed on the deep
   and the darkness of night,
   bringing the promise of light.

2. Then in the fullness of time
   came the same Spirit sublime
   breathed on the womb
   of the Virgin of grace,
   called her the chosen of God.

3. Wond'rous the moment that
   heard
   you say 'Amen' to the Word;

Son of the Father,
and Light of his light,
face of the Godhead unveiled.

4. Mary, our Lady of light,
   you are the Father's delight:
   pray for us sinners
   to Jesus, your Son,
   show us the light of the world.

   *John Glynn*

# 556

**My God, my God,**
**don't ever desert me,**
**my God, my God,**
**I need you beside me.**
**My life is so lonely,**
**my heart is so empty,**
**my God, only you**
**can comfort me.**

1. In this cold, forbidding world
   where man seeks only himself,
   I can find no one who'll love
   or who'll help. There is only you.

2. In my joy I look for laughter,
   in my sorrow I seek a friend;
   but I see only fleeting shadows,
   and then I turn and find you there.

3. None but you know how I'm
   aching,
   you alone give the solace I seek.
   You alone give me kindness and
   care
   whenever I despair.

   *Ronald Gokool*

# 557

My God, you fathom my heart and
you know me.

**My God, you fathom my heart and you know me.**

Nothing in me lies concerned from your eyes;
everything I do, you already know it.
**You already know it.**

How could I ever flee from your spirit,
or where could I take refuge, you see me everywhere.
**You see me everywhere.**

I climb to the heavens, you are in the heavens:
in the depths of the earth I find you even there.
**I find you even there.**

And should I flee away with the dawn or
to the furthermost shores of the sea;
yes, even there shall your hand be to help me.

**Yes, even there shall your hand be to help me.**

How wond'rous are your plans for me.
My God, how complete your designs.
**My God, how complete your designs.**

How can I count them, they are too plenty,
as the sands of the sea even then . . .
then I shall know still nothing of you.
**Then I shall know still nothing of you.**

*Huub Oosterhuis, tr. Tony Barr*
*From Psalm 138(139)*

# 558

**My soul is longing for your peace, near to you, my God.**

1. Lord, you know
   that my heart is not proud,
   and my eyes are not
   lifted from earth.

2. Lofty thoughts
   have never filled my mind,
   far beyond my sight
   all ambitious deeds.

3. In your peace
   I have maintained my soul,
   I have kept my heart
   in your quiet peace.

4. As a child
   rests on his mother's knee,
   so I place my soul
   in your loving care.

5. Israel,
   put all your hope in God,
   place your trust in him,
   now and evermore.

*Lucien Deiss*
*Based on Psalm 130(131)*

# 559

**New life! New life!**
**You came to bring us new life.**
**New life! New life!**
**We find such joy in your abundant life.**

1. You are the source of our great joy,
   the fountain of all life.
   You give us living water,
   you bid us come and drink.
   We come to you, we bless you, Lord,
   we glorify your name!
   We praise you, Lord,

we worship you,
we thank you for your gift
  of new life!

2. You are the source of our new life;
   in your light we see light.
   You show us your goodness;
     you bid us come and see.
   We come to you, we bless you,
     Lord,
   we glorify your name!
   We praise you, Lord
     we worship you,
   we thank you for your gift
     of new life!

*Carey Landry*

# 560

**No one can give to me that peace
which my risen Lord,
my risen King can give.
No one can give to me that peace
which my risen Lord,
my risen King can give.**

1. When I look around and see
   all the things that trouble me
   and I seem to lose my peace
   in a world that's not at ease.

2. For I take Christ's word as true:
   'My true peace I give to you,
     but not as the world might give,
   is my peace that makes you live.'

3. His true peace in me will stay,
   as I live from day to day
   and his joy will never end,
   and in Heaven it will extend.

4. All the world's in search of peace,
   but from sin they'll never cease
   how can they expect to find
   inner joys and peace of mind?

5. All injustice, hate and strife,
   sins of malice, sex and pride,
   stem from those who've never
     known,
   where the seeds of peace were
     sown.

6. Christ has risen from the dead,
   triumphed over sin and death
   and he'll never die again,
   but as Lord he'll live and reign.

*Douglas Rowe*

# 561

1. Now let your people depart in
     peace,
   for we've partaken in this your
     feast.
   You are the Saviour of all the
     earth,
   a light to guide us from our birth.

   **Ev'ry time I feel the Spirit
   moving in my heart I will pray!
   Ev'ry time I feel the Spirit
   moving in my heart, I will pray!**

2. Sing glory to the Creator Lord,
   and to the Spirit the comforter,
   and unto Jesus the blessed Son,
   forever three and ever one.

*John C. Ylvisaker*
*(From the Nunc Dimittis (Luke 2:29– 32)*

# 562

1. Now the tasks and toils are over
   and another day at its end,
   dear Lord, our drowsy spirits
   into your hands we commend.
   The day's familiar brightness
   is lost in the pathless night;

you alone will be our refuge,
and only you our light.

2. The moonlight through the
   branches
   by the evening wind is stirred,
   the stars stand in their places
   as faithful as your word:
   although we shall not hear it,
   though our eyes are held in sleep,
   yet our wakeful hearts turn to you
   their promises to keep.

3. Protect us from all evil,
   from the terrors darkness brings
   that we may rest securely
   in the shadow of your wings.
   O watchful Father, guide us,
   our strength and life restore,
   that we may wake at morning
   to hear your voice once more.

*Kevin Nichols*

# 563

1. Now watch for God's coming,
   be patient till then;
   like sunshine at noontime he'll
   brighten all men;
   who hope in the Lord will possess
   fertile land;
   the poor he will welcome and
   grasp by the hand.

2. Man's steps are directed, God
   watches his path;
   he guides him and holds him
   and saves him from wrath,
   and though he may fall he will not
   go headlong,
   for God gives sound footing and
   keeps him from wrong.

3. So wait for his coming, be
   patient till then;
   the wicked are armed and would
   kill honest men.
   Their arms shall be broken, no
   refuge they'll see,
   but saved are the needy by God's
   own decree.

4. Now those who do evil will wither
   like grass,
   like green of the springtime they
   fade and they pass,
   so trust in the Lord and to him
   give your life,
   he'll bring heart's desires and
   peace in our strife.

*Willard F. Jabusch*

# 564

1. Now with the fading light of day
   Maker of all, to Thee we pray
   that with Thy wonted care and
   love,
   Thou guard and protect us from
   above.

2. Take far away each hideous
   dream,
   things in the night that monstrous
   seem,
   wiles of our old arch-foe restrain
   lest faltering flesh contract a stain.

3. Father almighty, grace afford,
   grant it through Jesus Christ
   our Lord,
   who with the Holy Ghost and
   Thee
   is reigning for all eternity.

*Te lucis ante terminum (7th Century)*
*tr. Sebastian Bullough*

# 565

**O be joyful in the Lord!**
**O be joyful in the Lord!**
**Let us make a joyful noise,**
**let the whole earth rejoice!**
**O be joyful in the Lord,**
**all ye lands!**

1. Know that the Lord he is God;
   he has made us, we are his.
   We are the sheep of his pasture,
   the people of his hand.

2. Enter his gates with thanksgiving:
   come into his courts with praise.
   Be thankful unto him,
   and speak good of his name.

3. Know that the Lord, he is good:
   his love lasts for ever.
   He's faithful and true,
   through ev'ry generation.

*Psalm 99(100), paraphrased by*
*Jonathan Asprey*

# 566

1. O comfort my people
   and calm all their fear,
   and tell them the time of
   salvation draws near.
   O tell them I come to
   remove all their shame.
   Then they will forever
   give praise to my name.

2. Proclaim to the cities
   of Juda my word:
   that gentle yet strong is
   the hand of the Lord.
   I rescue the captives
   my people defend
   and bring them to justice
   and joy without end.

3. All mountains and hills shall
   become as a plain
   for vanished are mourning
   and hunger and pain.
   And never again shall
   these war against you.
   Behold I come quickly
   to make all things new.

*Isaiah 40, paraphrased by*
*Chrysogonus Waddell*

# 567

1. O food of travellers, angels' bread,
   manna wherewith the blest are fed,
   come nigh, and with thy sweetness
      fill
   the hungry hearts that seek thee
      still.

2. O fount of love, O well unpriced,
   outpouring from the heart of
      Christ,
   give us to drink of very thee,
   and all we pray shall answered be.

3. O Jesus Christ, we pray to thee
   that this presence which we see,
   though now in form of bread
      concealed,
   to us may be in heaven revealed.

*Maintzisch Gesangbuch, 1661,*
*tr. Walter H. Shewring and others*

# 568

1. O lady, full of God's own grace,
   whose caring hands the child
      embraced,
   who listened to the Spirit's word,
   believed and trusted in the Lord.

   **O virgin fair, star of the sea,**
   **my dearest mother, pray for me,**

O virgin fair, star of the sea,
my dearest mother, pray for me.

2. O lady, who felt daily joy
   in caring for the holy boy,
   whose home was plain and shorn
   of wealth,
   yet was enriched by God's own
   breath.

3. O lady, who bore living's pain
   but still believed that love would
   reign,
   who on a hill watched Jesus die
   as on the cross they raised him
   high.

4. O lady, who, on Easter day,
   had all your sorrow wiped away
   as God the Father's will was done
   when from death's hold he freed
   your Son.

*Estelle White*

# 569

1. O light forever dawning
   beyond the darkest night;
   O comfort of the mourning,
   our strength and our delight;
   receive our humble pleading
   for those whose course is run,
   lest pardon they be needing
   for any evil done.

2. To him who like the eagle
   arose on conqu'ring wing,
   the cross his banner regal,
   O death, where is your sting?
   There's surely no rejection
   for those who share his strife,
   but hope and resurrection
   and everlasting life.

*Denis E. Hurley*

# 570

1. O raise your eyes on high and see
   there stands our sovereign Lord,
   his glory is this day revealed,
   his Word a two-edged sword.

2. We glimpse the splendour and the
   power
   of him who conquered death,
   the Christ in whom the universe
   knows God's creating breath.

3. Of every creed and nation King
   in him all strife is stilled;
   the promise made to Abraham
   in him has been fulfilled.

4. The prophets stand and with great
   joy
   give witness as they gaze;
   the Father with a sign has sealed
   our trust, our hope, our praise.

5. This glory that today our eyes
   have glimpsed of God's own Son
   will help us ever sing with love
   of Three who are but One.

*Ralph Wright, OSB*

# 571

O, what a gift, what a wonderful
gift;
who can tell the wonder of the Lord?
Let us open our eyes, our ears,
and our hearts;
it is Christ the Lord, it is he!

1. In the stillness of the night, when
   the world was asleep,
   the Lord made his message
   known.

It was then that his Word came
down from on high,
from the Father's royal throne:
**Christ our Lord and our King!**

2. His mighty Word cuts quick and
clean,
far sharper than a two-edged
sword:
open your eyes, your ears,
and your hearts,
and hear the Word of the Lord:
**Christ our Lord and our King!**

3. He came to his people, the chosen
race,
that his Father's will would be
known;
Lion of Judah, Light of the Word,
our Redeemer came to his own,
**Christ our Lord and our King!**

4. He lived here among us, he
worked here among us,
morning, night, and day;
showed us his glory, gave us a
promise,
and then we turned away.
**Christ our Lord and our King!**

5. At the Passover meal on the night
before he died,
he lifted up his eyes and prayed.
Then he broke the bread,
then he shared the wine
the gift that God had made:
**Christ our Lord and our King!**

6. On the hill of Calvary, the world
held its breath;
and there for the world to see,
the Father gave his Son, his very
own Son
for the love of you and me.
**Christ our Lord and our King!**

7. Early on that morning when the
guards were asleep,
the Father revealed his might;
Christ in his glory arose from
the dead,
the Lord of Life and Light:
**Christ our Lord and our King!**

8. On the road to Emmaus, the
glory that is his,
the disciples could never see.
Then he broke the bread, then he
shared the wine;
it is the Lord, it is he:
**Christ our Lord and our King!**

9. Now look around you
and open your eyes;
remember the Spirit is here.
Here within his Church, his people
are one.
Look, the Lord is near:
**Christ our Lord and our King!**

*Pat Uhl and Michael Gilligan*


# 572

1. Of one that is so fair and bright,
velut maris stella,
brighter than the day is light,
parens et puella;
I cry to thee to turn to me,
lady, pray thy Son for me,
tam pia,
that I may come to thee,
Maria.

2. In sorrow, counsel thou art best,
felix fecundata:
for all the weary thou art rest,
mater honorata:
beseech him in thy mildest mood,
who for us did shed his blood

in cruce,
that we may come to him
in luce.

3. All this world was forlorn,
   Eva peccatrice,
   till our Saviour Lord was born
   de te genetrice;
   with thy ave sin went away,
   dark night went and in came day
   salutis.
   The well of healing sprang from
     thee,
   virtutis.

4. Lady, flower of everything,
   rosa sine spina,
   thou borest Jesus, heaven's king,
   gratia divina.
   Of all I say thou bore the prize,
   lady, queen of paradise,
   electa;
   maiden mild, mother
   es effecta.

   *Anonymous, medieval*

# 573

1. Of the Father's love begotten,
   ere the worlds began to be,
   he is Alpha and Omega,
   he the source, the ending he,
   of all things that are and have been
   and that future years shall see:
   **Evermore and evermore**

2. By his word was all created;
   He commanded, it was done:
   heaven and earth and depth of
     ocean,
   universe of three in one,
   all that grows beneath the shining
   of the light of moon and sun:

3. Blessed was the day for ever
   when the virgin, full of grace,

by the Holy Ghost conceiving,
bore the Saviour of our race,
and the child, the world's
  Redeemer,
first revealed his sacred face:

4. O, ye heights of heaven, adore
     him,
   Angels and archangels sing!
   Every creature bow before him
   singing praise to God our King;
   let no earthly tongue be silent,
   all the world with homage ring:

5. He, by prophets sung, is here now,
   promised since the world began,
   now on earth in flesh descended
   to atone for sins of man.
   All creation praise its Master,
   see fulfilment of his plan:

6. Glory be to God the Father,
   glory be to God the Son,
   glory to the Holy Spirit,
   persons three, yet Godhead one.
   Glory be from all creation
   while eternal ages run:

   *Aurelius C. Prudentius (348–c 413)*
   *tr. J.M. Neale (1818–66),*
   *H.W.Baker (1821–77) and others*

# 574

**Oh the word of my Lord, deep
  within my being,
oh the word of my Lord, you have
  filled my mind.**

1. Before I formed you in the womb
   I knew you through and through,
   I chose you to be mine.
   Before you left your mother's side
   I called to you, my child, to be
     my sign.

2. I know that you are very young,
   but I will make you strong
   – I'll fill you with my word;
   and you will travel through the
     land,
   fulfilling my command which you
     have heard.

3. And ev'rywhere you are to go
   my hand will follow you;
   you will not be alone.
   In all the danger that you fear
   you'll find me very near, your
     words my own.

4. With all my strength you will be
     filled:
   you will destroy and build,
   for that is my design.
   You will create and overthrow,
   reap harvests I will sow – your
     word is mine.

*Damian Lundy*
*Based on Jeremiah 1*

# 575

1. On a hill far away
   stood an old rugged cross,
   the emblem of suff'ring and
     shame;
   and I loved that old cross
   where the dearest and best
   for a world of lost sinners was
     slain.

**So I'll cherish the old rugged cross**
**'till my trophies at last I lay down;**
**I will cling to the old rugged cross**
**and exchange it someday for a**
  **crown.**

2. Oh that old rugged cross,
   so despised by the world,
   has a wondrous attraction for me:

for the dear Lamb of God
left his glory above
to bear it to dark Calvary.

3. In the old rugged cross,
   stained with blood so divine,
   a wondrous beauty I see.
   For 'twas on that old cross
   Jesus suffered and died
   to pardon and sanctify me.

4. To the old rugged cross
   I will ever be true,
   its shame and reproach gladly
     bear.
   Then he'll call me some day
   to my home far away
   there his glory for ever I'll share.

*George Bennard*

# 576

1. One day will come
   when this world which we roam
   will cease to produce sorrows
   from seeds which we have sown;
   that day there'll be such rejoicing,
   joy will banish all tears.
   One day when love conquers all
     our fears.

**That day a glow will surround us,**
**evil will be no more;**
**no wars, nor hatred around us**
**peace on earth will be sure.**
**One day when man's heart**
**returns to God;**
**the day when all men acclaim him**
**all pow'rful Lord;**
**with radiant gowns he'll adorn us.**
**'My true children', he'll say,**
**one day when love teaches us how**
  **to pray.**
**One day when love teaches us how**
  **to pray.**

2. Some day we'll learn
   how to control our lives.
   It's only then we'll be able
   to open our eyes
   to see the beauty around us,
   which God meant us to share.
   One day when love teaches us how
   to care.

   *Ronald Gokool*

# 577

1. Our Father, we have wandered
   and hidden from your face,
   in foolishness have squandered
   your legacy of grace.
   But now, in exile dwelling,
   we rise with fear and shame,
   as distant but compelling,
   we hear you call our name.

2. And now at length discerning
   the evil that we do,
   behold us Lord, returning
   with hope and trust to you.
   In haste you come to meet us
   and home rejoicing bring.
   In gladness there to greet us
   with calf and robe and ring.

3. O Lord of all the living,
   both banished and restored,
   compassionate, forgiving
   and ever caring Lord,
   grant now that our transgressing,
   our faithlessness may cease.
   Stretch out your hand in blessing
   in pardon and in peace.

   *Kevin Nichols*

# 578

*Antiphon:*

Our help is the name of the Lord
who made the earth and the
   heavens.
He is for us a most merciful
   Father,
and his faithfulness has no end.
**Our help is the name of the Lord
and his faithfulness has no end.**

1. He calls my life from out of the
   grave,
   he fills my days with happiness,
   and like an eagle my youth is
   restored.
   Our help is in the name of the Lord
   and his faithfulness has no end.
   **Our help is the name of the Lord
   and his faithfulness has no end.**

2. This God of ours does not
   condemn us,
   never repays us evil for evil.
   For he is greater than our sins.
   Our help is in the name of the Lord
   and his faithfulness has no end.
   **Our help is the name of the Lord
   and his faithfulness has no end.**

3. As any man shows mercy to his
   sons
   he is a merciful Father to us.
   He knows us through for he made
   us.

*Antiphon:*

Our help is the name of the Lord
who made the earth and the
   heavens.
He is for us a most merciful
   Father,

and his faithfulness has no end.
**Our help is in the name of the Lord
and his faithfulness has no end.**

*From Psalm 102(103):3–5,8–10.13–14
Antiphon based on Psalm 120(121):2
Versified by Huub Oosterhuis,
tr. Tony Barr*

# 579

1. Our Saviour Jesus Christ
   proclaimed
   that when we gather in his name
   he would be there to love and
   guide,
   lead us towards the Father's side.

   **Our hearts are longing for you,
   Lord,
   give us the faith to trust your word.**

2. He told us, 'Ask, you will receive,
   seek and you'll find if you believe.
   Knock at the door of love and
   truth
   and we shall open it for you.'

3. His hands brought healing to the
   blind,
   his words brought ease to troubled
   minds.
   He said his friends could do the
   same
   by invocation of his name.

4. He came to earth in form of man
   to give to us his Father's plan.
   We are the branches, he the vine,
   we too can share his life divine.

*Estelle White*

# 580

1. Out of deep unordered water
   God created land and life;
   world of beast and bird and later
   twosome people, man and wife.

There is water in the river
bringing life to tree and plant.
Let creation praise its giver:
there is water in the font.

2. Water on the human forehead,
   birthmark of the love of God,
   is the sign of death and rising,
   through the sea there runs a road.

3. Standing round the font reminds
   us
   of the Hebrew's climb ashore.
   Life is hallowed by the knowledge
   God has been this way before.

*Fred Kaan*

# 581

**'Peace is my parting gift to you,
my own peace.
Peace is my parting gift to you,'
says the Lord.**

1. Set your troubled hearts at rest,
   and banish all your fears, for . . .
   *(Jn 14:27)*

2. I will give you peace such as
   the world,
   it cannot give, for . . .
   *(Jn 14:27)*

3. Come to me all who are weary
   and in need of rest, for . . .
   *(Mk 11:28)*

4. You will find my yoke is easy,
   and my burden light, for . . .
   *(Mk 11:30)*

5. As the Father sent me, so now
   I am sending you, for . . .
   *(Jn 20:21)*

6. In my Spirit's power
   all your sins will be forgiven,
   for . . .
   *(Jn 20:22-23)*

7. Go and take my gift of peace
   to all throughout the world, for . . .
   *(Mk 16:15 and Mt 28:18)*

   *Sr. Gabriel (verse 1 and response)*
   *and Robert B. Kelly (verses 2–7)*

# 582

1. Peace, perfect peace,
   in this dark world of sin?
   The blood of Jesus whispers
   peace within.

2. Peace, perfect peace,
   by thronging duties pressed?
   To do the will of Jesus, this is rest.

3. Peace, perfect peace,
   with sorrows surging round?
   On Jesus' bosom nought
   but calm is found.

4. Peace, perfect peace,
   with loved ones far away?
   In Jesus' keeping we are safe,
   and they.

5. Peace, perfect peace,
   our future all unknown?
   Jesus we know, and he is on
   the throne.

6. Peace, perfect peace,
   death shadowing us and ours?
   Jesus has vanquished death
   and all its powers.

7. It is enough; earth's troubles
   soon shall cease,

and Jesus call us to heaven's
perfect peace.

*E.H. Bickersteth (1823–1906)*

# 583

Peacetime, peacetime,
time for making peace.
Peacetime, peacetime,
time to say I forgive you,
time for saying 'I love you',
time to live as friends.

1. Happy are they
   who are makers of peace;
   Happy are they
   who forgive;
   happy are they
   who know how to love;
   they're the sons
   and daughters of God.

2. Happy are they
   who are gentle of heart;
   happy are those
   who care;
   happy are they
   who seek the good of all;
   they're the ones
   so close to God's heart.

*Carey Landry*

# 584

1. Praise the Lord for the heavens
   above!
   Praise the Lord for the sun and
   the moon!
   Praise the Lord for the stars
   shining bright!
   Yes praise, O praise the Lord!

2. Praise the Lord for the breezes
   and the winds!
   Praise the Lord for the cold and
   heat!
   Praise the Lord for the showers
   so cool!
   Yes praise, O praise the Lord!

3. Praise the Lord for the nights
   and the days!
   Praise the Lord for the weeks
   and the months!
   Praise the Lord for the years
   as they pass!
   Yes praise, O praise the Lord!

4. Praise the Lord for redemption
   from sin!
   Praise the Lord for salvation is
   ours!
   Praise the Lord for that glorious
   day!
   Yes praise, O praise the Lord!

5. Praise the Lord for his passion
   and death!
   Praise the Lord for his sufferings
   so cruel!
   Praise the Lord for arising
   from death!
   Yes praise, O praise the Lord!

*Douglas Rowe, SJ.*

# 585

1. Praise the Lord! Ye heavens,
   adore him;
   praise him, angels, in the height;
   sun and moon, rejoice before him,
   praise him, all ye stars of light.
   Praise the Lord! for he hath
   spoken;
   worlds his mighty voice obeyed:

laws, which never shall be broken,
for their guidance he hath made.

2. Praise the Lord! for he is glorious;
   never shall his promise fail:
   God hath made his saints
   victorious;
   sin and death shall not prevail.
   Praise the God of our salvation;
   hosts on high, his power proclaim;
   heaven and earth and all creation,
   laud and magnify his name!

3. Worship, honour, glory, blessing,
   Lord, we offer to thy name;
   young and old, thy praise
   expressing,
   join their Saviour to proclaim.
   As the saints in heaven adore thee,
   we would bow before thy throne;
   as thine angels serve before thee,
   so on earth thy will be done.

*Verses 1–2 from the Foundling
Hospital Collection (1796)
Verse 3 by E. Osler (1798–1863)*

# 586

**Praise to the Lord! Praise him!
Praise to the Lord!**

1. Shout to God, all you heavens,
   and clap your hands you on earth.
   Enter into his presence
   exulting and singing for joy!

2. Know that God is our Father;
   he made us, we are his own.
   Come to him with thanksgiving
   extolling and blessing his name.

3. Merciful to us, sinners,
   compassionate to his sons,
   he has sent his beloved
   to guide us in justice and peace!

4. Praise him, then, with full voices
   and sing to him from the heart!
   Gather, Christians, together,
   together, to joyfully sing.

5. Praise the Lord with trumpet.
   O praise his name with the dance;
   celebrate with the cymbal,
   exalt him with drum, pipe and
   string!

*Paschal Jordan*

# 587

**Rain down justice,
you heavens, from above;
let the earth bring forth for us
the one who is to come.**
*(Isaiah 45:8)*

1. Be not angry, O Lord,
   and remember no longer our
   sinfulness.
   Our city, the city of your Holy
   One,
   has become a desert.
   Sion is lying in the ruins;
   Jerusalem having fallen, lies
   desolate.
   Is this the House of your glory
   and your holiness,
   where our Fathers came to praise
   you?

2. We have sinned and stand before
   you unclean,
   we have chosen to walk our own
   ways.

We have fallen as the leaves of
   the autumn,
scattered by the wind.
Just as the ravage of earth
   by the winter storms,
we have blotted your memory
   from our sight.
You have hidden your face away
   from us,
you have crushed us with the
   weight of our evil.

3. See the sorrow of your People,
   O Lord;
   send the Saviour, the one who
   is to come.
   Send us the Lamb to take away
   the sins of the world,
   to take away our burdens.
   Send us a Lord to rule the earth,
   to this city built on your holy
   mountain.
   Then he shall free us from all
   that has enslaved us,
   the day he takes away the yoke
   of our captivity.

4. Be comforted, be comforted, my
   People,
   your salvation is very close at
   hand.
   Why are your hearts so full of
   sorrow,
   why does such grief so estrange
   you?
   Do not be afraid any more.
   I am the Promised One, the hope
   of ages.
   You are my People and soon I
   come to rescue you
   I am the Holy One, the Lord
   your Redeemer.

*Tony Barr
Based on Rorate, caeli*

# 588

Rejoice, and shout for joy
sing out in praise for what the
  Lord has done.
It's right to praise him and sing
  a new song.
Play it loudly. Sing so joyfully.
For his love it fills the earth.

1. O the words of the Lord are true
   and his works are worthy of trust.
   He loves what we do that's
     righteous
   and what we do that's just.
   He merely spoke and the world
     began
   the heav'ns were formed with
     moons and stars.
   He made the oceans by pouring
     them
   into vast reservoirs.

2. With one breath he can scatter
   the plans of a whole nation.
   His intentions are the same
   for ev'ry generation.
   Happy is the nation
   whose God is the Lord.
   Not the king whose army
   can boast a powerful sword.

3. O the Lord looks down from
     heaven
   and he knows ev'ry thing we do.
   He watches over those who obey
     him
   and trust in his love so true.
   O the Lord he saves and helps us
   and protects us like a shield.
   We depend on him. He is our
     hope.
   To him alone we yield.

*Anne Seymour, from Psalm 32(33)*

# 589

Rejoice, rejoice, rejoice!
Come, let us praise the Lord! (3)
Praise the Lord! Praise the Lord!
  Praise the Lord!

1. Holy, holy, holy! (3)
   O, holy is the Lord!

2. Glory, glory, glory! (3)
   O, glory to the Lord!

*Norbert Farrell*

# 590

1. 'Remember, man, that you are
     dust,
   and unto dust you shall return.'
   **O who are we, mere creature clay,**
   **that we should dare to call you**
     **'Lord'?**

2. 'Fear not, my child, I am your
     God.
   For you I came; for you I died.'
   **What gift is this – a creature God!**
   **– And in return, what can we give?**

3. 'O lift your heart, your heart of
     stone:
   no longer lost, you are my own.'
   **O, we have sinned, deserve to die:**
   **how can our pride admit your love?**

4. O Lord of love, we turn to you:
   forgive, and heal, and make us
     new.
   **No eye can see, no ear can hear,**
   **no mind conceive what hope you**
     **bring,**
   **what hope you bring.**

*John Glynn*

# 591

**Return to the Lord, return,
O Israel!
He calls to you.
For the Lord is full of love
and tender mercy;
he waits for your heart.**

1. What shall I do with you,
   O my people?
   This love of yours so quickly
   disappears. *(Hosea 6:4)*

2. When will you share your bread
   with the hungry?
   When will you welcome in the
   homeless poor? *(Isaiah 58:7)*

3. I do not take delight in burnt
   off'ring.
   Give me yourself, your crushed
   and broken heart. *(Psalm 51:17)*

4. And I will plant my law deep
   within you.
   Deep in your heart will I inscribe
   my name. *(Jeremiah 31:31)*

5. I love you with a love everlasting;
   I hold you constantly close to
   my heart. *(Jeremiah 31:31)*

*Paschal Jordan*

# 592

1. Rock of ages, cleft for me,
   let me hide myself in thee;
   let the water and the blood,
   from thy riven side which flowed,
   be of sin the double cure:
   cleanse me from its guilt and
   power.

2. Not the labours of my hands
   can fulfill thy law's demands;
   could my zeal no respite know,
   could my tears for ever flow,
   all for sin could not atone:
   thou must save, and thou alone.

3. Nothing in my hand I bring,
   simply to thy Cross I cling;
   naked, come to thee for dress;
   helpless, look to thee for grace;
   foul, I to the fountain fly;
   wash me, Saviour, or I die.

4. While I draw this fleeting breath,
   when my eyelids close in death,
   when I soar through tracts
   unknown,
   see thee on thy judgement throne;
   rock of ages, cleft for me,
   let me hide myself in thee.

*A.M. Toplady (1740–1778)*

# 593

1. Seek ye first the Kingdom of God,
   and his righteousness,
   and all these things shall be added
   unto you;
   allelu, alleluia.

   **Alleluia, alleluia, alleluia,
   alleluia, alleluia.**

2. Ask and it shall be given unto you,
   seek and ye shall find;
   knock and it shall be opened
   unto you;
   allelu, alleluia.

*Karen Lafferty*

# 594

1. Send forth your Spirit, God
   our Father,
   as you have sent him in the past:
   at Gabriel's word, by Jordan's
   water,
   as Jesus went to pray and fast.

2. In this same Spirit he proclaimed
   you
   on Juda's hills, by Galilee,
   he called us to your heav'nly
   kingdom,
   he died and rose triumphantly.

3. And now though seen by us no
   longer
   he rests not from the task begun,
   but breathes the Spirit of his
   sonship
   on men of ev'ry race and tongue.

4. May he be with us at this moment
   and give us of your Spirit still,
   that we may do the work that
   waits us
   and strive your purpose to fulfil.

*At confirmation*

5. May all who come for
   confirmation
   be richly with your Spirit sealed:
   to love and serve you in their
   brothers,
   until your glory is revealed.

                    *Denis E. Hurley*

# 595

**Send forth your Spirit, O Lord.**
**Send forth your Spirit**
**on these your chosen ones.**
**Send forth your Spirit of love.**

1. To show the love of the Father,
   to show the love of the Son.
   To show the love of Jesus for all
   men;
   this is his new commandment.

**Send forth your Spirit, O Lord.**
**Send forth your Spirit**
**on these your chosen ones.**
**Send forth your Spirit of truth.**

2. To know the will of the Father,
   to know the will of the Son,
   to know the Gospel of Jesus the
   Lord,
   to proclaim to everyone.

**Send forth your Spirit, O Lord.**
**Send forth your Spirit**
**on these your chosen ones.**
**Send them to cast your fire on**
**earth.**

*Sung by Confirmation candidates*

3. Come upon us, O Spirit of the
   living God!
   Come upon us, O Spirit of truth!
   Come upon us, O Spirit of love
   and life!
   Send us to cast your fire on earth!

**Send forth your Spirit, O Lord.**
**Send forth your Spirit**
**on these your chosen ones.**
**Send them to cast your fire on**
**earth.**

**Send forth your Spirit, O Lord.**
**Send forth your Spirit**
**on these your chosen ones.**
**Send forth your Spirit of love.**

                    *Garfield Rochard*

# 596

**Send forth your Spirit, O Lord, that the face of the earth be renewed.**

1. O my soul, arise and bless the Lord God,
   O Lord, in majesty,
   enrobed with pow'r and eternal might.

2. You are clothed with splendour and with beauty,
   O God, and heav'nly light
   is like a cloud that conceals your face.

3. You have built your palace on the waters;
   on wings of winds and fire
   you reign in heav'n, rule supreme on earth.

4. Like the winds your angels fly before you;
   as fire and flaming light,
   your ministers stand before your throne.

5. For the earth you fixed on its foundations;
   indeed, it shall stand firm,
   and not be moved for unending years.

6. On the earth the waters spread their mantle;
   and seas filled all the land;
   above the earth stood the rising flood.

7. When they heard on high your voice of thunder,
   in fear they took to flight;
   at your reproach, they dispersed and fled.

8. By your word, there sprang up hills and mountains;
   on earth the dry land rose,
   and in their place, rested glens and vales.

9. Your command sets bounds on all the waters,
   and they shall not return;
   they may not pass limits you have set.

10. Torrents fill the valleys at your order;
    while streams and rivers flow,
    refresh the beasts, slake the thirst of man.

11. From their nests, the birds give praise and glory
    to you, O Lord of hosts,
    from ev'ry branch, join in songs of praise.

12. In green fields you feed your sheep and cattle,
    and all your creatures, Lord;
    and yet to men, you have given more.

13. There is wine to cheer the heart of mankind;
    the wheat for man makes bread;
    and oil is used to anoint his head.

14. While I live, I sing the praise of Yahweh,
    O Lord, your glorious praise,
    my lips proclaim: Blessed be the Lord.

15. Praise to God, the author of these marvels,
    to God, the mighty One,
    who made the earth, glory to his name.

16. Praise to God, the Father, Son
    and Spirit,
    to God who gives us life,
    our thanks return, now and
    evermore.

*Lucien Deiss, from Psalm 103(104)*

# 597

1. Shepherd of souls, in love come
   feed us.
   Life-giving bread for hungry
   hearts.
   To those refreshing waters lead us
   where dwells that grace your peace
   imparts.
   May we, the wayward in your fold,
   by your forgiveness rest consoled.

2. Life-giving vine, come, feed and
   nourish,
   strengthen each branch with life
   divine.
   Ever in you O may we flourish,
   fruitful the branches of the vine.
   Lord, may our souls be purified
   so that in Christ we may abide.

3. Sinful are we who stand before
   you
   worthy of you is Christ alone.
   So in Christ's name we do implore
   you;
   rich are the mercies you have
   shown.
   Say but the word, O Lord divine,
   then are our hearts made pure like
   thine.

4. Following you, O Lord, who led
   them,
   Multitudes thronged the
   mountainside;

Filled with compassion, Lord,
    you fed them,
Fed them with loaves you
    multiplied.
Come, feed us now, O Lord, we
    pray:
Lifegiving bread give us this day.

5. Help us, dear Lord, prepare a
   dwelling
   worthy of you who made us all;
   cleanse thou our hearts, our guilt
   dispelling,
   purify us who heed your call.
   'Take this and eat' were words
   you said,
   so we have gathered for this bread.

*J. Clifford Evers*

# 598

1. Show me your ways that I may
   follow you,
   lead me, O master, on my way.
   Guide me in all the things that
   I must do,
   direct my steps that I don't go
   astray.

   **In you I place my confidence
   and trust,
   O Lord, have your way with me
   for I am yours.**

2. Guard me when temptation calls
   on me to sin.
   Protect me when the enemy is
   near.
   Strengthen me to turn to you
   that I may win,
   and bless me, Jesus, that I
   persevere.

**The spirit's willing but the flesh
is weak, O Lord.
But your support is all I'll ever need.**

3. Show me your ways that I may
   follow you,
   lead me, O Master, on my way.
   Guide me in all the things that
   I must do,
   direct my steps that I don't go
   astray.

*Sebastian Temple*

# 599

1. Sing a simple song unto the Lord;
   sing a simple song unto the Lord,
   sing it with your heart,
   sing it with your soul,
   sing a simple song unto the Lord.

   **Oh Lord, I love you;
   O Lord, I see;
   Oh Lord, I love you,
   I see that you love me.**

2. Say a simple prayer . . .

3. Give a simple gift . . .

*Carey Landry*

# 600

1. Sing everyone
   a song to the Lord,
   a song to the Lord
   of all our hearts.
   He made us,
   we're the work of his hands,
   the work of his hands
   in all we are.

Lord, we offer you
everything we do,
sing everyone
a song to the Lord,
a song to the Lord
of all our hearts.

2. Come everyone
   who works for his life,
   who works for his life
   on this fair earth.
   He worked for
   us and left us himself,
   the gift of his life
   in bread and wine.
   Take our work and play,
   it's yours every day.
   Sing everyone
   a song to the Lord,
   a song to the Lord
   who makes us live.

3. Sing softly,
   for the Lord is around,
   he's there in the smallest
   summer breeze.
   Sing sweetly,
   for the Lord isn't harsh,
   he's gentle in voice,
   in giving, free.
   Lord, we love with you
   all those you give us now.
   Sing loudly,
   for the love of the Lord,
   the love of the Lord
   is all our joy.

*Anne Conway*

# 601

1. Sing praises to the Lord; (3)
   alleluia, alleluia!

2. And holy be his Name; (3)
   alleluia, alleluia!

3. For he is kind and good, (3)
   alleluia, alleluia!

4. He died that we might live;
   he rose again to life;
   he lives no more to die,
   alleluia, alleluia!

*Derick Clouden*

# 602

**Sing to the Lord a song,
sing to the Lord a psalm.
Sing to the Lord, you nations!
Praise his name! (2)**

1. He made heaven, he made the
   earth;
   the sea, the sky and all there is,
   He made Adam out of naught,
   and told him these were his.

2. Now, Adam was a lonely man,
   and God decided he would give
   a helping-mate to this new man:
   created the woman Eve.

3. Then God told Adam what to do:
   'Go forth, good man, into the
   world,
   multiply and fill the earth
   and bless thy holy name.'

*Helena Warner*

# 603

**Sing to the Lord, alleluia,
sing to the Lord.**

1. Bless his name,
   announce his salvation
   day after day,
   alleluia.

2. Give to him,
   you families of peoples
   glory and praise,
   alleluia.

3. Great is he,
   and worthy of praises
   day after day,
   alleluia.

4. He it is
   who gave us the heavens,
   glory to God,
   alleluia.

5. Tell his glories,
   tell all the nations,
   day after day,
   alleluia.

6. Bring your gifts
   and enter his temple,
   worship the Lord,
   alleluia.

*John Foley SJ.
from Psalm 95(96)*

# 604

**Sing to the mountains, sing to the
sea.
Raise your voices, lift your hearts.
This is the day the Lord has made.
Let all the earth rejoice.**

1. I will give thanks to you, my Lord.
   You have answered my plea.
   You have saved my soul from
   death.
   You are my strength and my song.

2. Holy, holy, holy Lord.
   Heaven and earth are full of your
   glory.

3. This is the day that the Lord has made.
Let us be glad and rejoice.
He has turned all death to life.
Sing of the glory of God.

*Bob Dufford, SJ.*

# 605

1. Sing to the world of Christ our sov'reign Lord;
tell of his birth which brought new life to all.
Speak of his life, his love, his holy word;
let ev'ry nation hear and know his call.
Sing to the World of Christ our Sov'reign Lord.

2. Sing to the world of Christ the Prince of peace,
showing to me the Father's loving care,
pleading that love should reign and wars might cease,
teaching we need the love of God to share.
Sing to the world of Christ the Prince of peace.

3. Sing to the world of Christ our steadfast friend,
off'ring himself to live the constant sign;
food for our souls until we meet life's end,
gives us his flesh for bread, his blood for wine.
Sing to the world of Christ our steadfast friend.

4. Sing to the world of Christ our Saviour King,
born that his death mankind's release should win;
hung from a cross, forgiveness he could bring;
buried, he rose to conquer death and sin.
Sing to the world of Christ our Saviour King.

5. Sing to the world of Christ at God's right hand,
praise to the Spirit both have sent to men,
living in us till earth shall reach its span,
time be no more, and Christ shall come again.
Sing to the world of Christ at God's right hand.

*Patrick Lee*

# 606

1. Son of God and son of David,
priest devoid of dignity,
slave to ransom the enslaved,
butt of jibes and jealousy:
you were like us, struggling and trying,
till your dying
for our liberty.

2. Every creature should, with gladness,
kneel before your majesty;
every man, through joy and sadness,
witness to your sanctity,
bring you a rich credit balance
from his talents
and activity.

3. Jesus' name in condemnation
nailed to that torturing tree,
'King of Jews' that provocation
you forgave in agony.
Hear, Lord, this sinner's petition
for remission,
life eternally.

*Ds Willem Barnard,*
*tr. Bonaventure Hinwood*

# 607

1. Son of the Father, Jesus,
    Lord and slave,
   born among the cattle in the
    squalor of a cave,
   one with God, you made yourself
   one with man, shunning wealth;
   Lord, we worship you with heart
    and mind.

2. Son of the Father, Jesus,
    workers' friend,
   you whom Joseph taught the skills
    of working with your hands,
   man, at home in builder's yard,
   one with man, toiling hard;
   Lord, we worship you with hand
    and mind.

3. Son of the Father, author of our
    faith,
   choosing men to follow you
    from every walk of life,
   who with them, in boats, on shore,
   troubles shared, burdens bore;
   Lord, we worship you with hand
    and mind.

4. Seed of the Father, from life's
    furrow born,
   teaching men in parables
    from agriculture drawn,
   Jesus, lover of the soil,

man of earth, son of toil;
Lord, we worship you with hand
 and mind.

5. Father and Spirit, Jesus, Lord
    and Man,
   bless us in the work you have
    appointed to be done.
   Lift our spirits, guide our wills,
   steer our hands, use our skills;
   Lord, we worship you with hand
    and mind.

*Fred Kaan*

# 608

1. Take my life, and let it be
   consecrated, Lord, to thee;
   take my moments and my days,
   let them flow in ceaseless praise.

2. Take my hands, and let them move
   at the impulse of thy love.
   Take my feet, and let them be
   swift and purposeful for thee.

3. Take my voice, and let me sing
   always, only, for my King.
   Take my intellect, and use
   every power as thou shalt choose.

4. Take my will, and make it thine:
   it shall be no longer mine.
   Take my heart; it is thine own:
   it shall be thy royal throne.

5. Take my love; my Lord, I pour
   at thy feet its treasure-store.
   Take myself, and I will be
   ever, only, all for thee.

*Frances R. Havergal (1836–79)*

# 609

1. Tell out, my soul, the greatness
   of the Lord!
   Unnumbered blessings, give my
   spirit voice;
   tender to me the promise of his
   word;
   in God my Saviour shall my heart
   rejoice.

2. Tell out, my soul, the greatness
   of his name!
   Make known his might, the deeds
   his arm has done;
   his mercy sure, from age to age
   the same;
   his holy name – the Lord, the
   Mighty One.

3. Tell out, my soul, the greatness
   of his might!
   Powers and dominions lay their
   glory by.
   Proud hearts and stubborn wills
   are put to flight,
   the hungry fed, the humble lifted
   high.

4. Tell out, my soul, the glories
   of his word!
   Firm is his promise, and his
   mercy sure.
   Tell out, my soul, the greatness
   of the Lord
   to children's children and for
   evermore!

*Timothy Dudley-Smith*
*Based on Luke 1:46–55*

# 610

1. That which we have heard
   we have seen with our own eyes;
   that which we have felt and
   touched:

   **The Word who is life,**
   **the Word who is life,**
   **the Word who is life for us.**
   **To him be glory,**
   **all honour and praise.**
   **To him be glory:**
   **Jesus, our Saviour and Lord.**

2. He is the Light of lights;
   our redeemer King;
   he is the Lord of lords.

3. He is the bread of life;
   wonder-counsellor;
   he is Prince of peace.

*Carey Landry*
*Based on 1 John 1:1*

# 611

1. The angel Gabriel from heaven
   came,
   his wings as drifted snow, his eyes
   as flame;
   'All hail,' he said, 'thou lowly
   maiden Mary,
   most highly favoured lady.' *Gloria!*

2. 'For know, a blessed Mother thou
   shalt be,
   all generations laud and honour
   thee,
   thy Son shall be Emmanuel, by
   seers foretold;
   most highly favoured lady.'
   *Gloria!*

3. Then gentle Mary meekly bowed
      her head,
   'To me be as it pleaseth God,'
      she said,
   'my soul shall laud and magnify
      his holy name':
   most highly favoured lady. *Gloria!*

4. Of her, Emmanuel, the Christ
      was born
   in Bethlehem, all on a Christmas
      morn,
   and Christian folk throughout
      the world will ever say
   'most highly favoured lady.'
      *Gloria!*

*Basque carol paraphrased by*
*Sabine Baring-Gould (1834–1924)*

# 612

1. The Church is wherever God's
      people are easing
   burdens of others in love and
      good will.
   The Church is wherever the cross
      of the Saviour
   is borne by believers who follow
      him still.

2. The Church is wherever God's
      people are trusting;
   facing hard trials with hope,
      not despair.
   The Church is wherever a
      miracle follows
   beyond human power, in answer
      to prayer.

3. The Church is wherever his own
      come to Jesus,
   stirred by a longing and need
      to be whole.

The Church is wherever God's
      people adore him
in worship that rises from heart,
      mind and soul.

4. The Church is wherever disciples
      of Jesus
   turn to their Master each step
      of the way.
   The Church is wherever the love
      of the Saviour
   is seen in his followers' lives
      day by day.

*Pat Regehr*

# 613

1. The King shall come when
      morning dawns
   and light triumphant breaks,
   when beauty gilds the eastern hills
   and life to joy awakes.

2. Not as of old a little child,
   to bear and fight and die,
   but crowned with glory like the
      sun
   that lights the morning sky.

3. O brighter than the rising morn
   when he, victorious, rose,
   and left the lonesome place of
      death,
   despite the rage of foes.

4. O brighter than that glorious
      morn
   shall this fair morning be,
   when Christ our King in beauty
      comes,
   and we his face shall see!

5. The King shall come when
      morning dawns
   and light and beauty brings;
   "Hail, Christ the Lord!" your
      people pray,
   "Come quickly, King of kings!"

*John Brownlie (1859–1925)*

# 614

**The light of Christ
has come into the world,
the light of Christ
has come into the world.**

1. We must all be born again
   to see the kingdom of God;
   the water and the Spirit
   bring new life in God's love.

2. God gave up his only Son
   out of love for the world
   so that ev'ryone who believes in
      him
   will live for ever.

3. The Light of God has come to us
   so that we might have salvation,
   from the darkness of our sins, we
      walk
   into glory with Christ Jesus.

*Donald Fishel*

# 615

1. The Lord is my shepherd.
   He provides all I need
   in the rich grassland,
   where he lets me feed.
   He brings me to water
   my life to renew.

He guides me on true paths
because he is true.

2. I walk through the darkness,
   with nothing to fear;
   his right hand protects me
   when danger is near.
   He lays me a table
   in spite of my foes.
   He fills me with gladness,
   my cup overflows.

3. Each day he is goodness,
   each day he's my song.
   I live in his household
   the whole of life long.
   The Lord is my shepherd.
   He provides all I need
   in the rich grassland,
   where he lets me feed.

*Hubert Richards
Based on Psalm 22(23)*

# 616

The seed is Christ's, the harvest his:
may we be stored within God's barn.
The sea is Christ's, the fish are his:
may we be caught within God's net.
From birth to age, from age to death,
enfold us, Christ, within your arms.
Until the end, the great re-birth,
Christ, be our joy in Paradise.

*Traditional Irish, tr. James Quinn,
SJ.*

# 617

**The Spirit is moving all over,
all over this land.**

1. People are gathering, the Church
      is born;

the Spirit is blowing on a world reborn.

2. Doors are opening as the Spirit comes;
his fire is burning in his people now.

3. Filled with his Spirit we are sent to serve;
we are called out as brothers, we are called to work.

4. The world, born once, is born again;
we recreate it in love and joy.

5. Old men are dreaming dreams;
and young men see the light.

6. Old walls are falling down;
and people are speaking with each other.

7. The Spirit fills us with his power
to be his witnesses to all we meet.

8. The Spirit urges us to travel light
to be people of courage who spread his fire.

9. God has poured out his Spirit
on all; on all creation.

*Carey Landry*

# 618

1. The Spirit lives to set us free,
**walk, walk in the light.**
He binds us all in unity,
**walk, walk in the light.**

**Walk in the light, (3)
walk in the light of the Lord.**

2. Jesus promised life to all,
The dead were wakened by his call.

3. He died in pain on Calvary,
to save the lost like you and me.

4. We know his death was not the end,
He gave his Spirit to be our friend.

5. By Jesus' love our wounds are healed,
The Father's kindness is revealed.

6. The Spirit lives in you and me,
His light will shine for all to see.

*Damian Lundy*

# 619

**The Spirit of God rests upon me,
the Spirit of God consecrates me,
the Spirit of God bids me go forth
to proclaim his peace his joy.**

1. The Spirit of God sends me forth,
called to witness the kingdom of Christ
among all the nations;
called to proclaim
the good news of Christ to the poor.
My spirit rejoices in God, my Saviour.

2. The Spirit of God sends me forth,
called to witness the kingdom of Christ
among all the nations;
called to console
the hearts overcome with great sorrow.
My spirit rejoices in God, my Saviour.

3. The Spirit of God sends me forth,
   called to witness the kingdom of
   Christ
   among to comfort
   the poor who mourn and who
   weep.
   My spirit rejoices in God, my
   Saviour.

4. The Spirit of God sends me forth,
   called to witness the kingdom of
   Christ
   among all the nations;
   called to announce
   the grace of salvation to men.
   My spirit rejoices in God, my
   Saviour.

5. The Spirit of God sends me forth,
   called to witness the kingdom of
   Christ
   among all the nations;
   called to reveal
   his glory among all the people
   My spirit rejoices in God, my
   Saviour.

*Lucien Deiss*
*Based on Isaiah 61:1–2 and Luke*
*4:18–19*

# 620

1. There is a river that flows from
   God above
   there is a fountain that's filled
   with his great love.

   **Come to the waters; there is a**
   **great supply;**
   **there is a river that never shall**
   **run dry.**

2. Wash me with water, and then
   I shall be clean;
   white as the new snow, if you
   remove my sin. *(Psalm 50)*

3. Plunged in the water, the tomb
   of our rebirth,
   so may we rise up to share in
   Christ's new life.

4. All who are thirsty, now hear
   God as he calls;
   come to the Lord's side, his life
   pours out for all. *(Jn 19: 33-35)*

5. Safe in the new Ark, the Church
   of Christ our Lord,
   praise God for water, his sign
   to save the world.

*Verse 1 traditional*
*Verses 2–5 Robert B. Kelly*

# 621

**There is one Lord,**
**there is one faith,**
**there is one baptism,**
**one God, who is Father.**

1. We were called to be one in the
   Spirit of God,
   in the bond of peace, we sing
   and proclaim.

2. We were called to form one body
   in one spirit,
   we sing and proclaim.

3. We were called in the same hope
   in Christ the Lord,
   we sing and proclaim.

*Lucien Deiss*
*Based on Ephesians 4:5*

# 622

1. Thine be the glory, risen,
   conquering Son,
   endless is the victory thou o'er
   death hast won;

angels in bright raiment rolled
the stone away,
kept the folded grave-clothes,
where thy body lay.

**Thine be the glory, risen,
conquering Son,
endless is the victory thou o'er
death hast won.**

2. Lo, Jesus meets us, risen from
the tomb;
lovingly he greets us, scatters
fear and gloom;
let the church with gladness,
hymns of triumph sing,
for her Lord is living, death has
lost its sting.

3. No more we doubt thee, glorious
Prince of life;
life is nought without thee: aid
us in our strife;
make us more than conquerors,
through thy deathless love:
bring us safe through Jordan to
thy home above.

*Edmond Louis Budry (1854–1932)*
*tr. Richard Birch Hoyle (1875–1939)*

# 623

1. This is my body, broken for you,
bringing you wholeness, making
you free.
Take it and drink it, and when
you do,
do it in love for me.

2. This is my blood poured out for
you,
bringing forgiveness, making you
free.
Take it and drink it, and when

you do,
do it in love for me.

3. Back to my Father soon I shall go.
Do not forget me; then you will see
I am still with you, and you will
know
you're very close to me.

4. Filled with my Spirit, how you
will grow!
You are my branches; I am the
tree.
If you are faithful, others will
know
you are alive in me.

5. Love one another – I have loved
you,
and I have shown you how to be
free;
serve one another, and when you
do,
do it in love for me.

*Verses 1 and 2 Jimmy Owens*
*Verses 3–5 Damian Lundy*

# 624

**This is the day
that the Lord has made,
let us rejoice and shout
"Alleluia!"**

1. We were asleep,
it seemed like death
but now the morning's broken.

2. The winter's past,
the grass is green
and Spring is life in our land.

3. The Lord of life
has passed through death
and still he lives among us.

*Anne Conway*
*Based on Psalm 117(118)*

# 625

1. This is the day (2)
   that the Lord has made. (2)
   We will rejoice, (2)
   and be glad in it. (2)
   This is the day
   that the Lord has made.
   We will rejoice
   and be glad in it.
   This is the day
   that the Lord has made.

2. This is the day
   when he rose again . . .

3. This is the day
   when the Spirit came . . .

*Author Unknown*

# 626

This is the feast of vict'ry for
   our God
for the Lamb who was slain has
   begun his reign
has begun his reign, alleluia!
This is the feast of vict'ry for
   our God
for the Lamb who was slain
has begun his reign, alleluia!

1. Worthy is Christ, the Lamb who
   was slain,
   whose blood set us free to be
   people of God.
   Power, riches, wisdom and
   strength
   and honour, blessing and glory
   are his.

2. Sing with all the people of God
   and join in the hymn of all

creation:
Blessing, honour, glory and might
be to God and the Lamb for ever.
Amen.

*John Ylvisaker*
*Based on Revelation 4:9–14*

# 627

This is the night
when God delivered our forefathers
   from their chains,
led them dry shod through the sea,
   out of slavery.
Free your people once again.

This is the night
when Christ has ransomed us
and paid the price of sin.
The Paschal Lamb was slain
   bringing peace through pain.
We will follow where he's been.

This is the night,
this is the night he rose triumphant
   from the grave,
opened what was sealed,
   forgave, and blessed, and healed
those he suffered death to save.

O happy fault!
O necessary sin!
A New Day rushes in!

This is the night
the pillar of fire becomes a beacon
   of belief
to lead the people on, when hope
   is nearly gone,
unwav'ring joy consuming grief.

This is the night,
this is the night of nights
   awaited since the Fall,
when death is our rebirth,

with heaven wed to earth,
reconciling one and all.

This is the night,
this is the night of joy,
of solemn songs of praise,
washing guilt away.
The night shall be as day,
mourning turned to dancing all
our days.

O happy fault!
O necessary sin!
A New Day rushes in!

*Miriam Therese Winter*
*Based on the Exsultet*

# 628

That is what Yahweh asks of you,
only this:
that you act justly, that you
love tenderly,
that you walk humbly, with your
God.

1. 'My children, I am with you such
a little while,
and where I go now you cannot
come,
a new commandment I give to
you:
as I have loved you, so love each
other.'

2. 'Do not let your hearts be
troubled;
trust in God now, and trust in me.
I go to prepare a place for you,
and I shall come again to take
you home.'

3. 'Peace is the gift I leave with you,
a peace the world can never give.

If you keep my word, my Father
will love you,
and we will come to you to make
our home.'

*Mary McGann, RSCJ*

# 629

1. Thou whose almighty Word
chaos and darkness heard,
and took their flight;
hear us, we humbly pray,
and where the Gospel-day
sheds not its glorious ray
let there be light!

2. Thou who didst come to bring
on thy redeeming wing
healing and sight,
health to the sick in mind,
sight to the inly blind,
ah! now to all mankind
let there be light!

3. Spirit of truth and love,
life-giving, holy dove,
speed forth thy flight!
Move on the waters' face,
bearing the lamp of grace,
and in earth's darkest place
let there be light!

4. Blessed and holy Three,
glorious Trinity,
wisdom, love, might;
boundless as ocean tide
rolling in fullest pride,
through the world far and wide
let there be light!

*J. Marriott (1780–1825)*

## 630

Though the mountains may fall,
  and the hills turn to dust,
yet the love of the Lord will stand
as a shelter for all who will call on
  his name.
Sing the praise and the glory of
  God.

1. Could the Lord ever leave you?
  Could the Lord forget his love?
  Though the Mother forsake her
    child,
  he will not abandon you.

2. Should you turn and forsake him,
  he will gently call your name.
  Should you wander away from
    him,
  he will always take you back.

3. Go to him when you're weary;
  he will give you eagle's wings.
  You will run, never tire,
  for your God will be your
    strength.

4. As he swore to you Fathers,
  when the flood destroyed the land.
  He will never forsake you;
  he will swear to you again.

*Daniel L. Schutte, SJ.*

## 631

1. Through all the changing scenes
  of life,
  in trouble and in joy,
  the praises of my God shall still
  my heart and tongue employ.

2. Of his deliverance I will boast,
  till all that are distressed,
  when learning this, will comfort
    take
  and calm their griefs to rest.

3. O magnify the Lord with me,
  with me exalt his name;
  when in distress to him I called
  he to my rescue came.

4. The hosts of God encamp around
  the dwellings of the just;
  deliverance he affords to all
  who on his succour trust.

5. O make but trial of his love;
  experience will decide
  how blest are they, and only they,
  who in his truth confide.

6. Fear him, ye saints, and you will
    then
  having nothing else to fear;
  make you his service your delight,
  your wants shall be his care.

*Psalm 33(34):1–9*
*Nahum tate (1625–1715) and*
*Nicholas Brady (1659–1726), alt.*

## 632

To be the body of the Lord in
  this world,
to have his Spirit coursing through
  my soul,
to know the passion of my Jesus
in his love for every man,
to show his mercy in the shadows of
  this land.

1. Come, walk with me; come, share
  my life,
  you must know the shadows
  if you would know the light.

2. No eyes have I, no ears to hear,
   you must be my Body and show
   my Father's care.

3. Open your eyes, see what I see.
   For this world how I suffer.
   Share my destiny.

4. I am the vine, branches are you.
   Life from me eternal to make
   your world anew.

5. One bread, one cup; one heart
      and mind.
   One great human people
   in fellowship divine.

*Clyde Harvey*

# 633

1. To God our Father be the praise,
   be glory ever given,
   for to this world he sent his Son
   that we might be forgiven.

2. The world in sin and darkness lay;
   goodness was put to flight;
   and in the fulness of his time
   God sent his Son, the Light.

3. 'In him was life' the Gospel says,
   'this life was light of men.'
   The darkness has been overcome,
   the Light of God shines on.

4. The Light of God is in the world,
   but shines not everywhere;
   he shines alone in human lives
   when he's invited there.

5. 'Behold at the door of your life I
      stand
   the Light, the Life, the Love;
   I will come in,' he says 'and will
   illuminate your soul.'

6. Rejoice then, you who sing this
      hymn;
   real life, real joy and light
   shall be for you eternally,
   if you will welcome him.

*William Armitage*

# 634

**Together we journey on the
   highway of God,
to the mountain of glory and grace;
and together we'll seek for the pearl
   of great price
till we meet with the Lord face to
   face.**

1. There's one on that journey
      who's burdened with sorrow,
   bitterness hidden by grief:
   yet we shall bear it,
      together we'll share it,
   united in heart and in mind.

2. Another who travels is joyful
      and trusting,
   clothed with the garment of peace:
   so we shall wear it, together we'll
      share it,
   united in heart and mind.

3. And all we who journey have
      gladness and sorrow
   somewhere on God's holy way:
   so we shall bear them,
      together we'll share them,
   united in heart and in mind.

*John Glynn*

# 635

**Trust in the Lord; you shall not tire.
Serve you the Lord; you shall not
   weaken.
For the Lord's own strength will**

**uphold you.
You shall renew your life and live.**

1. The Lord is our eternal God.
   He neither faints nor grows weary.
   Our hearts he probes from afar,
   knowing our ways, knowing our
      ways.

2. Young hearts may grow faint and
      weak,
   youths may collapse, stumble and
      fall,
   they that hope in the Lord will
      renew their courage;
   they'll soar with eagle's might.

3. Old men shall dream new dreams;
   young men will find wisdom in
      visions.
   The Lord will speak in our
      lifetime,
   show his face to those who wait.

*Robert F. O'Connor, SJ,
Based on Isaiah 40:28–31*

# 636

**Unite us, Lord, in peace
and uphold us with your love.**

1. Our faults divide and hinder;
   your grace can make us one;
   we wonder at your rising,
   your light is like the sun.

2. You are our expectation
   in loneliness and pain;
   your healing and your pardon
   are greater than our sin.

3. Lord, look upon the starving
   and set the captive free.

Share out among our brothers
the bread of unity.

4. How happy are the people
   who strive to be at one,
   who learn to live as brothers,
   who lay their hatred down.

5. O Lord, whose silent spirit
   enlightens and endows,
   make us in faith receptive
   and help us love your house.

6. Your cross will draw together
   the circle of mankind;
   in you shall all the people
   their true communion find.

7. Death can no longer hurt us,
   triumphant is your word.
   Let life now grow and blossom,
   O Jesus, risen Lord!

*Dominique Ombrie, tr. Fred Kaan*

# 637

1. Upon thy table, Lord, we place
   these symbols of our work and
      thine,
   life's food won only by thy grace,
   who giv'st to all the bread and
      wine.

2. Within these simple things there
      lie
   the height and depth of human
      life,
   the thought of man, his tears and
      toil,
   his hopes and fears, his joy and
      strife.

3. Accept them, Lord; from thee
   they come:

we take them humbly at thy hand.
these gifts of thine for higher use
we offer, as thou dost command.

*M.F.C. Willson (1884–1944)*

# 638

**Veni Sancte Spiritus (4)**

*Some or all of these verses may be sung by a soloist.*

1. Holy Spirit, Lord of light,
   radiance give from celestial height.
   Come thou Father of the poor,
   come now with treasures that
      endure:
   Light of all who live.

2. Thou of all consolers the best.
   Thou the soul's delightful guest;
   refreshing peace bestow.
   Thou in toil my comfort sweet,
   thou coolness in the heat.
   Thou my solace in time of woe.

3. Light immortal, light divine;
   fire of love, our hearts refine,
   our inmost being fill.
   Take thy grace away
   and nothing pure in man will stay,
   all his good is turned to ill.

4. Heal our wounds, our strength
      renew,
   on our dryness pour thy dew;
   wash guilt away, bend the
      stubborn heart
   melt the frozen, warm the chill
   and guide the steps that go astray.

5. Sevenfold gifts on us be pleased
      to pour,
   who thee confess and thee adore;
   bring us thy comfort when we die;

give us life with thee on high;
give us joys, give us joys that
   never end.

*Attr. to Stephen Langton*
*(c 1160–1228),*
*tr. Edward Caswall (1814–1878),*
*altered by Christopher Walker*

# 639

1. 'Wake, awake! For night is dying,'
   the watchmen on the heights are
      crying,
   'Awake, Jerusalem, at last!'
   Midnight hears the welcome
      voices,
   and at the thrilling cry rejoices:
   'Come forth, you virgins, night is
      past;
   the bridegroom comes; awake,
   your lamps with gladness take,
   hallelujah!
   and for his marriage feast prepare,
   for you must go to meet him
      there.'

2. Sion hears the watchmen singing,
   and all her heart with joy is
      springing;
   she wakes, she rises from her
      gloom:
   for her Lord comes down
      all-glorious,
   the strong in grace, in truth
      victorious;
   her star is risen, her light is come.
   Now come, O blessed one,
   God's own beloved Son;
   hallelujah!
   we follow to the festal hall
   to sup with you, the Lord of all.

3. Now let earth and heaven adore
      you,
   as men and angels sing before you

with harp and cymbal's joyful
tone;
of one pearl each shining portal,
where we join with the choirs
immortal
of angels round your dazzling
throne.
No eye has seen, nor ear
is yet attuned to hear,
such great glory;
hallelujah, as here we sing
our praise to you, eternal King!

*Philipp Nicolai (1556–1608),*
*tr. Catherine Winkworth (1827–78),*
*alt.*

# 640

**Wake up! the dawn is near;**
**no time for sleeping, this:**
**our God is sending us his gift,**
**his Son, the Lord of bliss.**

1. Come, Lord of all the world,
   creation's source and sum;
   break through these barren,
   wintry skies
   and show your mercy – come!

2. Our sins are multiplied,
   yet yours alone we stand –
   you shaped us as the clay is shaped
   beneath the potter's hand.

3. See how we stray from you,
   so deeply have we sinned,
   swept on by wickedness; like
   leaves
   before the autumn wind.

4. Yet still we trust your word,
   your pardon precious-priced,
   your wisdom sweetly ruling all,
   the chosen one, your Christ.

*Luke Connaughton (1919–79)*

# 641

**We are bound for the promised**
**land,**
**we're bound for the promised land;**
**Oh, who will come and go with us?**
**We are bound for the promised**
**land.**

1. We seek you, Lord, and all your
   strength
   your presence constantly,
   rememb'ring all your marv'lous
   works,
   and all that you can be.

2. You are the Lord, you are the God
   whose judgements fill this earth;
   you're mindful of your covenant;
   we can trust you at your Word.

3. To Abraham you made a vow,
   a promise to his son:
   'I'll give to you the promised land!
   Your inheritance is won.'

4. Give glory to the Father, Son,
   and Spirit, One in Three;
   as it was in the beginning,
   it shall forever be.

*John C. Ylvisaker*
*From Psalm 104(105)*

# 642

**We cry, 'Hosanna, Lord,' yes,**
**'Hosanna, Lord,'**
**yes, 'Hosanna, Lord' to you.**
**We cry, 'Hosanna, Lord,' yes**
**'Hosanna, Lord,'**
**yes, 'Hosanna, Lord,' to you.**

1. Behold, our Saviour comes.
   Behold, the Son of our God.
   He offers himself and he comes
   among us,

a lowly servant to men.

2. Children wave their palms
as the King of all kings rides by.
Should we forget to praise our
God,
the very stones would sing.

3. He comes to set us free.
He gives us liberty.
His vict'ry over death is
th'eternal sign of God's love for
us.

*Mimi Farra*

# 643

1. We form one Church, one
Christian folk,
redeemed by God's own Son;
refreshed by clear and saving
streams,
we share in graces won.
We break the Bread of heaven
to feed us on our way,
we take the cup that holds his
blood
to celebrate his day.

2. We know the kindness of his love;
we know his will to save;
we know he's won the victory
o'er sin and o'er the grave.
To each of us is given
the fullness of his grace,
to live in joy a life of love
until we see his face.

3. Our hope is based on Jesus Christ,
our faith is in his name;
we know he seeks the sinful one,
for that is why he came;
he cares for those who suffer,

he loves both young and old,
a man of sorrows, risen now,
as he himself foretold!

*Willard F. Jabusch*

# 644

1. We gather together to ask the
Lord's blessing,
he chastens and hastens his will
to make known;
the wicked oppressing now cease
from distressing,
sing praises to his Name; he
forgets not his own.

2. Beside us to guide us, our God
with us joining,
ordaining, maintaining his
kingdom divine;
so from the beginning the fight
we were winning:
thou, Lord, wast at our side: all
glory be thine!

3. We all do extol thee, thou leader
triumphant.
And pray that thou still our
defender wilt be.
Let thy congregation escape
tribulation:
thy Name be ever praised! O Lord,
make us free!

*Theodore Baker (1851–1934)*

# 645

1. We praise you and thank you
our Father above,
who offer us peace in your
kingdom of love.
Your people are saved by the

death of your Son
who leads us to glory
where all will be one.
Accepting this Gospel we honour
Saint Patrick,
who taught in our land what
your kindness has done.

2. Your Word has revealed what
our future will be,
'Raised up from the earth
I draw all men to me.'
May we, like Saint Patrick,
bear witness to you,
reflecting your love in whatever
we do.
He came to our country which
once had enslaved him,
to preach the good news that
God makes all things new.

*Donal Murray*

# 646

1. We praise you, God, confessing
you as Lord!
Eternal Father, all earth worships
you!
Angelic choirs, high heavens,
celestial powers,
cherubs and seraphs praise you
ceaselessly:
'All-holy Lord, O God of heavenly
hosts,
your glorious majesty fills heaven
and earth.'

2. Blessed apostles join in praise
of you
with prophets famed and martyrs
clothed in white,
singing with holy Church
throughout the earth:
'Father, we praise your boundless

majesty!
We praise your glorious, true
and only Son!
We praise you, Holy Spirit,
Paraclete!'

3. You are the King of glory,
Jesus Christ!
You are the Father's everlasting
Son!
Born for mankind from lowly
Virgin's womb,
death you have conquered,
opening heaven to faith;
throned now in glory at the
Father's side
you shall return in glory as our
judge.

4. We pray you, therefore, give
your servants aid,
whom you have ransomed with
your precious blood,
let them be ranked in glory
with your saints;
save, Lord, the people who are
wholly yours,
bless them, for they are your
inheritance,
and, as their ruler, ever raise
them up.

5. Throughout each single day,
we bless you Lord,
for all eternity we praise your
name.
Keep us this day, Lord, free
from every sin;
have mercy on us, Lord;
have mercy, Lord;
show us your love, as we have
hoped in you!
You are my hope, Lord; you shall
fail me not!

*Te Deum laudamus,*
*tr. James Quinn, SJ.*

# 647

We thank you, Father, for the gift of faith
through Jesus Christ your son
and for the gift of life with each other
in this our family.
May your Good News be a constant
source of strength and joy,
for all of us who share in your
wonderful love each day.

To live in the Spirit is to grow in
liberty.
Without love our freedom cannot be
real.

*Gregory Norbet, OSB,
and Mary David Callahan, OSB*

# 648

1. Welcome all ye noble saints of old,
   as now before your very eyes
   unfold
   the wonders all so long ago
   foretold.

   **God and man at table are sat
   down. (2)**

2. Elders, martyrs, all are falling
   down,
   prophets, patriarchs are gath'ring
   round;
   what angels longed to see, now
   man has found.

3. Who is this who spreads the vict'ry
   feast?
   Who is this who makes our waring
   cease?
   Jesus risen, Saviour, Prince of
   Peace.

4. Beggars lame, and harlots also
   here;

repentant publicans are drawing
near;
wayward sons come home without
a fear.

5. Worship in the presence of the
   Lord
   with joyful songs, and hearts in
   one accord,
   and let our host at table be adored.

6. When at last this earth shall pass
   away,
   when Jesus and his bride are one
   to stay,
   the feast of love is just begun that
   day.

*Robert J. Stamp*

# 649

1. What child is this, who, laid to
   rest,
   on Mary's lap is sleeping?
   Whom angels greet
   with anthems sweet,
   while shepherds watch are
   keeping?
   This, this is Christ the King,
   whom shepherds guard and angels
   sing:
   come greet the infant Lord,
   the Babe, the Son of Mary!

2. Why lies he in such mean estate,
   where ox and ass are feeding?
   Good Christians, fear:
   for sinners here
   the silent Word is pleading.
   Nails, spear, shall pierce him
   through,
   the cross be born for me, for you:
   hail, hail the Word made flesh,
   the Babe, the Son of Mary!

3. So why bring him incense, gold
   and myrrh,
   come peasant, king, to own him.
   The King of kings
   salvation brings,
   let loving hearts enthrone him.
   Raise, raise the song on high,
   the Virgin sings her lullaby:
   joy, joy for Christ is born,
   the Babe, the Son of Mary!

*W.C. Dix (1837–98)*

# 650

1. What do you ask of me?
   What would you have me do?
   I give myself
   within these gifts I offer you.
   This bread is food for life.
   This wine is spirit of love for you.

2. What can I offer you?
   You've given life to me.
   You're part of all I am.
   What would you have me be?
   This bread is food for life,
   This wine is spirit of love for me.

*Miriam Therese Winter*

# 651

1. When Jesus comes to be baptised,
   he leaves the hidden years behind,
   The years of safety and of peace,
   to bear the sins of all mankind.

2. The Spirit of the Lord comes
   down,
   anoints the Christ to suffering,
   to preach the word, to free the
   bound,
   And to the mourner, comfort
   bring.

3. He will not quench the dying
   flame,
   and what is bruised he will not
   break,
   but heal the wound injustice dealt,
   and out of death his triumph
   make.

4. Our everlasting Father, praise,
   with Christ, his well-beloved Son,
   who with the Spirit reigns serene,
   untroubled Trinity in One.

*The Benedictines of Stanbrook*

# 652

1. When morning gilds the skies,
   my heart awaking cries,
   may Jesus Christ be praised:
   alike at work and prayer
   to Jesus I repair;
   may Jesus Christ be praised.

2. To God, the word on high
   the hosts of angels cry:
   may Jesus Christ be praised!
   let mortals, too, upraise
   their voice in hymns of praise:
   May Jesus Christ be praised!

3. Let earth's wide circle round
   in joyful notes resound:
   May Jesus Christ be praised!
   let air, and sea, and sky,
   from depth to height, reply:
   May Jesus Christ be praised!

4. Does sadness fill my mind?
   A solace here I find,
   may Jesus Christ be praised:
   or fades my earthly bliss?
   My comfort still is this,
   may Jesus Christ be praised.

5. The night becomes as day,
   when from the heart we say,

may Jesus Christ be praised:
the powers of darkness fear,
when this sweet chant they hear,
may Jesus Christ be praised.

6. Be this, while life is mine,
my canticle divine,
may Jesus Christ be praised:
be this the eternal song
through ages all along,
may Jesus Christ be praised.

*German, 19th Century,*
*tr. E. Caswall (1814–78)*

# 653

1. When the time came to stretch
out his arms,
and to lay down his life for his
friends
God's only Son in the breaking
of bread,
gave his own flesh as food for
mankind,
gave his own flesh as food for
mankind.

2. This is my flesh, O take it and eat.
This is my blood, O take it and
drink
and to proclaim my death for
mankind,
this must you do, until I return,
this must you do, until I return.

3. Hunger and thirst no longer we
fear,
Christ's holy flesh becomes now
our food.
And when we raise his chalice
to drink,
joy overflows, our hope is
renewed,
joy overflows, our hope is
renewed.

4. O bread of life, O Banquet Divine,
sign of the love that makes us all
one,
We who now share this gift from
above,
surely have seen the goodness of
God,
surely have seen the goodness of
God.

5. Through Jesus Christ, the perfect
high Priest,
and in the Spirit source of our
peace.
For this great feast which you have
prepared,
Father above, O praised be your
name,
Father above, O praised be your
name.

*Michel Scouarnec,*
*tr. Margaret Daly*

# 654

**Whey he day? Whey he day?**
**Whey he day, mi Lard?**
**Whey he day? Whey he day?**
**Whey he day? mi Lard?**
**Whey he day? Whey he day?**
**Whey he day, mi Lard?**
**Ah cyant fine he, fine he at all.**

1. Ah want to see de man from
Galalee,
Ah want to see de man who set
me free,
Ah want to see de man who died
for me,
Ah cyant fine he, fine he at all.

2. Ah want to see de man who bleed
for me,
Ah want to see de man dey scourge

for me,
Ah want to see dis man from
   Galalee,
Ah cyant fine he, fine he at all.

3. Whey de man who make de bline
      to see?
   Whey de man who set de captive
      free?
   Whey de man who make de lame
      to walk?
   An de li'l dumb boy to talk?

*Anthony Pierre*

# 655

1. Who is she that stands
      triumphant,
   rock in strength, upon the rock,
   like some city crowned with
      turrets,
   braving storm and earthquake
      shock?
   Who is she her arms extending,
   blessing thus a world restored,
   all the anthems of creation
   lifting to creation's Lord?

   **Hers the kingdom, hers the sceptre;**
   **fall, ye nations, at her feet;**
   **hers that truth whose fruit is**
      **freedom;**
   **light her yoke, her burden sweet.**

2. As the moon its splendour
      borrows
   from a sun unseen at night,
   so from Christ, the sun of justice,
   evermore she draws her light.
   Touch'd by his, her hands have
      healing,
   bread of life, absolving key:
   Christ incarnate is her

bridegroom,
God is hers, his temple she.

3. Empires rise and sink like billows,
   vanish, and are seen no more;
   glorious as the star of morning
   she o'erlooks the wild uproar.
   Hers the household all-embracing,
   hers the vine that shadows earth:
   blest thy children, mighty mother;
   safe the stranger at thy hearth.

*Aubrey de Vere (1814–1902)*

# 656

1. Who wants to live as God here
      on this earth *(repeat)*
   must go the way of all seed,
   in doing so find mercy. *(repeat)*

2. Must go the way of all things
      born of earth, *(repeat)*
   must share the fate, with heart
      and soul,
   of all things bound for dying.

   *(repeat)*

3. Both sun and rain will touch each
      of his days: *(repeat)*
   the smallest seed, come rain
      or shine,
   must die so as to live. *(repeat)*

4. So people live to die for one
      another, *(repeat)*
   the smallest seed, as living bread,
   to feed, sustain each other.

   *(repeat)*

5. And that is how our Lord and
      God has shown himself,

   *(repeat)*

   and so becomes his living self
   for each of us on earth. *(repeat)*

*Huub Oosterhuis,*
*tr. Tony Barr*

# 657

A. Wind and fire, the signs of pow'r
   giv'n by God at Pentecost,
   to Apostles, full of joy,
   when their waiting days were past.

1. Wind, which at creation's start
   stirred dark waters into life;
   living Spirit, vital breath,
   breathing life through man and
      wife.

*Repeat Refrain A*

2. Out they burst into the streets;
   stirred the people with their news;
   set explosive in men's minds
   then God's Spirit lit the fuse.

B. Wind and fire, the signs of pow'r
   giv'n by God to us today;
   fire, to set our hearts ablaze:
   wind, to blow our fears away.

3. Hearts ablaze and free from fear,
   we'll amaze the world again,
   and God's wind and fire will still
   surge into the minds of men.

*Repeat Refrain B*

   *Alan Gaunt and John Marsh*

# 658

Would you like to be happy?
Would you like to be good?
Then obey God's law of love,
obey as children should.

1. You should love the Lord your
      God,
   with your head and hand and
      heart;
   you should love the Lord your
      God,
   body, soul and ev'ry part.

2. When your head thinks, think
      with love;
   when your hand works, work
      with love;
   when your heart beats, beat
      with love;
   ev'ry part must work with love.

3. You should love the Lord your
      God,
   you should love him best of all.
   Love all people as yourself
   for he made and loves them all.

   *Source unknown*

# 659

Yahweh, I know you are near,
standing always at my side.
You guard me from the foe
and you lead me in ways
   everlasting.

1. Lord, you have searched my heart
   and you know when I sit and when
      I stand.
   Your hand is upon me, protecting
      me from death,
   keeping me from harm.

2. When can I run from your love?
   If I climb to the heavens, you are
      there.
   If I fly to the sunrise or sail beyond
      the sea
   still I'd find you there.

3. You know my heart and its ways,
   you who formed me before I was
      born,
   in secret of darkness, before I saw
      the sun,
   in my mother's womb.

4. Marvellous to me are your works;
   how profound are your thoughts,
      my Lord!

Even if I could count them, they
number as the stars,
you would still be there.

*Daniel L. Schutte, SJ.*

# 660

1. You, Israel, return now;

   **return to God, your Father,
   your only great Creator;
   return to God, your Father.**

2. You won't be disappointed;

3. Although you have offended;

4. Although your sins are many;

5. He's sure to listen to you;

6. For he is calling to you;

7. Now seek your Lord's
   forgiveness;

8. He calls you all to hear him;

9. And give yourselves to him now;

10. For he is your redeemer;

11. The people's liberator;

12. Return now, O return now;

13. You lonely and you lost ones;

14. Now pray to him his people;

15. And he will quickly answer;

16. So come now all you people;

*Tom Colvin*
*Based on a Tumbuka hymn by N.Z.Tembo*

# 661

1. You must cry out the Word of
   the Lord!
   You must cry out the Word of
   the Lord!
   For you can heal a wounded man,
   or make a poor man rich,
   if you sing out the Word of the
   Lord!

2. You are called to the Word of
   the Lord!
   You are called to the Word of
   the Lord!
   For the Lord has come in power;
   if you believe, he lives in you,
   you must breathe out the Word of
   the Lord!

3. O my people, don't wait any
   longer!
   O my people, don't wait any
   longer!
   For my children are starving
   for my living water,
   you must cry out the Word of
   the Lord!

4. You must cry out the Word of
   the Lord!
   You must cry out the Word of
   the Lord!
   For you can heal a wounded man,
   or make a poor man rich,
   if you give out the Word of the
   Lord!

*Carol Gordon*

# 662

1. You servants of God, now give
   him praise: alleluia!
   Sing out, for his goodness fills our
   days: alleluia!

His name let us praise now and
always: alleluia!

2. His name let us praise eternally:
alleluia!
Sing praise, night and day, on land
and sea: alleluia!
The Lord's name for ever blest will
be: alleluia!

3. Above all creation is the Lord:
alleluia!
By all may he ever be adored:
alleluia!
For God has our fallen life
restored: alleluia!

4. The weak, and the poor, and all in
need: alleluia!
The Lord without fail their pray'r
will heed: alleluia!
Above others they are blest
indeed: alleluia!

5. Give praise to the Father, and the
Son: alleluia!
Give praise to the Spirit, three in
one: alleluia!
Whose reign is for evermore:
alleluia!

*Jean-Paul Lécot*
*Based on Psalm 112(113)*
*tr. R. Kelly and W.R. Lawrence*

# 663

1. You shall cross the barren desert,
but you shall not die of thirst.
You shall wander far in safety
though you do not know the way.
You shall speak your words to
foreign men
and they will understand.
You shall see the face of God
and live.

**Be not afraid, I go before you
always.**
**Come, follow me, and I will give
you rest.**

2. If you pass through raging waters
in the sea,
you shall not drown.
If you walk amid the burning
flames,
you shall not be harmed.
If you stand before the pow'r of
hell
and death is at your side,
know that I am with you through
it all.

3. Blessed are your poor,
for the kingdom shall be theirs
blest are you that weep and
mourn,
for one day you shall laugh.
And if wicked men insult and
hate you
all because of me,
blessed, blessed are you!

*Robert J. Dufford, SJ.*
*Based on Isaiah 43 and Luke 6*

# 664

1. The eyes of the blind shall be
opened,
the ears of the deaf shall hear.
The chains of the lame will be
broken,
streams will flow in deserts of fear.

**Your kingdom come, your will be
done,**
**now that we have become your sons.**
**Let the prayer of our hearts daily
be:**

'God, make us your family;
God make us your family.'

*(Final time, add:)*
God, make us your family.'

2. The ransomed of the Lord shall
    return,
   the islands will sing his songs at
    last.
   The chaff from the wheat shall be
    burned,
   his kingdom on earth it shall come
    to pass.

3. The nations will see their shame,
   the one true God will be adored.
   They turn from their fortune
    and shame,
   his holy mountain shall be
    restored.

*Tim Whipple*
*Based on Isaiah 35*

## THE PSALMS

# 665
*Psalm 8*

**How great is your name, O Lord our
God through all the earth!**

or

**What is mortal man that you care for
him?**

1. Your majesty is praised above the
    heavens;
   on the lips of children and of
    babes
   you have found praise to foil
    your enemy,
   to silence the foe and the rebel.

2. When I see the heavens, the work
    of your hands,
   the moon and stars which you
    arranged,
   what is man that you should keep
    him in mind,
   mortal man, that you care for
    him?

3. Yet you have made him little less
    than a god;
   with glory and honour you
    crowned him,
   gave him power over the works
    of your hand,
   put all things under his feet.

4. All of them, sheep and cattle,
   yes, even the savage beasts,
   birds of the air, and fish
   that make their way through the
    waters.

5. (Give glory to the Father almighty,
   to his Son, Jesus Christ, the Lord,
   to the Spirit who dwells in our
    hearts
   both now and for ever./Amen.)

*The Grail*

# 666
*Psalm 18 (19) 8-15*

**You, O Lord, have the message of
eternal life.**

or

**Your words are spirit, Lord, and they
are life.**

1. The law of the Lord is perfect,
   it revives the soul.
   The rule of the Lord is to be
    trusted,
   it gives wisdom to the simple.

2. The precepts of the Lord are right,
they gladden the heart.
The command of the Lord is clear,
it gives light to the eyes.

3. The fear of the Lord is holy,
abiding for ever.
The decrees of the Lord are truth,
and all of them just.

4. They are more to be desired than
gold,
than the purest of gold;
and sweeter are they than honey,
than honey from the comb.

5. So in them your servant finds in
instruction,
great reward is in their keeping.
But who can detect all his errors?
From hidden faults acquit me.

6. From presumption restrain your
servant,
and let it not rule me.
Then shall I be blameless,
clean from grave sin.

7. May the spoken words of my
mouth,
the thoughts of my heart,
win favour in your sight, O Lord,
my Rescuer, my Rock!

8. (Praise the Father, the Son and
holy Spirit
both now and for ever,
the God who is, who was and who
will be,
world without end.)

*The Grail*

# 667

My shepherd is the Lord, nothing
indeed shall I want.

or

His goodness shall follow me always
to the end of my days.

or

The Lord himself will give me repose.

1. The Lord is my shepherd,
there is nothing I shall want.
Fresh and green are the pastures
where he gives me repose.
near restful waters he leads me,
to revive my drooping spirit.

2. He guides me along the right path:
he is true to his name.
If I should walk in the valley of
darkness
no evil would I fear.
You are there with your crook
and your staff,
with these you give me comfort.

3. You have prepared a banquet
for me
in the sight of my foes.
My head you have anointed
with oil;
my cup is overflowing.

4. Surely goodness and kindness shall
follow me
all the days of my life.
In the Lord's own house shall I
dwell
for ever and ever.

5. (Give glory to the Father
Almighty,
to his Son, Jesus Christ, our Lord,
to the Spirit who dwells in our
hearts.)

*The Grail*

# 668

**Seek the face of the Lord and yearn for him.**

or

**Open wide, O you gates eternal, and let the King of glory enter.**

or

**Hosanna to the Son of David!**

or

**Hosanna in the highest heaven!**

1. The **Lord's** is the **earth** and its **full**ness,
   the **world** and **all** its **peoples.**
   It is **he** who **set** it on the **seas;**
   on the **waters** he **made** it **firm.**

2. Who shall **climb** the **moun**tain
   of the **Lord?**
   Who shall **stand** in his **holy place?**
   The **man** with **clean hands** and
   pure **heart,**
   who **desires** not **worthless things.**

3. He shall re**ceive blessings** from
   the **Lord**
   and **reward** from the **God** who
   **saves** him.
   **Such** are the **men** who **seek** him,
   **seek** the **face** of the **God** of **Jacob.**

4. O **gates,** lift **high** your **heads;**
   grow **higher, ancient doors.**
   let him **enter,** the **king** of **glory!**

5. **Who** is the **king** of **glory?**
   The **Lord,** the **mighty,** the **valiant,**
   the **Lord,** the **valiant** in **war.**

6. O **gates,** lift **high** your **heads;**
   grow **Higher, ancient doors,**
   let him **enter,** the **king** of **glory!**

7. **Who** is **he,** the **king** of **glory?**
   **He,** the **Lord** of **armies,**
   he is the **king** of **glory.**

8. (Give **glory** to **Father Almighty,**
   to his **Son,** Jesus **Christ,** the **Lord,**
   to the **Spirit,** who **dwells** in our
   **hearts.)**

*The Grail*

# 669

**To you, O Lord, I lift up my soul.**

1. Lord, make me <u>know</u> your ways.
   Lord, teach <u>me</u> your paths.
   Make me walk in your <u>truth</u>, and
   teach me:
   for you are <u>God</u> my saviour.

2. Remember your <u>mercy</u>, Lord,
   and the love you have shown <u>from</u>
   of old.
   In your love re<u>member</u> me,
   because of your <u>goodness</u>, O Lord.

3. The Lord is <u>good</u> and upright.
   He shows the path to <u>those</u> who
   stray,
   he guides the humble in <u>the</u> right
   path;
   he teaches his way <u>to</u> the poor.

4. His ways are faithful<u>ness</u> and love
   for those who keep his <u>covenant</u>
   and will.
   The Lord's friendship is for those
   <u>who</u> revere him;
   to them he re<u>veals</u> his covenant.

5. (Glory be to the Father, and <u>to</u>
   the Son,
   and to the <u>Holy</u> Spirit,

as it was in the beginning, is now,|
   and ever shall be,
world without end. Amen.)

# 670   *Ps 26(27):1, 3-5, 7-9, 13-14*

*Accents are for use with the
alternative (simple) setting*

**The Lord is my light and my help.**
or
**One thing I ask of the Lord,
for this I long,
to live in the house of the Lord,
all the days of my life.**
or
**I am sure I shall see the Lord's
goodness in the land of the living.**

1. The Lórd is my light and my hélp.
   When shall I féar?
   The Lórd is the strónghold of my
      life,
   before whóm shall I shrínk?

2. Though ármies do báttle against
      me,
   my héart will not féar.
   Though wár and destrúction
      break fórth,
   even thén would I trúst.

3. For thére in his hoúse I am sáfe,
   in évil's dark hóur.
   He hídes me and shélters my soúl,
   my defénder, my róck.

4. There is óne thing I ásk of the
      Lord,
   for thís I lóng;
   to live in the house of the Lord|
   all the dáys of my life,
   to sávour the sweétness of the
      Lórd,
   to behóld his témple.

5. O Lórd, hear my voíce when I cáll,
   have mércy and ánswer.
   Of yoú my héart has spóken:
   'Seek his fáce'.

6. Your fáce, indeéd I seék it;
   hide it nót from mé.
   Dismiss not your sérvant in ánger,
   for yoú are my hélp.

7. I knów I shall seé the Lord's
      goódness,
   in his prómised lánd.
   Take héart and stand firm, O my
      soúl,
   put your hópe in the Lórd.

*The Grail
(slightly adapted)*

# 671   *Psalm 41 (42): 1-6*

**My soul is thirsting for the Lord.
When shall I see him face to face?**

or

**I will pour clean water over you,
and cleanse you from all your sin.**

1. Like the **deer** that **yearns**
   for **running streams,**
   so my **soul** is **yearning**
   for **you,** my **God.**

2. My **soul** is **thirsting** for **God,**
   the **God** of my **life;**
   **when** can I **enter** and **see**
   the **face** of **God?**

3. My **tears** have be**come** my **bread,**
   by **night,** by **day;**
   as I **hear** it **said** all day **long:**
   '**Where** is your **God?**'

4. **These** things will **I** remember
   as **I pour** out my **soul:**
   how I would **lead** the rejoicing
      **crowd**

into the **house** of **God.**

5. **Why** are you cast **down**, my **soul**,
why **groan** within me?
   Hope in **God,** I will **praise** him
   **still,**
   my **Saviour** and my **God.**

6. (Praise the **Father,** the **Son** and
   Holy **Spirit,**
   both **now** and for ever,
   the God who **is,** who **was** and
   who **will** be,
   **world** without **end.**)

*The Grail*

# 672

*Psalm 42 (43)*

**I will go to the altar of God, praise
the God of my joy.**

or

**Hope in God. I will praise him still,
my Saviour and my God.**

1. **Defend** me, O **God,** and plead my
   **cause**
   against a **godless** nation:
   from **deceitful** and **cunning** men
   **rescue** me, O **God.**

2. Since **you,** O **God,** are my
   **stronghold,**
   **why** have you rejected me?
   **Why** do I go **mourning,**
   **oppressed** by the **foe?**

3. O **send** forth your **light** and your
   **truth,**
   let **these** be my **guide;**
   let them **bring** me to your **holy**
   **mountain,**
   to the **place** where you **dwell.**

4. **And I will come** to the altar of
   **God,**

the **God** of my **joy.**
My **Redeemer,** I will **thank** you
   on the **harp,**
O **God,** my **God!**

5. **Why** are you cast **down,** my **soul,**
why **groan** within me?
   Hope in **God,** I will **praise him still,**
   my **Saviour** and my **God.**

6. (Praise the **Father,** the **Son** and
   Holy **Spirit,**
   both **now** and for ever,
   the God who **is,** who **was** and who
   **will** be,
   **world** without **end.**)

*The Grail*

# 673

*Psalm 50 (51)*

**Have mercy on us, O Lord, for we have
sinned.**

or

**A pure heart create for me, O God.**

1. Have **mercy** on me, **God,** in your
   **kindness.**
   In your **compassion** blot **out** my
   **offence.**
   O **wash** me more and **more** from
   my **guilt**
   and **cleanse** me **from** my **sin.**

2. My **offences** truly I **know** them;
   my **sin** is **always** before me.
   Against **you,** you **alone,** have I
   **sinned;**
   what is evil in your **sight** I have
   **done.**

3. That you may be **justified when**
   you give **sentence**
   and be **without** reproach when you

judge,
O see, in guilt I was born,
a sinner was I conceived.

4. Indeed you love truth in the heart;
   then in the secret of my heart
      teach me wisdom.
   O purify me, then I shall be clean;
   O wash me, I shall be whiter than
      snow.

5. Make me hear rejoicing and
      gladness,
   that the bones you have crushed
      may thrill.
   From my sins turn away your face
   and blot out all my guilt.

6. A pure heart create for me,
      O God,
   put a steadfast spirit within me.
   Do not cast me away from your
      presence,
   nor deprive me of your holy spirit.

7. Give me again the joy of your
      help;
   with a spirit of fervour sustain me,
   that I may teach transgressors
      your ways,
   and sinners may return to you.

8. O rescue me, God, my helper,
   and my tongue shall ring out your
      goodness.
   O Lord, open my lips,
   and my mouth shall declare your
      praise.

9. For in sacrifice you take no
      delight,
   burnt offering from me you would
      refuse,
   my sacrifice, a contrite spirit.
   A humbled, contrite heart you will
      not spurn.

10. (Give glory to the Father
       almighty,
    to his Son, Jesus Christ, the Lord,
    to the Spirit who dwells in our
       hearts,
    both now and for ever. Amen.)

*The Grail*

# 674     *Psalm 62 (63): 1-6, 8-9*

O God, you are my God,
for you my soul is thirsting.

1. O God, you are my God, for you
      I long;
   for you my soul is thirsting.
   My body pines for you
   like a dry, weary land without
      water. (R)

2. So I gaze on you in the sanctuary
   to see your strength and your
      glory.
   For your love is better than life,
   my lips will speak your praise. (R)

3. So I will bless you all my life,
   in your name I will lift up my
      hands.
   My mouth shall be filled as with
      a banquet,
   my mouth shall praise you with
      joy. (R)

4. For you have been my help;
   in the shadow of your wings I
      rejoice.
   My soul clings to you;
   your right hand holds me fast. (R)

5. (Glory be to the Father, and to
      the Son,
   and to the Holy Spirit,
   as it was in the beginning, is now,
      and ever shall be,
   world without end. Amen.)

*The Grail*

# 675

How lovely is your dwelling place,
Lord God of hosts.

or

Lord, God of hosts, happy the man
who trusts in you.

1. My soul is longing and yearning,
   is yearning for the courts of the
   Lord.
   My heart and my soul ring out
   their joy
   to God, the living God.

2. The sparrow herself finds a home
   and the swallow a nest for her
   brood;
   she lays her young by your altars.
   Lord of hosts, my King and my
   God.

3. They are happy who dwell in your
   house,
   for ever singing your praise.
   They are happy, whose strength
   is in you,
   in whose hearts are the roads to
   Sion.

4. As they go through the Bitter
   Valley,
   they make it a place of springs,
   they walk with ever growing
   strength.
   They will see the God of gods in
   Sion.

5. O Lord God of hosts, hear my
   prayer,
   give ear, O God of Jacob.
   Turn your eyes, O God our shield,
   look on the face of your anointed.

6. One day within your courts

is better than a thousand elsewhere.
The threshold of the house of God
I prefer to the dwellings of the
   wicked.

7. For the Lord God is a rampart, a
   shield;
   he will give us his favour and glory.
   The Lord will not refuse any good
   to those who walk without blame.

8. (Give praise to the Father
   Almighty,
   to his Son, Jesus Christ, the Lord,
   to the Spirit who dwells in our
   hearts,
   both now and for ever. Amen.)

*The Grail*

# 676

Let us see O Lord, your mercy
and give us your saving help.

or

Come, Lord, and save us (2)

1. I will hear what the Lord God has
   to say,
   a voice that speaks of peace.
   His help is near for those who fear
   him
   and his glory will dwell in our land.

2. Mercy and faithfulness have met;
   justice and peace have embraced.
   Faithfulness shall spring from the
   earth
   and justice look down from
   heaven.

3. The Lord will make us prosper
   and our earth shall yield its fruit.
   Justice shall march before him
   and peace shall follow his steps.

4. (Give glory to the Father almighty,
   to his Son, Jesus Christ, the Lord,
   to the Spirit who dwells in our hearts
   both now and for ever. Amen.)

*The Grail*

# 677 *Psalm 90 (91)*

**Call upon the Lord and he will hear you,**

or

**Be with me, Lord, in my distress.**

1. He who dwells in the shelter of the Most High
   and abides in the shade of the Almighty
   says to the Lord: 'My refuge,
   my stronghold, my God in whom I trust!'

2. It is he who will free you from the snare
   of the fowler who seeks to destroy you;
   he will conceal you with his pinions
   and under his wings you will find refuge.

3. You will not fear the terror of the night
   nor the arrow that flies by day,
   nor the plague that prowls in the darkness
   nor the scourge that lays waste at noon.

4. A thousand may fall at your side,
   ten thousand fall at your right,
   you, it will never approach;
   his faithfulness is buckler and shield.

5. Your eyes have only to look
   to see how the wicked are repaid,
   you who have said: 'Lord, my refuge!'
   and have made the Most High your dwelling.

6. Upon you no evil shall fall,
   no plague approach where you dwell.
   For you has he commanded his angels,
   to keep you in all your ways.

7. They shall bear you upon their hands
   lest you strike your foot against a stone.
   On the lion and the viper you will tread
   and trample the young lion and the dragon.

8. His love he set on me, so I will rescue him;
   protect him for he knows my name.
   When he calls I shall answer: 'I am with you.'
   I will save him in distress and give him glory.

9. With length of life I will content him;
   I shall let him see my saving power.
   (To the Father, the Son and Holy Spirit
   give praise for ever./Amen.)

*The Grail*

# 678 *Psalm 92 (93)*

**The Lord is King for evermore.**

or

**Alleluia, alleluia, alleluia!**

1. The Lord is king, with majesty

enrobed;
the Lord has robed himself with
   might,
he has girded himself with power.

2. The world you made firm,
      not to be moved;
   your throne has stood firm from
      of old;
   from all eternity, O Lord, you are.

3. The waters have lifted up, O Lord,
   the waters have lifted up their
      voice,
   the waters have lifted up their
      thunder.

4. Greater than the roar of mighty
      waters,
   more glorious than the surgings
      of the sea,
   the Lord is glorious on high.

5. Truly, your decrees are to be
      trusted.
   Holiness is fitting to your house,
   O Lord, until the end of time.

6. (Give glory to the Father
      Almighty,
   to his Son, Jesus Christ, the Lord,
   to the Spirit who dwells in our
      hearts.)
                              *The Grail*

# 679     *Psalm 94 (95)*

O come, let us worship the Lord.

or

O that today you would listen to his
voice:
harden not your hearts.

1. Come, ring out our joy to the Lord;
   hail the Rock who saves us.

Let us come before him, giving
   thanks,
with songs let us hail the Lord.

2. A mighty God is the Lord,
   a great king above all gods;
   in his hand are the depths of the
      earth;
   the heights of the mountains are
      his.
   To him belongs the sea, for he
      made it,
   and the dry land shaped by his
      hands.

3. Come in, let us bow and bend low;
   let us kneel before the God who
      made us,
   for he is our God and we
   the people who belong to his
      pasture,
   the flock that is led by his hand.

4. O that today you would listen to
      his voice!
   'Harden not your hearts as at
      Meribah,
   as on that day at Massah in the
      desert
   when your fathers put me to the
      test,
   when they tried me, though they
      saw my work.'

5. For forty years I was wearied of
      these people
   and I said: 'Their hearts are astray,
   these people do not know my ways.'
   Then I took an oath in my anger:
   'Never shall they enter my rest.'

6. Give glory to the Father
      Almighty,
   to his Son, Jesus Christ, the Lord,
   to the Spirit who dwells in our
      hearts,
   both now and for ever. Amen.
                              *The Grail*

# 680

*Psalm 99 (100)*

Arise, come to your God, sing him your
songs of rejoicing.

or

We are his people, the sheep of his
flock.

or

Alleluia, alleluia, alleluia!

1. Cry out with joy to the Lord, all
   the earth.
   Serve the Lord with gladness.
   Come before him, singing for joy.

2. Know that he, the Lord is God.
   He made us, belong to him,
   we are his people, the sheep of his
   flock.

3. Go within his gates, giving thanks.
   Enter his courts with songs of
   praise.
   Give thanks to him and bless his
   name.

4. Indeed, how good is the Lord,
   eternal his merciful love;
   he is faithful from age to age.

5. (Give glory to the Father
   Almighty,
   to his Son, Jesus Christ, the Lord,
   to the Spirit who dwells in our
   hearts.)
                                    *The Grail*

# 681

*Psalm 102 (103): 1-4, 8, 10, 12-13*

The Lord is compassion and love,
alleluia, alleluia.

or

The Lord has set his sway in heaven,
alleluia, alleluia.

1. My soul, give thanks to the Lord,
   all my being, bless his holy name.
   My soul, give thanks to the Lord
   and never forget all his blessings.

2. It is he who forgives all your guilt,
   who heals every one of your ills,
   who redeems your life from the
   grave,
   who crowns you with love and
   compassion.

3. The Lord is compassion and love,
   slow to anger and rich in mercy.
   He does not treat us according to
   our sins
   nor repay us according to our
   faults.

4. As far as the east is from the west
   so far does he remove our sins.
   As a father has compassion on his
   sons,
   the Lord has pity on those who
   fear him.

5. (Give glory to the Father
   almighty,
   to his Son, Jesus Christ, the Lord,
   to the Spirit who dwells in our
   hearts
   both now and for ever./Amen.)
                                    *The Grail*

# 682

*Psalm 103 (104) 1-2, 5-6,
24, 27-30, 10-14,*

Send forth your Spirit, O Lord,
and renew the face of the earth.

1. Bless the Lord, my soul!
   Lord God, how great you are,

clothed in majesty and glory,
wrapped in light as in a robe!

2. You founded the earth on its base,
to stand firm from age to age.
You wrapped it with the ocean
like a cloak:
the waters stood higher than the
mountains.

3. You make springs gush forth in the
valleys:
they flow in between the hills.
On their banks dwell the birds
of heaven;
from the branches they sing
their song.

4. From your dwelling you water
the hills;
earth drinks its fill of your gift.
You make the grass grow for the
cattle
and the plants to serve man's
needs.

5. How many are your works, O
Lord!
In wisdom you made them all.
The earth is full of your riches.
Bless the Lord, my soul!

6. All creatures look to you
to give them their food in due
season.
You give it, they gather it up:
you open your hand, they have
their fill.

7. You take back your spirit, they die,
returning to the dust from which
they came.
You send forth your spirit, they
are created;
and you renew the face of the
earth.

8. May the glory of the Lord last for
ever!
May the Lord rejoice in his works!
May my thoughts be pleasing to
him.
I find my joy in the Lord.

9. (Give glory to the Father
almighty,
to his Son, Jesus Christ, the Lord,
to the Spirit who dwells in our
hearts
both now and for ever./Amen.)

*The Grail*

# 683     *Psalms 114/115 (116)*

**I will walk in the presence of the Lord
in the land of the living.**

or

**How can I repay the Lord for his
goodness?**

1. I love the Lord for he has heard
the cry of my appeal;
for he turned his ear to me
in the day when I called him.

2. They surrounded me, the snares of
death,|
with the anguish of the tomb;
they caught me, sorrow and
distress.
I called on the Lord's name.
O Lord my God, deliver me!

3. How gracious is the Lord, and
just;
our God has compassion.
The Lord protects the simple
hearts;
I was helpless so he saved me.

4. He has kept my <u>soul</u> from death,
my eyes from tears|
and my <u>feet</u> from stumbling.
I will walk in the presence <u>of</u> the
    Lord
in the land <u>of</u> the living.

5. (Glory be to the Father, and <u>to</u>
    the Son,
and to the <u>Holy</u> Spirit,
as it was in the beginning, is now,|
    and <u>ev</u>er shall be,
world without <u>end</u>. Amen.)

*The Grail*

# 684        *Psalm 115*

1. My vows to the Lord I <u>will</u> fulfill
before <u>all</u> his people.
O precious in the eyes <u>of</u> the Lord
is the death <u>of</u> his faithful.

2. Your servant, Lord, your serv<u>ant</u>
    am I;
you have loos<u>ened</u> my bonds.
A thanksgiving sacri<u>fice</u> I make:
I will call on the Lor<u>d</u>'s name.

3. My vows to the Lord I <u>will</u> fulfill
before <u>all</u> his people,
in the courts of the house <u>of</u> the
    Lord,
in your midst, <u>O</u> Jerusalem.

4. I trusted, even <u>when</u> I said:
'I am sore<u>ly</u> afflicted,'
and when I said in <u>my</u> alarm:
'No man <u>can</u> be trusted.'

5. How can I re<u>pay</u> the Lord
for his good<u>ness</u> to me?
The cup of salvation <u>I</u> will raise;
I will call on the Lor<u>d</u>'s name.

6. (Glory be to the Father, and <u>to</u>
    the Son,

and to the <u>Holy</u> Spirit,
as it was in the beginning, is now,|
    and <u>ev</u>er shall be,
world without end. Amen.)

*The Grail*

# 685        *Psalm 116 (117)*

**Alleluia, alleluia.**

*Response is repeated throughout.*

*Meanwhile, choir/cantor sings:*

O praise the Lord, all you nations,
acclaim him, all you peoples!
Strong is his love for us;
he is faithful for ever.

*Repeat ad libitum.*

*Final time coda:*

Alleluia!        *The Grail*

# 686

*Psalm 117 (118) 1-2, 16-17, 22-23*

**Alleluia, alleluia, alleluia!**

or

**This day was made by the Lord;
we rejoice and we are glad.**

1. Give thanks to the Lord
for he is good,
for his love has no end.
Let the sons of Israel say:
'His love has no end
his love has no end.'

2. The Lord's right hand
has triumphed;
his right hand raised me up.

I shall not die, I shall live
and recount his deeds,
recount his deeds.

3. The stone which the
     builders rejected
has become the corner stone.
This is the work of the Lord,
a marvel in our eyes,
a marvel in our eyes.

*The Grail*

# 687
*Psalm 121*

Give your peace, O Lord, to those
     who count on you.

or

I rejoiced when I heard them say:
     Let us go to God's house!

or

Let us go to God's house, rejoicing.

1. I rejoic'd when I heard them say:
     'Let us go to God's house.
     And now our feet are standing
          within your gates,
     O Jerusalem.'

2. Jerusalem is built as a city
     strongly compact.
     It is there that the tribes go up,
          the tribes
     of the Lord.

3. For Israel's law it is
     there to praise the Lord's name.
     There were set the thrones of
          judgement, of the
     house of David.

4. For the peace of Jerusalem, pray:
     'Peace be to your homes!'
     May peace reign in your walls, in

your
palaces, peace!'

5. (Praise the Father, the Son and
          Holy Spirit,
     both now and forever:
     the God who is, who was and who
          will be,
     world without end.)

*The Grail*

# 688
*Psalm 125 (126)*

Those who sow in tears and sorrow,
     one day will reap with joy.

or

What marvels the Lord worked for us!
Indeed we were glad.

1. When the Lord delivered Sion
          from bondage,
     it seemed like a dream.
     Then was our mouth filled with
          laughter,
     on our lips there were songs.

2. The heathens themselves said:
          'What marvels
     the Lord worked for them!'
     What marvels the Lord worked
          for us!
     Indeed, we were glad.

3. Deliver us, O Lord, from our
          bondage,
     as streams in dry land.
     Those who sow in tears
     will sing when they reap.

4. They go out, they go out, full of
          tears,
     carrying seed for the sowing;
     they come back, they come back,
          full of song,
     carrying their sheaves.

5. (Praise the Father, the Son and
      Holy Spirit,
   both now and for ever,
   the God who is, who was and who
      will be,
   world without end.)

*The Grail*

# 689

*Psalm 129 (130)*

I place all my trust in you my God,
all my hope is in your saving word.

or

I wait for the Lord; I count on his word.

or

With the Lord there is mercy
   and fullness of redemption.

1. Out of the depths I cry to you,
      O Lord,
   Lord, hear my voice!
   O let your ears be attentive
   to the voice of my pleading.

2. If you, O Lord, should mark
      our guilt,
   Lord, who would survive?
   But with you is found forgiveness:
   for this we revere you.

3. My soul is waiting for the Lord,
   I count on his word:
   my soul is longing for the Lord
   more than watchman for
      day-break.

4. Because with the Lord there is
      mercy
   and fullness of redemption,
   Israel indeed he will redeem
   from all its iniquity.

5. (To the Father almighty give glory,
   give glory to his Son,

to the Spirit most holy give praise,
whose reign is for ever.)

*The Grail*

# 690

*Psalm 135 (136)*

1. O give thanks to the Lord for he is
      good,
   great is his love, love without end.
   Give thanks to the God of gods,
   great is his love, love without end.
   Give thanks to the Lord of lords,
   great is his love, love without end.

2. Who alone has wrought
      marvellous works,
   great is his love, love without end;
   whose wisdom it was made the
      skies,
   great is his love, love without end;
   who fixed the earth on the seas,
   great is his love, love without end.

3. It was he who made the great
      lights,
   great is his love, love without end,
   the sun to rule in the day,
   great is his love, love without end,
   the moon and stars in the night
   great is his love, love without end.

4. The first-born of the Egyptians he
      smote,
   great is his love, love without end.
   He brought Israel out from their
      midst,
   great is his love, love without end;
   arm outstretched, with power in
      his hand,
   great is his love, love without end.

5. He divided the Red Sea in two,
   great is his love, love without end;
   he made Israel pass through the
      midst,

great is his love, love without end;
flung Pharoah and his force in the
sea,
great is his love, love without end.

6. Through the desert his people he
led,
great is his love, love without end.
Nations in their greatness he
struck,
great is his love, love without end.
Kings in their splendour he slew,
great is his love, love without end.

7. He let Israel inherit their land,
great is his love, love without end.
On his servant their land he
bestowed,
great is his love, love without end.
He remembered us in our distress,
great is his love, love without end.

8. And he snatched us away from our
foes,
great is his love, love without end.
He gives food to all living things,
great is his love, love without end.
To the God of heaven give thanks,
great is his love, love without end.

*The Grail*

# 691 *Psalm 144 (145) 1-2, 8-18*

**I will bless your name for ever,
O God my King.**

or

**You open wide your hand; O Lord,
you grant our desires.**

1. I will give you glory, O God my
King.
I will bless your name for ever.
I will bless you day after day
and praise your name for ever.

2. The Lord is kind and full of
compassion,
slow to anger, abounding in love.
How good is the Lord to all,
compassionate to all his creatures.

3. All your creatures shall thank you,
O Lord,
and your friends shall repeat their
blessing.
They shall speak of the glory of
your reign
and declare your might, O God.

4. To make known to men your
mighty deeds
and the glorious splendour of
your reign.
Yours is an everlasting kingdom;
your rule lasts from age to age.

5. The Lord is faithful in all his
words
and loving in all his deeds.
The Lord supports all who fall
and raises all who are bowed
down.

6. The eyes of all creatures look to
you
and give them their food in due
time.
You open wide your hand,
grant the desires of all who live.

7. The Lord is just in all his ways
and loving in all his deeds.
He is close to all who call him,
who call on him from their hearts.

8. (Glory be to the Father, and to
the Son,
and to the Holy Spirit,
as it was in the beginning, is now,
and ever shall be,
world without end. Amen.)

*The Grail*

# 692

**Alleluia, alleluia, alleluia.**

1. Praise God for his holy dwelling;
   praise him on his mighty throne;
   praise him for his wonderful
      deeds;
   praise him for his sov'reign
      majesty.

2. Praise him with the blast of
      trumpet;
   praise him now with lyre and
      harps;
   praise him with the timbrel and
      dance;
   praise him with the sound of string
      and reed.

3. Praise him with resounding
      cymbals;
   with cymbals that crash give
      praise;
   O let everything that has breath,
   let all living creatures praise the
      Lord.

4. Praise God the almighty Father;
   praise Christ his beloved Son;
   give praise to the Spirit of love,
   for ever the triune God be praised.

*Omer Westendorf*

# 693

### The Benedictus

Blessed be the Lord, the God of
   Israel!
He has visited his people and
   redeemed them.

He has raised up for us a mighty
saviour
in the house of David his servant,
as he promised by the lips of holy
   men,
those who were his prophets from
   of old.

A saviour who would free us from
   our foes,
from the hands of all who hate us.
So his love for our fathers is fulfilled
and his holy covenant remembered.

He swore to Abraham our father to
   grant us,
that free from fear, and saved from
   the hands of our foes,
we might serve him in holiness and
   justice
all the days of our life in his presence.

As for you, little child,
you shall be called a prophet of God,
   the Most High.
You shall go ahead of the Lord
to prepare his ways before him.

To make known to his people their
   salvation
through forgiveness of all their sins,
the loving-kindness of the heart of
   our God
who visits us like the dawn from on
   high.

He will give light to those in darkness
those who dwell in the shadow of
   death,
and guide us into the way of peace.

Glory be to the Father, and to the
   Son,
and to the Holy Spirit,
as it was in the beginning, is now and
   ever shall be,
world without end, Amen.

*The Grail*

# 694

## The Magnificat (Luke 1: 46-55)

**The Lord has done marvels for me, holy is his name.**

1. My soul glorifies the Lord,
   my spirit rejoices in God, my
   Saviour.

2. He looks on his servant in her
   nothingness;
   henceforth all ages will call me
   blessed.

3. The Almighty works marvels for
   me.
   Holy his name!

4. His mercy is from age to age,
   on those who fear him.

5. He puts forth his arm in strength
   and scatters the proud-hearted.

6. He casts the mighty from their
   thrones
   and raises the lowly.

7. He fills the starving with good
   things,
   sends the rich away empty.

8. He protects Israel, his servant,
   remembering his mercy.

9. The mercy promised to our
   fathers,
   for Abraham and his sons for ever.

10. (Praise the Father, the Son, and
    Holy Spirit,
    both now and forever, world
    without end.)
    *The Grail*

*Other settings of the Magnificat
are numbers 414, 479 and 749*

# 695

## Nunc Dimittis (Luke 2- 29-32)

**Guard us, O Lord, while we sleep
and keep us in peace.**

or

**My eyes have seen your salvation:
the light of all peoples.**

1. At last, all powerful Master,
   you give leave to your servant to
   go
   in peace, according to your
   promise.

2. For my eyes have seen your
   salvation
   which you have prepared for all
   nations
   the light to enlighten the Gentiles
   and give glory to Israel, your
   people.

3. Give praise to the Father almighty,
   to his Son, Jesus Christ, the Lord.
   to the Spirit, who dwells in our
   hearts,
   both now and forever. Amen.
   *The Grail*

*Another setting of the Nunc Dimittis
is number 561*

# ROUNDS, CANONS AND REFRAINS

## 696

Adoramus te Domine.

*MUSIC: see after hymn 723*

## 697
## 698

These are settings of the Alleluia which are found in the melody line and full music editions.

## 699

**The Beatitudes (Mt 5:3-10)**

**Blessed are they who follow God's law**
**and walk in his way:**
**the Kingdom is theirs.**

*The chorus is sung continuously. The cantor sings verses as required.*

1. Blest the poor in spirit,
   for theirs is the kingdom of Heaven.

2. Blest the gentle,
   for they shall inherit the earth.

3. Blest those who mourn,
   for they shall be comforted.

4. Blest those who hunger and thirst for justice,
   for they shall be satisfied.

5. Blest the merciful
   for they shall have mercy shown them.

6. Blest the pure in heart,
   for they shall see God.

7. Blest the peacemakers
   for they shall be called sons of God.

8. Blest those who suffer for righteousness,
   for theirs is the kingdom of Heaven.

*Stephen Dean*

## 700

1. Breath of life overflow in us, crying:
   at last we are born again.

2. Breath of life overflow in us, laughing:
   at last we are born again.

3. Breath of life overflow in us, knowing:
   at last we are born again.

*Huub Oosterhuis*
*tr. Tony Barr*

## 701

1. Dona nobis pacem, pacem.
   Dona nobis pacem.

2. Dona nobis pacem.
   Dona nobis pacem.

3. Dona nobis pacem.
   Dona nobis pacem.

# 702

Glory be to God the Father, God
  the Father,
God the Son and Holy Spirit, Holy
  Spirit,
as it was and shall be evermore.

# 703

[1]Go out to the [2] whole world,
  [3] proclaim the [4] Good News.

*(Mark 16: 15)*

# 704

[1]I rejoiced[2] when [3]I heard them say
'Let us go to God's house.'
Alleluia!

*Psalm 121 (122):1*

# 705

1. Jesus Christ, little Lord,
  God and Saviour he,
  born into this sinful world
  to set the people free.

2. Sing, Jesus come to us
  and teach us how to pray,
  we will share your joy and love,
  and peace this Christmas Day.

*Roger Humphrey*

# 706

Jubilate Deo, jubilate Deo, alleluia.
*MUSIC: see after hymn 723*

# 707

[1]Jubilate Deo [2]omnis terra.
Servite Domino in laetitia.
Alleluia, alleluia, in laetitia.
Alleluia, alleluia, in laetitia!
*MUSIC: see after hymn 723*

# 708

[1]Let us go forth into the world
[2]with the good news, spreading his
  word, for we're
[3]Easter people, saved by Christ.

*Estelle White*

# 709

**Misericordias Domini in aeternum
cantabo.**

1. From age to age through all
  generations,
  my mouth shall proclaim your
  truth, O Lord.

2. Who, O God, who in the universe
  can compare with you?

3. Blest be the Lord for ever,
  throughout eternity. Amen!
  Amen!
*MUSIC: see after hymn 723*

*From Psalm 88 (89)*
*Taizé*

# 710

O Lord, hear my prayer,
O Lord, hear my prayer:
when I call, answer me.
O Lord, hear my prayer,
O Lord, hear my prayer.
Come and listen to me.
*MUSIC: see after hymn 723*

*Taizé*

# 711

Ostende nobis Domine,
    misericordiam tuam. Amen!
    Amen!
Maranatha! Maranatha!

*MUSIC: see after hymn 723*

*Taizé*

# 712

1. Sing alleluia to the Lord.
2. Sing alleluia to the Lord.
1. Sing alleluia to the Lord.
2. Sing alleluia.
1. Sing alleluia, sing alleluia,
2. Alleluia.
1 & 2. Sing alleluia to the Lord.

*Linda Stassen*

# 713

¹Sing and rejoice in the
²Lord in your hearts with
    thanksgiving,
³sing and rejoice in him.

*Hermann Stern*

# 714

¹Stand and stare not at what used to
    be
²and remain not in the past. For
³I, says he, make new beginnings.
    Look,
⁴all things are new now, do you not
    see?

*Huub Oosterhuis*
*tr. tony Barr*

## LATIN HYMNS

# 715 Christus Vincit

Christus vincit: Christus regnat:
    Christus imperat.
**Christus vincit: Christus regnat:**
    **Christus imperat.**
Exaudi Christe.
**Exaudi Christe.**
Summo Pontifici et universali Papae
    vita.
**Salvator mundi:**
**tu illum adjuva.**
Sancta Maria:
**tu illum adjuva.**
Sancte Petre:
**tu illum adjuva.**
Sancte Paule:
**tu illum adjuva.**
Sancte Gregori:
**tu illum adjuva.**
**Christus vincit: Christus regnat:**
    **Christus imperat.**
Rex regnum!
**Christus vincit.**
Rex noster!
**Christus regnat.**
Gloria nostra!
**Christus imperat.**
Ipsi soli imperium
gloria et potestas,
per immortalia saecula saeculorum.
    Amen.
**Christus vincit: Christus regnat:**
    **Christus imperat.**

*9th Century*

# 716 Pange Lingua

1. Pange, lingua, gloriosi
   corporis mysterium,
   sanguinisque pretiosi,
   quem in mundi pretium
   fructus ventris generosi
   Rex effudit gentium.

2. Nobis datus, nobis natus
   ex inacta Virgine;
   et in mundo conversatus,
   sparso verbi semine,
   sui moras incolatus
   miro clausit ordine.

3. In supremae nocte coenae
   recumbens cum fratribus,
   observata lege plene
   cibis in legalibus:
   cibum turbae duodenae
   se dat suis manibus.

4. Verbum caro, panem verum
   Verbo carnem efficit:
   fitque sanguis Christi merum;
   et si sensus deficit,
   ad firmandum cor sincerum
   sola fides sufficit.

5. Tantum ergo Sacramentum
   veneremur cernui:
   et antiquum documentum
   novo cedat ritui:
   praestet fides supplementum
   sensuum defectui.

6. Genitori, genitoque
   laus, et jubilatio,
   salus, honor, virtus quoque
   sit et benedictio:
   procendenti ab utroque
   compar sit laudatio. Amen.

*St Thomas Aquinas (1227–74)*

# 717 Regina cæli

Regina cæli, lætare, alleluia,
quia quem meruisti portare, alleluia,
resurrexit sicut dixit, alleluia.
Ora pro nobis Deum, alleluia.

*Author Unknown*
*(11th Century)*

# 718 Salve Regina

Salve Regina, Mater misericordiæ:
vita dulcedo, et spes nostra, salve.
Ad te clamamus, exules filii hevæ.
Ad te suspiramus, gementes et
   flentes,
in hac lacrimarum vale.
Eja ergo, Advocata nostra,
illos tuos misericordes oculos
ad nos converte.
Et Jesum benedictum fructum
   ventris tui,
nobis post hoc exsilium ostende.
O clemens, O pia, O dulcis Virgo
   Maria.

*Author Unknown*
*(11th Century)*

# 719 Te Deum Laudamus

Te Deum laudamus: te Dominum
   confitemur.
Te æternum Patrem omnis terra
   veneratur.
Tibi omnes Angeli, tibi cæli et
   universæ potestates:
tibi Cherubim et Seraphim
   incessabili voce proclaimant:
Sanctus: Sanctus: Sanctus
   Dominus Deus Sabaoth.
Pleni sunt cæli et terra majestatis

gloriæ.
Te gloriosus Apostolorum chorus:
Te Prophetatum laudabilis numerus:
Te Martyrum candidatus laudat
exercitus.
Te per orbem terrarum sancta
confitetur Ecclesia:
Patrem immensæ majestatis:
Venerandum tuum verum et unicum
Filium:
Sanctum quoque Paraclitum
Spiritum.
Tu Rex gloriæ, Christe.
Tu Patris sempiternus es Filius.
Tu ad liberandum suscepturus
hominem,
non horruisti Virginis uterum.
Tu devicto mortis aculeo,
aperuisti credentibus regna cælorum.
Tu ad dexteram Dei sedes, in gloria
Patris.
Judex crederis esse venturus.
Te ergo quæsumus, tuis famulis
subveni,
quos pretioso sanguine redemisti.
Æterna fac cum sanctis tuis in gloria
numerari.
Salvum fac populum tuum Domine,
et benedic hære ditate tuæ.
Et rege eos, et extolle illos usque in
æternum.
Per singulos dies, benedicimus te.
Et laudamus nomen tuum in
sæculum, et in sæculum sæculi.
Dignare Domine die isto
sine peccato nos custodire.
Miserere nostri Domine, miserere
nostri.
Fiat misericordia tua Domine super
nos,
quem admodum speravimus in te.
In te Domine speravi:
non confundar in æternum.
*Author Unknown (4th Century)*

# 720 Veni, Creator Spiritus

1. Veni, Creator Spiritus,
   mentes tuorum visita,
   imple superna gratia,
   quae tu creasti pectora.

2. Qui diceris Paraclitus,
   Altissimi donum Dei,
   fons vivus, ignis, caritas,
   et spiritalis unctio.

3. Tu septiformis munere,
   digitus paternae dexterae,
   tu rite promissum Patris,
   sermone ditans guttura.

4. Accende lumen sensibus,
   infunde amorem codibus,
   infirma nostri corporis
   virtute firmans perpeti.

5. Hostem repellas longius,
   pacemque dones protinus:
   ductore sic te praevio,
   vitemus omne noxium.

6. Per te sciamus, da, Patrem,
   noscamus atque Filium,
   teque utriusque Spiritum
   credamus omni tempore.

*Attr. to Rabanus Maurus (766–856)*

# 721 Victimae paschali laudes

Victimae paschali laudes
immolent Christiani.
Agnus redemit oves:
Christus innocens Patri
reconciliavit peccatores.
Mors et vita duello
conflixere mirando:
dux vitae mortuus
regnat vivus.

Dic nobis Maria
quid vidisti in via?
Sepulchrum Christi viventis
et gloriam vidi resurgentis:
Angelicos testes
sudarium et vestes.

Surrexit Christus spes mea:
praecedit suos in Galilaeam.
Scimus Christum surrexisse
a mortuis vere:
tu nobis, victor Rex, miserere.
Amen. (Alleluia.)

*Attr. to Wipo of Burgundy*
*(10th Century)*

## NATIONAL SONGS

# 722

1. I vow to thee, my country,
all earthly things above,
entire and whole and perfect,
the service of my love;
the love that asks no question,
the love that stands the test,
that lays upon the altar,
the dearest and the best;
the love that never falters,
the love that pays the price,
the love that makes undaunted
the final sacrifice.

2. And there's another country,
I've heard of long ago,
most dear to them that love her,
most great to them that know;
we may not count her armies,
we may not see her King;
her fortress is a faithful heart,
her pride is suffering;
and soul by soul and silently
her shining bounds increase,
and her ways are ways of
gentleness
and all her paths are peace.

*Sir Cecil Spring-Rice*

# 723

God save our gracious Queen,
Long live our noble Queen,
God save the Queen.
Send her victorious,
Happy and glorious,
Long to reign over us:
God save the Queen.

Thy choicest gifts in store
On her be pleased to pour,
Long may she reign.
May she defend our laws,
And ever give us cause
To sing with heart and voice,
God save the Queen.

# MUSIC for TAIZE CHANTS

**710**

O Lord hear my pray'r, O Lord hear my pray'r; when I call,

an - swer me. O Lord hear my pray'r, O Lord hear my pray'r.

Come and li - sten to me. O

**711**

*Principal Canon*

Os - ten - de no - bis Do - mi — ne, mi - se - ri - cor - di - am tu -

am. A - men! A - men! Ma - ra - na - tha! Ma - ra - na - tha! Os - ten - de. - tha.

A   Dm   Gm   A   A

*Guitar*

# NEW SONGS
# OF CELEBRATION

## Edited By
## Stephen Dean

**McCRIMMONS**
Great Wakering, Essex, England.

# 724 (1)

**All the ends of the earth**
**have seen the power of God;**
**All the ends of the earth**
**have seen the power of God.**

1 Sing to the Lord a new song,
  for he has done wondrous deeds;
  his right hand has won the vict'ry
     for him,
  his holy arm.

2 The Lord has made his salvation
     known,
  his justice revealed to all.
  Remembered his kindness and
     faithfulness
  to Israel.

3 All of the ends of earth have seen
  salvation by our God.
  Joyfully sing out all you lands,
  break forth in song.

4 Sing to the Lord with harp
     and song,
  with trumpet and with horn.
  Sing in your joy before the king,
  the king, our lord.

*Psalm 97 (98) 1-6 (R.v.4)*
*Adapted by David Haas and*
*Marty Haugen*

# 725 (2)

1 Awake! awake, and greet the new
     morn,
  for angels herald its dawning,
  sing out your joy, for soon he is
     born,
  Behold! the Child of our longing.

Come as a baby weak and poor,
to bring all hearts together,
he opens wide the heav'nly door
and lives now inside us for ever.

2 To us, to all in sorrow and fear,
  Emmanuel comes a-singing,
  his humble song is quiet and near,
  yet fills the earth with its ringing;
  music to heal the broken soul
  and hymns of loving kindness,
  the thunder of his anthems roll
  to shatter all hatred and blindness.

3 In darkest night his coming shall
     be,
  when all the earth is desparing,
  as morning light so quiet and free,
  so warm and gentle and caring.
  Then shall the mute break forth in
     song,
  the lame shall leap in wonder,
  the weak be raised above the
     strong,
  and weapons be broken asunder.

4 Rejoice, rejoice, take heart in the
     night,
  though dark the winter and cheer-
     less,
  the rising sun shall crown you with
     light,
  be strong and loving and fearless;
  love be our song and love our
     prayer,
  and love, our endless story,
  may God fill every day we share,
  and bring us at last into glory.

*Marty Haugen*

# 726 (3)

**As a tree planted
by streams of water,
is the one who delights
in the word of the Lord.**

1 Blessed are the poor in spirit,
  theirs is the Kingdom of heaven;
  Blessed are the ones who mourn,
  for they shall be comforted.

2 Blessed are the meek and lowly,
  they shall inherit the earth;
  Blessed are those who thirst for
      good,
  for they shall be satisfied.

3 Blessed are the merciful, for
  they shall have mercy shown
      them;
  Blessed are the pure in heart,
  for they shall see their God.

4 Blessed are the peaceful hearts, for
  they shall be called God's
      children;
  Bless'd those suff'ring for
      righteousness,
  the Kingdom of heaven is theirs.

*Refrain: Psalm 1:1,
verses Mt 5:1–112,
versified by Marty Haugen*

# 727 (4)

1 Before the heaven and earth
  were made by God's decree,
  the Son of God all glorious dwelt
  in God's eternity.

2 Though in the form of God
  and rich beyond compare,
  he did not stop to grasp his prize;
  nor did he linger there.

3 From heights of heaven he came
  to this world full of sin,
  to meet with hunger, hatred, hell,
  our life, our love to win.

4 The Son became true man
  and took a servant's role;
  with lowliness and selfless love,
  he came, to make us whole.

5 Obedient to his death
  that death upon the cross,
  no son had ever shown such love,
  nor father known such loss.

6 To him enthroned on high,
  by angel hosts adored,
  all knees shall bow, and tongues
      confess
  that Jesus Christ is Lord.

*Brian Black, from Philippians 2:6-11*

# 728 (5)

♩ = 76

Bless the Lord my soul and bless his ho-ly name.

Bless the Lord my soul, he res-cues me from death.

1 It is he who forgives all your guilt,
   who heals ev'ry one of your ills,
   who redeems your life from the
       grave,
   who crowns you with love and
       compassion.

2 The Lord is compassion and love,
   slow to anger and rich in mercy.
   He does not treat us according to
       our sins
   nor repay us according to our
       faults.

3 As a Father has compassion on his
       children,
   the Lord has pity on those who
       fear him;
   for he knows of what we are made,
   he remembers that we are dust.

*Psalm 102 (103):3-4.8,10.13-14*
*(R.cf.v.1)*
*Verses from the Grail Psalter.*
*Response from Taizé.*

# 729 (6)

1 Christ's church shall glory in his
       power
   and grow to his perfection;
   He is our rock, our mighty tower
   our life, our resurrection.
       So by his skilful hand
       the church of Christ shall stand;
       the master-builder's plan
       he works, as he began,
   and soon will crown with splen-
       dour.

2 Christ's people serve his wayward
       world
   to whom he seems a stranger;
   he knows its welcome from of old,
   he shares our joy, our danger.
       So strong, and yet so weak,
       the church of Christ shall speak;
       his cross our greatest need,
       his word the vital seed
   that brings a fruitful harvest.

3 Christ's living lamp shall brightly
burn,
and to our earthly city
forgotten beauty shall return,
and purity and pity.
　To give the oppresssed their
right
the church of Christ shall fight;
and though the years seem long
God is our strength and song,
and God is our salvation.

4 Christ's body triumphs in his
name;
one Father, sovereign giver,
one Spirit, with his love aflame,
one Lord, the same for ever.
　To you, O God our prize,
the church of Christ shall rise
beyond all measured height
to that eternal light,
where Christ shall reign all-holy.

*Christopher Idle*

# 730 (7)

1 Christ triumphant ever-reigning,
Saviour, Master, King,
Lord of heav'n, our lives sus-
taining,
hear us as we sing:

**Yours the glory and the crown,
the high renown,
the eternal name.**

2 Word incarnate, truth revealing,
Son of Man on earth!
Power and majesty concealing
by your humble birth:

3 Suffering servant, scorned, ill-
treated,
victim crucified!

Death is through the cross de-
feated,
sinners justified:

4 Priestly King, enthroned for ever
high in heaven above!
Sin and death and hell shall never
stifle hymns of love:

5 So, our hearts and voices raising
through the ages long,
ceaselessly upon you gazing,
this shall be our song:

*Michael Saward*

# 731 (8)

1 Come, rejoice before your Maker
all you peoples of the earth;
serve the Lord your God with
gladness,
come before him with a song!

2 Know for certain, our Creator
is the true and only God;
we are his, for he has made us,
we are sheep within his fold.

3 Come with grateful hearts before
him,
enter now his courts with praise;
show your thankfulness towards
him,
give due honour to his name.

4 For the Lord our God is gracious
everlasting in his love,
and to every generation
his great faithfulness endures.

*Michael Baughen (from Psalm 100)*

# 732 (9)

**Come Saviour, come like dew on
the grass;
break through the clouds like
gentle rain.**

1 Be angry, Lord, no more with us;
remember no longer our transgression.
See the city of God
laid waste and desolate:
Zion is turned to wilderness,
Jerusalem, ravaged and ruined,
your dwelling place
and the Holy of holies,
the house of your glory;
silent are those voices now
that once proclaimed your praise.

2 We have gone astray;
in the multitude of our sins
we have been made unclean,
fallen, fallen,
stricken as the leaves of autumn.
The stormwind carries us away,
the tempest of our evil deeds;
you have turned away from us
the face of your mercy,
and our iniquity has crushed us
like a potter's vessel.

3 O Lord our God,
look upon your people
in their affliction:
be mindful of your promises.
Send us the Lamb who will
set up his dominion
from the Rock of the Wilderness
to Zion
throned on her mountain.
There is no other whose power
can break our chains
and set us free.

4 Be comforted, be comforted,
take heart, my people:
you shall quickly see your salvation.
Why do you waste yourself with
grief,
though you have walked so long
with sorrow?
I am your Saviour, be afraid no
more.
For am I not God,
the Lord your God whom you
worship,
the Holy One of Israel,
come to redeem you?

*Alternative reponse*
**Rorate caeli desuper
et nubes pluant justum.**

Rorate Caeli, *Anon,
tr. Luke Connaughton (1919-1979)*

# 733 (10)

**Come to set us free,
come to make us your own.
Come to show the way
to your people, your chosen.
Open our lives to the
light of your promise.
Come to our hearts with healing,
come to our minds with power,
come to us and bring us your life.**

1 You are light which shines in
darkness,
Morning Star which never sets.
Open our eyes which only dimly
see
the truth which sets us free.

2 You are hope which brings us
    courage,
  you are strength which never fails.
  Open our minds to ways we do not
    know,
  but where your Spirit grows.

3 You are promise of salvation,
  you are God in human form.
  Bring to our world of emptiness
    and fear
  the word we long to hear.

*Bernadette Farrell*

# 734 (11)

1 Come, we that love the Lord,
  and let our joys be known;
  join in a song with sweet accord
  and thus surround the throne.
    **Hosanna, hosanna,**
    **Rejoice, give thanks and sing.**

2 Sing till we feel our hearts
  ascending with our tongues;
  sing till the love of sin departs
  and grace inspires our songs.

3 You pilgrims on the road
  to Zion's city, sing;
  rejoice now in the Lamb of God,
  in Christ, the eternal King.

4 There shall each rapturous tongue
  his endless praise proclaim,
  and sing in sweeter notes the song
  of Moses and the Lamb.

5 Then let our songs abound
  and let our tears be dry;
  We're marching through
    Emmanuel's ground
  to fairer worlds on high.

*1 & 5, Isaac Watts (1674-1748) 2-4,*
*William Hammond (1719-83)*

# 735 (12)

Con-fi-te-mi-ni Do-mi-no quo — ni — am bo - nus,

Con-fi-te-mi-ni Do-mi-no, Al-le-lu — ia!

*Taizé chant,*
*from Pss 105 (106) and 117 (118)*

## 736 (13)

1 Early morning. 'Come, prepare
   him,
   to the tomb your spices bring;
   death is cold and death decaying.
   We must beautify our King.'

2 Early morning, women excited,
   seeking Peter everywhere;
   telling of a man who told them,
   'He is risen; don't despair'.

3 Peter racing, early morning,
   to the tomb and rushing in;
   seeing shrouds of death dispensed
   with,
   finding new-born faith begin.

4 Early morning, Mary weeping,
   asking if the gardener knew;
   knowing, as his voice says, 'Mary',
   'Lord, Rabbuni, it is you'.

5 'Mary, you can live without me,
   as I now to God ascend;
   peace be with you; I am with you
   early morning without end.'

6 Early morning, stay for ever,
   early morning, never cease;
   early morning, come to all men
   for their good and power and
   peace.

*John Gregory*


## 737 (14)

**Eye has not seen,
ear has not heard
what God has ready for those
who love him;**

**Spirit of love, come give us
the mind of Jesus,
teach us the wisdom of God.**

1 When pain and sorrow weigh us
   down,
   be near to us, oh Lord,
   forgive the weakness of our faith,
   and bear us up within your peaceful word.

2 Our lives are but a single breath,
   we flower and we fade,
   yet all our days are in your hands,
   so we return in love what love has
   made.

3 To those who see with eyes of
   faith,
   the Lord is ever near,
   reflected in the faces
   of all the poor and lowly of the
   world.

4 We sing a myst'ry from the past,
   in halls where saints have trod,
   yet ever new the music rings,
   to Jesus, living song of God.

*Marty Haugen
(refrain based on I Cor 2:9-10)*


## 738 (15)

1 Father, we come in prayer
   to witness to your love,
   to make two hearts as one.
   Father, we give ourselves to you,
   we give our life to you,
   we give our lives anew
   for all time.

Wherever you must go
I'll be always at your side.
Wherever you live you'll find me there,
for your God is mine.

2 Jesus, we ask your help
to conquer for all time
the darkness in our land.
Jesus, where we live you live too,
unite our hearts with you
in your love.

3 Spirit, we feel your pow'r
your presence in our hearts:
be with us in each day,
Spirit, may we be one in you,
make all we say and do
give you praise.

*Anthony Sharpe
(based on the book of Ruth)*

# 739 (16)

*Cantors*
Father, we come to you,
God of all power and might.
Show us your glory:
give us your life.

*ALL*
**Father, we come to you,
God of all power and might.
Show us your glory:
give us your life.**

*Cantors*
You have united us,
bound us in love and peace:
God in the midst of us,
holy, unseen.

*ALL*
**Blessed is he who comes,
piercing the night of sin.
Open your hearts to him.
Great is his name.**

*Cantors*
Bread of life shared with us,
body of Christ the Lord,
broken and died for us:
life for the world.

*ALL*
**Father, we come to you,
God of all power and might.
Show us your glory:
give us your life.
Blessed is he who comes
piercing our night of sin.
Open our hearts to you:
great is your name.
Open our hearts to you:
great is your name!**

*James Walsh OSB*

# 740 (17)

1 For call to faith,
for gift of faith,
thank God who calls, who gives;
for call to life,
for gift of life,
thank God who ever lives.

2 For truth of God,
for word of God,
thank God that we can learn
the ways of God,
his law, his love,
and love him in return,

3 For Son of God,
  for Son of Man,
  thank God for Christ his Son;
  For Jesus, Saviour,
  Saviour-King,
  and our salvation won.

4 For sacrifice,
  for sacrament,
  thank God with priestly prayer;
  for food of life,
  for bread of life,
  for Christ, our own to share.

5 Pray to the Father
  and the Son
  their Holy Spirit's praise,
  for faith professed,
  for love possessed
  in his confirming grace.

6 Pray praise, pray love,
  pray thanks to God,
  pray every kind of prayer;
  Pray, everyone,
  for everyone
  to praise God everywhere.

*Brian Foley*

# 741 (18)

1 For the beauty of the earth,
  for the beauty of the skies,
  for the love which from our birth
  over and around us lies,
  Christ our God, to you we raise
  this our sacrifice of praise.

2 For the beauty of each hour
  of the day and of the night,
  hill and vale, and tree and flower,
  sun and moon and stars of light.
  Christ our God, to you we raise
  this our sacrifice of praise.

3 For the joy of ear and eye,
  for the heart and mind's delight,
  for the mystic harmony
  linking sense to sound and sight.
  Christ our God, to you we raise
  this our sacrifice of praise.

4 For the joy of human love,
  brother, sister, parent, child,
  friends on earth and friends above,
  pleasures pure and undefiled,
  Christ our God, to you we raise
  this our sacrifice of praise.

5 For each perfect gift divine
  to our race so freely given,
  joys bestowed by love's design,
  flowers of earth and fruits of
    heaven,
  Christ our God, to you we raise
  this our sacrifice of praise.

*F.S. Pierpoint (1835-1917)*

# 742 (19)

**For You, O Lord, my soul
  in stillness waits,
truly my hope is in you.**

1 O Lord of Light,
  our only hope of glory,
  your radiance shines in all
    who look to you,
  come, light the hearts of all
    in dark and shadow.

2 O Spring of Joy, rain down
    upon our spirits,
  our thirsty hearts are yearning
    for Your Word,
  come, make us whole, be comfort
    to our hearts.

3 O Root of Life, implant your seed
    within us,
  and in Your advent, draw us all to
    you,
  our hope reborn in dying
    and in rising.

4 O Key of Knowledge, guide us
    in our pilgrimage,
  we ever seek, yet unfulfilled re-
    main,
  open to us the pathway of Your
    peace.

5 Come, let us bow before the God
    who made us,
  let ev'ry heart be opened
    to the Lord,
  for we are all the people of His
    hand.

6 Here we shall meet the Maker
    of the heavens,
  Creator of the mountains
    and the seas,
  Lord of the stars, and present
    to us now.

*Marty Haugen*
*based on the 'O' Antiphons*

# 743 (20)

1 'Forgive our sins as we forgive,'
  you taught us, Lord, to pray,
  but you alone can grant us grace
  to live the words we say.

2 How can your pardon reach and
    bless
  the unforgiving heart
  that broods on wrongs and will not
    let
  old bitterness depart?

3 In blazing light your Cross reveals
  the truth we dimly knew:
  what trivial debts are owed to us,
  how great our debt to you!

4 Lord, cleanse the depths within
    our souls
  and bid resentment cease.
  Then, bound to all in bonds of
    love,
  our lives will spread your peace.

*Rosalind Herklots*

# 744 (21)

1 Forth in the peace of Christ we go:
  Christ to the world with joy we
    bring;
  Christ in our minds, Christ on our
    lips,
  Christ in our hearts, the world's
    true King.

2 King of our hearts, Christ makes
    us kings;
  kingship with him his servants
    gain;
  with Christ, the Servant-Lord of
    all,
  Christ's world we serve to share
    Christ's reign.

3 Priests of the world, Christ sends
    us forth
  this world of time to consecrate,
  this world of sin by grace to heal,
  Christ's world in Christ to re-
    create.

4 Prophets of Christ, we hear his
      word:
   he claims our minds, to search his
      ways,
   he claims our lips, to speak his
      truth,
   he claims our hearts, to sing his
      praise.

5 We are his Church, he makes us
      one:
   here is one hearth for all to find,
   here is one flock, one Shepherd-
      King,
   here is one faith, one heart, one
      mind.

*James Quinn SJ*
*See also hymn 78*

# 745 (22)

1 Free as is the morning sun
   Christ's new people Christ will
      lead
   to that homeland he has won;
   **Christ is risen, Lord indeed,**
   **Christ is risen, Lord indeed.**

2 One man for the people dies,
   Christ, the paschal lamb decreed,
   one man in whom all may rise;

3 We, like those who crossed dry-
      shod
   Egypt's marches and the reed,
   praise in liberty our God;

4 God himself his people saves,
   harvest of the dying seed
   springing lively from the graves;

*Hamish F.G. Swanston*

# 746 (23)

1 God is my great desire,
   his face I seek the first;
   to him my heart and soul aspire,
   for him I thirst.
   As one in desert lands,
   whose very flesh is flame,
   in burning love I lift my hands
   and bless his name.

2 God is my true delight,
   my richest feast his praise,
   through silent watches of the
      night,
   through all my days.
   To him my spirit clings,
   on him my soul is cast;
   beneath the shadow of his wings
   he holds me fast.

3 God is my strong defence
   in ev'ry evil hour;
   in him I face with confidence
   the tempter's power.
   I trust his mercy sure,
   with truth and triumph crowned:
   my hope and joy for evermore
   in him are found.

*Timothy Dudley-Smith*

# 747 (24)

1 God who spoke in the beginning,
   forming rock and shaping spar,
   set all life and growth in motion,
   earthly world and distant star;
   he who calls the earth to order
   is the ground of what we are.

2 God who spoke through men and
      nations,
  through events long past and
      gone,
  showing still today his purpose
  speaks supremely through his
      Son;
  he who calls the earth to order
  gives his word and it is done.

3 God whose speech becomes incar-
      nate,
  Christ is servant, Christ is Lord!
  calls us to a life of service,
  heart and will to action stirred;
  he who uses man's obedience
  has the first and final word.

*Albert J. Bayly (1901–84)*


# 748 (25)

**God, your glory we have seen
  in your Son,
full of truth, full of heavenly grace;
in Christ make us live,
his love shine on our face,
and the nations will see in us
the triumph you have won.**

1 In the fields of this world
  his good news he has sown,
  and sends us out to reap
  till the harvest is done.

2 In his love like a fire
  that consumes he passed by:
  the flame has touched our lips;
  let us shout: 'Here am I!'

3 He was broken for us,
  God-forsaken his cry,
  and still the bread he breaks:
  to ourselves we must die:

4 He has trampled the grapes
  of new life on his Cross;
  now drink the cup and live:
  he has filled it for us:

5 He has founded a kingdom
  that none shall destroy;
  the corner-stone is laid:
  Go to work, build with joy!

*Didier Rimaud, tr. Brian Wren*


# 749 (26)

1 Great is the Lord my soul pro-
      claims,
  in him my spirit sings for joy;
  for he who saves has looked on me
  with boundless love to raise me
      high.

2 Ages to come shall know that I
  am blessed and favoured by the
      Lord:
  his name is holy, mighty God;
  his wondrous power on me is
      poured.

3 All those who fear him find his
      love,
  in every age, in every land.
  His strong right arm puts down
      the proud,
  disperses them like grains of sand.

4 Down from their thrones he casts
      the strong,
  and raises up the meek of heart.
  He gives the hungry choicest food;
  in emptiness the rich depart.

5 Israel his servant knows his help,
in keeping with the promise sworn
to Abraham and all his race:
God's love will never be with-
 drawn.

6 Glory to God: the Father, Son,
and Spirit – Trinity sublime.
All honour, thanks and praise be
 theirs
across the spans of endless time.

*The Magnificat (Lk 1:46-55)*
*versified by Paul Inwood*

# 750 (27)

**Who calls my life again from the
 grave?
and like an eagle renews my
 youth?**

1 You are the forgiveness of our
 sins,
for you are greater than our sins.

2 As parents protecting their children,
so are you for us, most tender and
 loving.

3 You know us well, you have not
 forgotten
that we are made from the dust of
 the earth.

4 People, their days are just like the
 grass,
the bloom as the flowers in the
 open field.

5 The wind blows up, and they
vanish for good,
but God's love shall have no end.

*Huub Oosterhuis, tr. Tony Barr*
*From Ps 102 (103)*

# 751 (28)

**Hear us, almighty Lord,
show us your mercy,
sinners we stand here before
 you.**

1 Jesus our Saviour,
Lord of all the nations,
Christ our Redeemer,
 hear the prayers we offer,
Spare us and save us,
 comfort us in sorrow.

2 Word of the Father,
 keystone of God's building,
source of our gladness,
 gateway to the Kingdom,
free us in mercy from the sins
 that bind us.

3 God of compassion,
 Lord of might and splendour,
graciously listen,
 hear our cries of anguish,
Touch us and heal us
 where our sins have wounded.

4 Humbly confessing that we have
 offended,
stripped of illusions, naked in our
 sorrow,
pardon, Lord Jesus, those your
 blood
 has ransomed.

5 Innocent captive, you were
    led to slaughter,
  sentenced by sinners
    when they brought false
      witness.
  Keep from damnation
    those your death has rescued.

*Alternative response*

**Attende Domine et miserere
quia peccavimus tibi.**

Attende Domine, c.10,
tr. *Ralph Wright OSB*

# 752 (29)

1 Here in this place, new light is
    streaming,
  now is the darkness vanished
    away.
  See, in this space, our fears and
    our dreamings,
  brought here to you in the light of
    this day.
  Gather us in the lost and forsaken,
  gather us in the blind and the
    lame;
  call to us now, and we shall
    awaken,
  we shall arise at the sound of our
    name.

2 We are the young – our lives are a
    mystery,
  we are the old – who yearn for
    your face,

we have been sung throughout all
  of history,
called to be light to the whole
  human race.
Gather us in the rich and the
  haughty,
gather us in the proud and the
  strong;
give us a heart so meek and so
  lowly,
give us the courage to enter the
  song.

3 Here we will take the wine and the
    water,
  here we will take the bread of new
    birth,
  here you shall call your sons and
    your daughters,
  call us anew to be salt for the
    earth.
  Give us to drink the wine of com-
    passion,
  give us to eat the bread that is you;
  nourish us well, and teach us to
    fashion,
  lives that are holy and hearts that
    are true.

4 Not in the dark of buildings con-
    fining,
  not in some heaven, light years
    away, but
  here in this place, the new light is
    shining,
  now is the Kingdom, now is the
    day.
  Gather us in and hold us for ever,
  gather us in and make us your
    own;
  gather us in all peoples together,
  fire of love in our flesh and our
    bone.

*Marty Haugen*

## 753 (30)

1 How shall they hear the Word of
     God
  unless his truth is told?
  How shall the sinful be set free,
  the sorrowful consoled?
      To all who speak the truth today
      impart your Spirit, Lord, we
      pray.

2 How shall they call to God for help
  unless they have believed?
  how shall the poor be given hope,
  the prisoner reprieved?
      To those who help the blind to
      see
      give light and love and clarity.

3 How shall the gospel be pro-
     claimed
  if heralds are not sent?
  how shall the world find peace at
     last
  if we are negligent?
      So send us, Lord, for we rejoice
      to speak of Christ with life and
      voice.

*Michael Perry*

## 754 (31)

**I received the living God,
and my heart is full of joy.
I received the living God,
and my heart is full of joy.**

1 He has said: I am the Bread
  kneaded long to give you life;
  you who will partake of me
  need not ever fear to die.

2 He has said: I am the Way,
  and my Father longs for you;
  so I come to bring you home
  to be one with him anew.

3 He has said: I am the Truth;
  if you follow close to me,
  you will know me in your heart,
  and my word shall make you free.

4 He has said: I am the Life
  far from whom no thing can grow,
  but receive this living bread,
  and my Spirit you shall know.

*Anonymous*

## 755 (32)

**I rejoiced when I heard them say
'Let us go to the house of the
     Lord,'
I rejoiced when I heard them say
'Let us go to the house of the
     Lord.'**

1 I rejoiced when I heard them say
  'Let us go to God's house,'
  and now our feet are standing
  in your gates, O Jerusalem.

2 Jerusalem is built
  as a city, strongly compact.
  It is there that the tribes go up,
  the tribes of the Lord!

3 For Israel's law it is
  there to praise the Lord's name.
  There were set the thrones of
     judgment
  of the house of Israel.

*Psalm 121(122), (Grail Version).*

# 756 (33)

**If God should lead us home from
  our exile,
what wondrous dream-world!
If God should lead us home from
  our exile,
what wondrous dream-world!**

1  We will be singing, laughing and
     revelling;
   then let the world say 'Their God
     works wonders.'
   Yes, you work wonders, God here
     among us,
   you, our gladness.

2  Then lead us home, restore us to
     life,
   just as the rivers in the desert,
   as the new rains fall, start flowing
     again.

   Sowing in sorrow, reaping in glad-
     ness!
   A man sets out in tears for the
     sowing,
   back he comes singing, sheaves on
     his shoulder!

   **If God should lead us home from
     our exile,
   what wondrous dream-world!
   If God should lead us home from
     our exile,
   what wondrous dream-world!**

*Huub Oosterhuis, tr. Tony Barr
From Psalm 125(126)*

# 757 (34)

**In the abundance of your com-
  passion
wash my sins away.**

**Show me your mercy, O God,
and cleansed in the water of your
  salvation,
I shall be whiter than snow.**

1  Put a new heart in me, O God
   and give me again a constant
     spirit.

2  We cannot live unless we die,
   unless we are born of water and
     spirit.

3  Trust in the Lord for He is good,
   His mercy endures, His love is un-
     ending.

*Owen Alstott*

# 758 (35)

**In the land there is a hunger,
in the land is a need
not for the taste of water,
not for the taste of bread.
In the land there is a hunger,
in the land there is a need
for the sound of the word of God
upon every word we feed.**

1  Hear O Lord my cry,
   Day and night I call.
   My soul is thirsting
   for you, my God.

2  Your word O Lord
   is spirit and life
   You have the words, Lord,
   of everlasting life.

3  Only in God
   is my soul at rest.
   He is my rock
   and my salvation.

*Mike Lynch*

## 759 (36)

In the Lord I'll be ev-er thank-ful, in the Lord I will re-joice! Look to him, do not be a-fraid; in him re-joic-ing: the Lord is near, in him re-joic-ing: the Lord is near. In the

*Taizé chant*

## 760 (37)

**In your love remember me,
in your love remember me,
in your great goodness, O Lord,
remember me.**

1 Lord, make me know your ways,
Lord, teach me your paths.
Make me walk in your truth
and teach me,
for you are God my Saviour.

2 Remember your mercy, Lord,
your eternal love.
In your mercy I ask forgiveness:
in your love remember me.

3 His way is faithfulness,
faithfulness and love.
To the humble He shows the right
path,
taches the way of poverty.

*Psalm 24 (25)
adapted by Chris O'Hara*

# 761 (38)

**It is good to give thanks to your name, O Lord,
and to honour your ways.
It is good to give glory to you, Most High,
so we lift our voices in your praise.**

1 We proclaim your love from daybreak,
from the first light of the sun.
Faithfully you guard your people
all through the night.

2 Praise your name for all creation,
for your deeds we give you thanks.
Great and true, your wondrous achievements
by your own right hand.

3 All of our days we sing your praises
your great wisdom we acclaim.
Deep your thoughts, the fool cannot know them.
Praise your Holy Name.

4 In your house, to give you glory,
forever we will sing:
To proclaim that Yahweh is faithful
Our God, our King.

*Ps 91 (92), versified by
Anthony Sharpe*

# 762 (39)

1 Jesus is Lord! creation's voice
proclaims it,
for by his power each tree and
flower was
planned and made.
Jesus is Lord! the universe declares it –
sun, moon and stars in heaven cry:
'Jesus is Lord!'
**Jesus is Lord, Jesus is Lord!
Praise him with alleluias,
for Jesus is Lord.**

2 Jesus is Lord! yet from his throne
eternal
in flesh he came to die in pain on
Calvary's tree.
Jesus is Lord! from him all life
proceeding –
yet gave his life a ransom thus
setting us free.

3 Jesus is Lord! o'er sin the mighty
conqueror;
from death he rose and all his foes
shall own his name.
Jesus is Lord! God sends his Holy
Spirit
to show by works of power that
Jesus is Lord.

*D.J. Mansell*

# 763 (40)

1 Jesus, lead the way
through our life's long day,
when at times the way is cheerless,
help us follow, calm and fearless;
guide us by your hand
to the promised land.

---

2 Jesus be our light,
   in the midst of night,
   let not faithless fear o'er-take us,
   let not faith and hope forsake us;
   may we feel you near
   as we worship here.

3 When in deepest grief,
   strengthen our belief.
   When temptations come alluring,
   make us patient and enduring;
   Lord we seek your grace
   in this holy place.

4 Jesus, still lead on
   'til our rest be won:
   if you lead us through rough
       places,
   grant us your redeeming graces.
   When our course is o'er,
   open heaven's door.

   *Nicholas von Zinzendorf (1700-60)*
   *tr. Jane Borthwick, 1813-97, alt.*

# 764 (41)

1 Jesus, Lord of life and love
   I greet your presence here
   in this holy sign of life
   your love is clear.

2 Jesus, Lord, your loving eyes
   a sinner's heart reveal,
   by this holy sign of faith
   my failure heal.

3 Jesus, Lord, who sorrow knew
   console all those who mourn;
   in this holy sign of Heaven
   may Joy be born.

4 Jesus, Lord, in teaching here
   man came to follow you;

in this holy sign, my Lord
inspire anew.

5 Jesus, Lord of all my heart,
   I pray that every day
   through this holy sign of love
   in peace I stay.

                        *Christopher Walker*

# 765 (42)

1 Jesus, you're the one I love;
   you're the one I know.
   You're the one who makes me
       strong,
   Spirit in my soul.
   From the clouds of yesterday,
   through the night of pain,
   teach me, Lord, to know your
       way,
   know it once again.

   **Bread, blessed and broken for us all,**
   **symbol of your love from the**
   **grain so tall.**
   **Bread, blessed and broken for us all,**
   **Bread of life you give to us,**
   **bread of life for all.**

2 May the bread we break today,
   may the cup we share
   lift the burdens of our hearts,
   lift them ev'rywhere.
   Passing on to each of us
   a measure of your love,
   love to make us whole again,
   as we share your Word.

3 Jesus, you're the one I love;
   you're the one I know.
   You're the one who makes me
       strong,
   Spirit in my soul.

                        *Michael Lynch*

# 766 (43)

Jubilate, ev'rybody,
serve the Lord in all your ways, and
come before his presence singing;
enter now his courts with praise.
For the Lord our God is gracious,
and his mercy everlasting.
Jubilate, jubilate, jubilate Deo!

*F. Dunn*

# 767 (44)

**Lead us from death to life,
from falsehood to truth,
from despair to hope,
from fear to trust,
lead us from hate to love,
from war to peace;
let peace fill our hearts,
let peace fill our world,
let peace fill our universe.**

1 Still all the angry cries,
still all the angry guns,
still now your people die,
earth's sons and daughters.
Let justice roll,
let mercy pour down,
come and teach us
your way of compassion.

2 So many lonely hearts,
so many broken lives,
longing for love to break
into their darkness.
Come, teach us love,
come, teach us peace,
come and teach us
your way of compassion.

3 Let justice ever roll,
let mercy fill the earth,
let us begin to grow
into your people.
We can be love,
we can bring peace,
we can still be
your way of compassion.

*Verses: Marty Haugen*
*Refrain: Anonymous*

# 768 (45)

1 Lord, the light of Your love is
   shining
in the midst of the darkness,
   shining;
Jesus, Light of the World, shine
   upon us,
set us free by the truth You now
   bring us,
shine on me, shine on me.

**Shine, Jesus, shine,
fill this land with the Father's
   glory;
blaze, Spirit, blaze,
set our hearts on fire.
Flow, river, flow,
flood the nations with grace and
   mercy;
send forth Your word,
Lord, and let there be light.**

2 Lord, I come to Your awesome
   presence,
from the shadows into Your
   radiance;
by the blood I may enter Your
   brightness,
search me, try me, consume all my
   darkness.
Shine on me, shine on me.

3 As we gaze on Your kingly brightness
  so our faces display Your likeness,
  ever changing from glory to glory,
  mirrored here may our lives tell
   Your story.
  Shine on me, shine on me.

*Graham Kendrick*

# 769 (46)

Majesty, worship His Majesty;
unto Jesus be glory, honour and
  praise.
Majesty, kingdom, authority,
flows from His throne unto His own,
His anthem raise.
So exalt, lift upon high,
  the name of Jesus,
magnify, come glorify,
  Christ Jesus the King.
Majesty, worship His Majesty,
Jesus who died, now glorifed,
King of all kings.

*Jack W. Hayford*

# 770 (47)

**My people, I hear you calling,**
**I will forgive you your sin, if you**
**believe.**
**My people, you know my love**
**outlasts all time,**
**so constant, forgiving, my love**
**will set you free.**

1 You who search in the desert,
  you who find my pardon there,
  You have found salvation,
  your God has come to you from
   afar.

2 All of you who are blind and lame
  all who are my scattered sheep
  You, I will bring back to me,
  my hand will gather you, from
   every land.

3 You who once turned away from
   me
  you who show regret and shame,
  you will now rejoice again;
  you are forgiven, give thanks and
   praise!

*Anthony Sharpe*
*adapted from Jeremiah 31*

# 771 (48)

1 My soul cannot be still,
  my heart cries in pain.
  Is now a plea to heaven in vain?
  Our land is empty now,
  our towns laid waste:
  God's anger the people have faced.

**Lord, show us your mercy,**
**O Lord hear our prayer;**
**O Lord, renew our hearts and**
**minds**
**with your all-healing love.**

2 We look to the mountains,
  we see their fear:
  the anger of your presence is near.
  The land is a wilderness,
  the trees are dead.
  The birds of heaven have fled.

3 O turn to your people, Lord,
  and we shall be healed,
  to live in your covenant resealed.
  O praise to the God of hope
  set high on his throne;
  we trust in your promise to relent.

*Anthony Sharpe*
*based on Jer. 4:19.23-25; 17:12-13*

## 772 (49)

1 New songs of celebration render
to him who has great wonders
done;
awed by his power his foes sur-
render
and fall before the mighty One.
He has made known his great
salvation
which all his friends with joy confess;
he has revealed to every nation
his everlasting righteousness.

2 Joyfully, heartily resounding,
let every instrument and voice
peal out the praise of grace
abounding,
calling the whole world to rejoice.
Trumpets and organs set in
motion
such sounds as make the heavens
ring:
all things that live in earth and
ocean
make music for your mighty King.

3 Rivers and seas and torrents
roaring,
honour the Lord with wild
acclaim;
mountains and stones look up
adoring
and find a voice to praise his name.
Righteous, commanding, ever
glorious,
praises be his that never cease:
just is our God, whose truth victorious
establishes the world in peace.

*Erik Routley (1917-82)*
*Psalm 98 (97)*

## 773 (50)

**Nothing can ever take away from
us
the love of God that we have
seen in Jesus;
Nothing can ever separate us
from the love of God made real
in Christ.**

1 If God is with us, who can be
against us?
If God forgives us, who can still
accuse?
If God has cleared us, who can call
us guilty?
No-one, no-one, no-one.

2 No hardship, no kind of depriva-
tion,
no persecution, suffering or pain,
in peace or war, no trouble, threat
or danger,
nothing, nothing, nothing.

3 Nothing on the earth or in the
heavens,
nothing that exists or is still to
come,
nothing in our life, not even
dying,
nothing, nothing, nothing.

*Hubert Richards*
*Based on Romans 8:31-39*

## 774 (51)

**Now in this banquet, Christ is
our bread;
here shall all hungers be fed.
Bread that is broken, wine that is
poured,
love is the Sign of our Lord.**

1 You who have touched us and
   graced us with love,
make us your people of goodness
   and light.

2 Let our hearts burn with the fire of
   your love;
open our eyes to the glory of God.

3 God who makes the blind to see,
God who makes the lame to walk,
bring us dancing into day,
lead your people in your way.

4 Hope for the hopeless,
   light for the blind,
"Strong" is your name, Lord,
   "Gentle" and "Kind".

5 Call us to be your light,
call us to be your love,
make us your people again.

5 Come, O Spirit! renew our hearts!
We shall arise to be children of
   light.

*Alternative texts for refrain:*

1 **God of our journeys, daybreak to
   night;
lead us to justice and light.
Grant us compassion, strength
   for the day,
wisdom to walk in your way.**

2 **Lord, you can open hearts that
are stone;
live in our flesh and our bone;
Lead us to wonder, mystery and
grace,
one in your loving embrace.**

*Marty Haugen*

# 775 (52)

1 O changeless Christ, for ever new,
   who walked our earthly ways,
still draw our hearts as once you
   drew
the hearts of other days.

2 As once you spoke by plain and
   hill
or taught by shore and sea,
so be today our teacher still,
O Christ of Galilee.

3 As wind and storm their master
   heard
and his command fulfilled,
may troubled hearts receive your
   word,
the tempest-tossed be stilled.

4 And as of old to all who prayed
your healing hand was shown,
so be your touch upon us laid,
unseen but not unknown.

5 In broken bread, in wine outpoured,
your new and living way
proclaim to us, O risen Lord,
O Christ of this our day.

6 O changeless Christ, till life is past
your blessing still be given;
then bring us home, to taste at last
the timeless joys of heaven.

*Timothy Dudley-Smith*

# 776 (53)

1 O Christ, the healer, we have come
to pray for health, to plead for friends.
How can we fail to be restored,
when reached by love that never ends?

2 From every ailment flesh endures
our bodies clamour to be freed;
yet in our hearts we would confess
that wholeness is our deepest need.

3 How strong, O Lord, are our desires,
how weak our knowledge of ourselves!
Release in us those healing truths
unconscious pride resists or shelves.

4 In conflicts that destroy our health
we recognise the world's disease;
our common life declares our ills:
is there no cure, O Christ, for these?

5 Grant that we all, made one in faith,
in your community may find
the wholeness that, enriching us,
shall reach the whole of human kind.

*Frederick Pratt Green*

# 777 (54)

*Taizé chant.*

*Verses from Psalms 22(23), 24(25), 33(34), 84(85) or 129(130) may be sung by the Cantor.*

# 778 (55)

**Oh God, I seek You,
my soul thirsts for You,
Your love is finer than life.**

1 As a dry and weary desert land,
so my soul is thirsting for my God,
and my flesh is faint for the God I seek,
for Your love is more to me than life.

2 I think of You when at night I rest,
   I reflect upon Your steadfast love.
   I will cling to You, oh Lord my God,
   in the shadow of Your wings I sing.

3 I will bless Your name all the days I live,
   I will raise my hands and call on You.
   My joyful lips shall sing Your praise,
   You alone have filled my hungry soul.

*Marty Haugen, based on Psalm 62(63)*

# 779 (56)

**O how lovely is your dwelling place,
dwelling of the Lord of hosts!
How we long for your house, O Lord,
singing out a song of joy to the living God!**

1 Even sparrows find a home with you,
   and swallows lay their young to rest.
   Blessed are those who dwell in you
   and sing your praise, O God!

2 Bless'd are those who find their strength in you,
   whose hearts are highways for your will.
   Bringing joy to those around them,
   they go from strength to strength.

3 Hear our prayer, O Lord God of hosts;
   receive our life into your hands!
   Look into the hearts of those you love
   and grant us all we need!

4 For one day within your house exceeds
   a thousand spent away from you.
   We would rather serve within your house
   than wealth and power receive.

5 For our God protects us from all harm;
   he gives his favour and his love.
   All good things will come to those who love
   the Lord, and walk with him.

*Randall DeBruyn,
based on Psalm 83 (84)*

# 780 (57)

**O Lord, be not mindful of our guilt and our sins;
O Lord, do not judge us for our faults and offences.
May your merciful love be upon us.**

1 Help your people, Lord,
   O God our Saviour,
   deliver us for the glory of your name!

2 Praise to you, O Lord,
   through all the ages without end,
   deliver us for the glory of your name!

*Lucien Deiss*

## 781 (58)

**O Lord, you are the centre of my
life:
I will always praise you,
I will always serve you,
I will always keep you in my
sight.**

1 Keep me safe, O God, I take
   refuge in you.
   I say to the Lord: "You are my
   God.
   My happiness lies in you alone;
   my happiness lies in you alone."

2 I will bless the Lord who gives me
   counsel,
   who even at night directs my
   heart.
   I keep the Lord ever in my sight:
   since he is at my right hand, I shall
   stand firm.

3 And so my heart rejoices, my soul
   is glad;
   even in safety shall my body rest.
   For you will not leave my soul
   among the dead,
   nor let your beloved know decay.

4 You will show me the path of life,
   the fullness of joy in your presence,
   at your right hand, at your right
   hand
   happiness for ever.

   *From Psalm 15 (16) (The Grail).
   Refrain by Paul Inwood*

## 782 (59)

1 O most high and glorious God,
   cast your light into the darkness of
   my heart.
   Give me right faith, and certain
   hope,
   and perfect, perfect charity.
   Give me true insight, Lord, and
   wisdom,
   that I may always live within your
   holy will.
   Lord, may your light within me
   burn,
   shining out in perfect charity.

2 O most high and glorious God,
   open wide the door that leads me
   to your love.
   Give me your firm, and gentle
   strength;
   may I live that perfect charity.
   Lord, may your peace be ever in
   me,
   that I may always seek to serve
   your children here on earth;
   that I may find my home in you,
   and live in perfect charity.

3 Then most high and thankful
   praise
   I will sing unto the glory of your
   name;
   to Father, Son and Spirit bright,
   Living Presence, Perfect Charity.
   Praise to the Love that shines in
   splendour,
   that lights the pathways of my
   heart,
   and brings me close to you.
   O Holy One, invite me in,
   where you live in perfect charity.

   *V.1 based on the 'Prayer of St Francis'
   Vv.2-3 by Randall DeBruyn*

## 783 (60)

**O that today you would listen to
his voice:
'Harden not your hearts.'**

1 Come, ring out our joy to the
    Lord;
  hail the rock, hail the rock who
    saves us.
  Let us come before him giving
    thanks,
  with songs let us hail the Lord.

2 Come in, let us bow and bend low;
  let us kneel to the God who made
    us;
  like a flock he leads us by his hand
  to pasture he guides us on.

3 'At Meribah you harden your
    hearts
  and at Massah you seek to test
    me.'
  Let us trust our God and hope in
    him;
  today let us seek his voice.

*Psalm 94 (95). Response
and v.1 from the Grail Psalter.
Vv 2-3 adapted by Chris O'Hara.*

## 784 (61)

*Repeat each line after the leader.*

1 Oh healing river,
  send down your waters,
  send down your waters
  upon this land.
  O healing river
  send down your waters
  and wash the blood
  from off the sand.

2 This land is parching,
  this land is burning,
  no seed is growing
  in the barren ground.
  O healing river
  send down your waters
  O healing river
  send your waters down.

3 Let the seed of freedom,
  awake and flourish,
  let the deep roots nourish
  let the tall stalks rise.
  O healing river
  send down your waters
  O healing river
  from out of the skies.

*American Baptist hymn*

## 785 (62)

1 One shall tell another,
  and he shall tell his friends:
  husbands, wives and children
  shall come following on.
  From house to house in families
  shall more be gathered in;
  and lights will shine in every
    street,
  so warm and welcoming.

**Come on in and taste the new
    wine,
the wine of the kingdom,
the wine of the kingdom of God:
here is healing and forgiveness,
the wine of the kingdom,
the wine of the kingdom of God.**

2 Compassion of the Father
  is ready now to flow;
  through acts of love and mercy
  we must let it show.
  He turns now from his anger
  to show a smiling face,

and longs that we should stand
   beneath
the fountain of his grace.

3 He longs to do much more
than our faith has yet allowed,
to thrill us and surprise us
with his sovereign power.
Where darkness has been darkest,
the brightest light will shine;
his invitation comes to us,
it's yours and it is mine.

*Graham Kendrick*

# 786 (63)

1 Peace I give to you, my friends.
peace the world can never know,
Given you now to share with each
   other,
peace I give to you, my friends.

2 Love I give . . .

3 Joy I give . . .

*Anthony Sharpe*

# 787 (64)

1 Praise now your God, every
   tongue, ev'ry nation,
tell the good news to the next
   generation:
Christ, the Redeemer, who rose
   from the dead,
stays with his people as life-giving
   Bread.

**Alleluia, God is great! Alleluia,
God is good!**

2 Christ gave his word at the multi-
   plication.
Bread and sweet wine are now
   Christ our oblation.
Cross and last Supper are with us
   today.
Life now abounds, and God's will
   we obey.

3 Here is your Saviour, give deep
   adoration,
sing of his glory in glad celebration.
Come, for his manna is food for
   the road,
strength for the journey, our glory
   foreshowed.

*C.J. Marivoet*

# 788 (65)

**Praise to you, O Christ, our
   Saviour,
Word of the Father, calling us to
   life;
Son of God who leads us to
   freedom:
glory to you, Lord Jesus Christ!**

1 You are the Word who calls us out
   of darkness;
you are the Word who leads us
   into light;
you are the Word who brings us
   through the desert:
glory to you, Lord Jesus Christ!

2 You are the one whom prophets
   hoped and longed for;
you are the one who speaks to us
   today;

you are the one who leads us to our
    future;
glory to you, Lord Jesus Christ

3 You are the Word who calls us
        to be servants;
    you are the Word whose only law
        is love;
    you are the Word-made-flesh who
        lives among us:
    glory to you, Lord Jesus Christ!

4 You are the Word who binds us
        and unites us;
    you are the Word who calls us to
        be one;
    you are the Word who teaches us
        forgiveness:
    glory to you, Lord Jesus Christ!

*Bernadette Farrell*

# 789 (66)

**Prepare ye the way of the Lord!
Make straight his paths!
Fill in the valleys, lay the hills low,
smooth the rough places where
    he will go,
and all the earth shall see
the saving power of God!**

1 Repent, for the Kingdom of God
        is at hand,
    the light which the darkness can
        never withstand.

2 Cry out with a voice that is strong
        and sure:
    'The flower will fade, but my word
        will endure!'

3 Get up the high mountain and
        shout the Good News:
    'Fear not, for the Lord God
        Almighty rules!'

4 Like a shepherd he shelters his
        flock from harm;
    and tenderly leads the young
        lambs with his arm.

*Stephen Dean*

# 790 (67)

Psal-li-te Do-mi-no in vo-ce psal - mi. Can-ta-te Do-mi-no can-ti cum no - vum.

Psal-li-te Do-mi-no in vo-ce psal - mi. Can-ta-te Do-mi-no can-ti cum no - vum.

Exsultate! Exsultate!
Cantate alleluia! Cantate alleluia!

Sing! Sing! Sing a new song!
Sing! Sing! Sing to the Lord!

All the ends of the earth have seen
the salvation of our God.
Shout to the Lord all the earth,
ring out your joy, alleluia!

*Taizé chant
from Psalm 97(98)*

## 791 (68)

1 Safe in the shadow of the Lord,
  beneath his hand and power,
    I trust in him,
    I trust in him,
  my fortress and my tower.

2 My hope is set on God alone
  though Satan spreads his snare;
    I trust in him,
    I trust in him
  to keep me in his care.

3 From fears and phantoms of the
    night,
  from foes about my way,
    I trust in him,
    I trust in him
  by darkness as by day.

4 His holy angels keep my feet
  secure from every stone;
    I trust in him,
    I trust in him
  and unafraid go on.

5 Strong in the everlasting name,
  and in my Father's care,
    I trust in him,
    I trust in him
  who hears and answers prayer.

6 Safe in the shadow of the Lord,
  possessed by love divine,
    I trust in him,
    I trust in him
  and meet his love with mine.

*Timothy Dudley-Smith*

## 792 (69)

1 Sing a new song to the Lord,
  he to whom wonders belong!

Rejoice in his triumph and tell of
    his power.
O sing to the Lord a new song!

2 Now to the ends of the earth
  see his salvation is shown;
  and still he remembers his mercy
    and truth
  unchanging in love to his own.

3 Sing a new song and rejoice,
  publish his praises abroad!
  Let voices in chorus, and trumpet
    and horn,
  resound for the joy of the Lord!

4 Join with the hills and the sea
  thunders of praise to prolong!
  In judgement and justice he comes
    to the earth,
  O sing to the Lord a new song!

*Psalm 98(97)*
*versified by Timothy Dudley-Smith*

## 793 (70)

1 Sing, all creation, sing to God in
    gladness!
  Joyously serve him, singing
    hymns of homage!
  chanting his praises, come before
    his presence!
  Praise the Almighty!

2 Know that our God is Lord of all
    the ages!
  He is our maker, we are all his cre-
    atures,
  people he fashioned, sheep he
    leads to pasture!
  Praise the Almighty!

3 Enter his temple, ringing out his
    praises!
  Sing in thanksgiving as you come
    before him!
  Blessing his bounty, glorify his
    greatness!
  Praise the Almighty!

4 Great in his goodness is the Lord
    we worship;
  steadfast his kindness, love that
    knows no ending!
  Faithful his word is, changeless,
    everlasting!
  Praise the Almighty!

*James Quinn SJ,*
*based on Psalm 100 (99)*

# 794 (71)

1 Sing of the Lord's goodness,
    Father of all wisdom,
  come to him and bless his name.
  Mercy he has shown us, his love is
    for ever,
  faithful to the end of days.

  **Come then all you nations,**
  **sing of your Lord's goodness,**
  **melodies of praise and thanks to**
    **God.**
  **Ring out the Lord's glory,**
  **praise him with your music,**
  **worship him and bless his name.**

2 Power he has wielded,
    honour is his garment,
  risen from the snares of death.
  His word he has spoken,
    one bread he has broken,
  new life he now gives to all.

3 Courage in our darkness,
    comfort in our sorrow,
  Spirit of our God most high;
  solace for the weary,
    pardon for the sinner,
  splendour of the living God.

4 Praise him with your singing,
    praise him with the trumpet,
  praise God with the lute and harp;
  praise him with the cymbals,
    praise him with your dancing,
  praise God till the end of days.

*Ernest Sands*

# 795 (72)

  **Sing it in the valleys,**
  **shout it from the mountain tops;**
  **Jesus came to save us,**
  **and his saving never stops.**
  **He is King of Kings,**
  **and new life he brings,**
  **sing it in the valleys,**
  **shout it from the mountain tops,**
    **(oh!)**
  **shout it from the mountain tops.**

1 Jesus you are by my side,
  you take all my fears.
  If I only come to you,
  you will heal the pain of years.

2 You have not deserted me,
  though I go astray.
  Jesus take me in your arms,
  help me walk with you today.

3 Jesus, you are living now,
  Jesus, I believe.
  Jesus, take me, heart and soul,
  Yours alone I want to be.

*Mike Anderson*

# 796 (73)

**From Daniel 3:**

1 All you heavens, bless the Lord.
  Stars of the heavens, bless the
      Lord.

2 Sun and moon, bless the Lord.
  And you, night and day, bless the
      Lord.

3 Frost and cold, bless the Lord.
  Ice and snow, bless the Lord.

4 Fire and heat, bless the Lord.
  And you, light and darkness, bless
      the Lord.

5 Spirits and souls of the just, bless
      the Lord.
  Saints and the humble hearted,
      bless the Lord.

**From Psalm 117 (118):**

1 Give thanks to the Lord for he is
      good,
  for his love has no end.

2 The Lord is my strength, the Lord
      is my song,
  he has been my Saviour.

3 I shall not die, I shall live,
  I shall live and recount his deeds.

*Taizé chant*
*Psalm verses*
*from the Grail version*

# 797 (74)

1 The gift of the Holy Spirit
   is the gift of God's great love.
   To us comes the touch of healing
   from the God of heaven above;
   joy and strength for our daily
      living,
   trust and love for the work of
      giving,
   and the spirit of true forgiving
      each one.

2 Anointed, we are Christ's witness
   in the walk of life each day,
   a comfort and light to others
   whom we meet along the way.
   We will cherish your life within
      us,
   show the mercy you show to
      sinners,
   by your suffering, you chose to
      win us from death.

3 Thanksgiving we bring, and
      honour,
   to the Father and the Son
   and, with them, the Holy Spirit,
   God for ever, Three in One.
   Praise and glory we give and
      blessing,
   one faith, one in truth confessing,
   one in love in your all-embracing
      design.

                    *Kathleen Boschetti MSC*


# 798 (75)

1 The kingdom of God is justice and
      joy;
   for Jesus restores what sin would
      destroy.
   God's power and glory in Jesus we
      know;
   and here and hereafter the king-
      dom shall grow.

2 The kingdom of God is mercy and
      grace;
   the captives are freed, the sinners
      find place,
   the outcast are welcomed God's
      banquet to share;
   and hope is awakened in place of
      despair.

3 The kingdom of God is challenge
      and choice:
   believe the good news, repent and
      rejoice!
   His love for us sinners brought
      Christ to his cross:
   our crisis of judgement for gain or
      for loss.

4 God's kingdom is come, the gift
      and the goal;
   In Jesus begun, in heaven made
      whole.
   The heirs of the kingdom shall
      answer his call;
   and all things cry 'Glory!' to God
      all in all.

                         *Christopher Idle*

# 799 (76)

1 The Master came to bring good
      news,
   the news of love and freedom,
   to heal the sick and seek the poor,
   to build the peaceful kingdom.

   **Father, forgive us!**
   **Through Jesus hear us!**
   **As we forgive one another!**

2 The Law's fulfilled through Jesus
   Christ,
   the man who lived for others,
   the law of Christ is: Serve in love
   our sisters and our brothers.

3 To seek the sinners Jesus came,
   to live among the friendless,
   to show them love that they might
   share
   the kingdom that is endless.

4 Forgive us, Lord, as we forgive
   and seek to help each other.
   Forgive us, Lord, and we shall live
   to pray and work together.

*Ralph Finn*

# 800 (77)

1 The voice of God goes out to all
   the world:
   his glory speaks across the universe.
   The Great King's herald cries
   from star to star;
   *with power, with justice, he will
   walk his way.*

2 Give glory to the mystery revealed,
   the voice of God, his image and his
   Word:
   his word of peace, the image of his
   grace:
   *with power, with justice, he will
   walk his way.*

3 The Lord has said: Receive my
   messenger,
   my promise to the world, my
   pledge made flesh,

a lamp to every nation, light from
light:
*with power, with justice, he will
walk his way.*

4 The broken reed he will not trample down,
   nor set his heel upon the dying
   flame.
   He binds the wounds, and health
   is in his hand:
   *with power, with justice, he will
   walk his way.*

5 Anointed with the Spirit and with
   power,
   he comes to crown with comfort
   all the weak,
   to show the face of justice to the
   poor:
   *with power, with justice, he will
   walk his way.*

6 His touch will bless the eyes that
   darkness held,
   the lame shall run, the halting
   tongue shall sing,
   and prisoners laugh in light and
   liberty:
   *with power, with justice, he will
   walk his way.*

*Luke Connaughton (1919-79)*

# 801 (78)

**The word of God is more desired
than gold;
the word of God is sweeter than
honey.
Light to our eyes, the Lord's
command is clear;
greater than gold: the message of
eternal life.**

1 The law of God is perfect,
   gives the soul new life.
   The Lord's decree is to be trusted,
   fills the simple heart with wisdom.

2 The precepts of the Lord
   fill our hearts with joy.
   The Lord's command is clear and
       truthful;
   giving light for the eyes.

3 Much more desired than gold,
   more than finest gold;
   the word of God is so much
       sweeter,
   sweeter than the honeycomb.

*Psalm 18(19) adapted by*
*Chris O'Hara*

# 802 (79)

1 Those who were in the dark
   are thankful for the sunlight;
   we who live, we who die
   are grateful for his gift,
   thankful for his love.

**Behold, behold the Lamb of**
   **God.**
**All who eat, all who drink shall**
   **live;**
**and all, all who dwell in God**
**shall come to know his glory.**

2 Peaceful now those whose hearts
   are blessed with understanding.
   Of the wheat, of the wine
   united with his Word
   and the love we share.

3 Gentle one, Child of God,
   join with us at this table.

Bless our lives, nourish all
who hunger for this feast;
shelter them with peace.

4 Lord of all, give us light;
   deliver us from evil.
   Make us one; be our shield.
   Make still the winds that blow;
   cradle us with love.

*Martin Willett*

# 803 (80)

1 To God be the glory, great things
       he has done!
   So loved he the world that he gave
       us his Son.
   Who yielded his life in atonement
       for sin,
   and opened the life-gate that all
       may go in.

**Praise the Lord! Praise the Lord!**
**Let the earth hear his voice!**
**Praise the Lord! Praise the Lord!**
**Let the people rejoice!**
**O come to the Father through**
   **Jesus his Son;**
**and give him the glory, great**
   **things he has done!**

2 O perfect redemption, the pur-
       chase of blood,
   to every believer the promise of
       God!
   And every offender who truly
       believes,
   that moment from Jesus a pardon
       receives.

3 Great things he has taught us,
       great things he has done,

and great our rejoicing through
  Jesus the Son;
but purer, and higher, and
  greater will be
our wonder, our rapture, when
  Jesus we see.

*Frances J. van Alstyne (1820-1915)*

# 804 (81)

1 To Jesus Christ, our sovereign
    King,
  who is the world's salvation,
  all praise and homage do we bring
  and thanks and adoration.

**Christ Jesus, Victor!
Christ Jesus, Ruler!
Christ Jesus, Lord and Re-
  deemer!**

2 Your reign extend, O King
    benign,
  to every land and nation;
  for in your Kingdom, Lord
    divine,
  alone we find salvation.

3 To you, and to your church, great
    king,
  we pledge our heart's oblation;
  until before your throne we sing
  in endless jubilation.

*Martin B. Hellriegel (1891-1981) alt.*

# 805 (82)

*Taizé chant*

Lento ♩ = 48

Wait for the Lord, his day is near. Wait for the Lord be strong take heart!

1 Prepare the way for the Lord.
  Make a straight path for him.
  *(Is.40)*

2 The glory of the Lord
  shall be revealed. *(Is.40)*

3 All the earth will see the Lord.
  *(Is.40)*

4 Rejoice in the Lord always.
  He is at hand. *(Phil.4)*

5 Seek first the kingdom of God,

  seek and you shall find. *(Mt.6-7)*

6 Joy and gladness
  for all who seek the Lord. *(Ps.69)*

7 I waited for the Lord;
  he heard my cry. *(Ps.39)*

8 Our eyes are fixed
  on the Lord our God. *(Ps.122)*

9 O Lord, show us your way.
  Guide us in your truth. *(Ps.118)*

10 Prepare the way for the Lord.

# 806 (83)

*Antiphon*
Be here among us, word freely given,
that I may hear you with heart and
  soul.

*Refrain*
**Wake your power, come, lead us to
  freedom!**
**Wake your power, come, lead us to
  freedom!**

1 Word freely given, God with us
    always,
  peace for our future, be here
    among us.
  Your will be done, your kingdom
    come,
  See us, accept us, keep us from
    falling.
*Refrain*

2 And may our lives be not empty or
    aimless.
  Keep us from falling back to the
    dust.
  Send your Spirit that we be
    recreated.
*Refrain*

3 That we may hear you, that we
    may live you,
  people for people, and all for all.
  And bring to fullness your word
    that is our peace.
  Wake your power, come, lead us
    to freedom.
*Refrain*
*Antiphon*
*Refrain*

*Huub Oosterhuis, tr. Tony Barr*

# 807 (84)

1 We are your people:
  Lord, by your grace,
  you dare to make us
  Christ to our neighbours,
  of every nation and race.

2 How can we demonstrate
  your love and care?
  Speaking or listening?
  Battling or serving?
  Help us to know when and where.

3 Called to portray you,
  help us to live
  closer than neighbours,
  open to strangers,
  able to clash and forgive.

4 Glad of tradition,
  help us to see
  in all life's changing
  where you are leading,
  where our best efforts should be.

5 Joined in community,
  breaking your bread,
  May we discover
  gifts in each other,
  willing to lead and be led.

6 Lord, as we minister
  in diff'rent ways,
  may all we're doing
  show that you're living,
  meeting your love with our praise.

*Brian Wren*

# 808 (85)

1 We give God thanks for those who
    knew
  the touch of Jesus' healing love;

they trusted him to make them whole,
to give them peace, their guilt remove.

2 We offer prayer for all who go
relying on his grace and power,
to help the anxious and the ill,
to heal their wounds, their lives restore.

3 We dedicate our skills and time
to those who suffer where we live,
to bring such comfort as we can
to meet their need, their pain relieve.

4 So Jesus' touch of healing grace
lives on within our willing care;
by thought and prayer and gift we prove
his mercy still, his love we share.

*Michael Perry*

# 809 (86)

1 We have a gospel to proclaim,
good news for men in all the earth;
the gospel of a saviour's name:
we sing his glory, tell his worth.

2 Tell of his birth at Bethlehem,
not in a royal house or hall
but in a stable dark and dim:
the Word made flesh, a light for all.

3 Tell of his death at Calvary,
hated by those he came to save;
in lonely suffering on the cross
for all he loved, his life he gave.

4 Tell of that glorious Easter morn:
empty the tomb, for he was free;

he broke the power of death and hell
that we might share his victory.

5 Tell of his reign at God's right hand,
by all creation glorified;
he sends his Spirit on his church
to live for him, the lamb who died.

6 Now we rejoice to name him king;
Jesus is Lord of all the earth;
the gospel-message we proclaim:
we sing his glory, tell his worth.

*Edward J. Burns*

# 810 (87)

1 We have a King who comes in splendour,
comes in clouds of glory!
Holding in his hand the sceptre,
holding all our lives.
His the might and his the power
stronger than the mountains!
**Son of God and still the Son of Mary,**
**Jesus, holy Lord.**

2 We call him King for so he is,
who sits beside the Father;
his to rule and his to judge
the living and the dead.
But his eyes are full of kindness,
mercy is his measure.

3 So listen to his words and heed them;
turn from sin and sorrow.
He will come and dwell among us,
finding here his home.
Live the life and taste the freedom,
share with him his glory!

*Willard F. Jabusch*

## 811 (88)

**We have been told, we've seen
  his face,
and heard his voice alive in our
  hearts;
'Live in my love with all your
  heart,
as the Father has loved me,
so I have loved you.'**

1 'I am the vine, you are the
    branches,
  and all who live in me will bear
    great fruit.'

2 'You are my friends, if you keep
    my commands,
  no longer slaves, I call you
    friends.'

3 No greater love is there than this:
  'to lay down one's life for a friend.'

*David Haas, from John 15:5.9.13-14*

## 812 (89)

**Unless a grain of wheat shall fall
upon the ground and die,
it remains but a single grain
with no life.**

1 If we have died with him
  then we shall live with him;
  if we hold firm we shall reign with
    him.

2 If anyone serves me
  then they must follow me;
  wherever I am my servants will be.

3 Make your home in me as I make
    mine in you;
  those who remain in me bear
    much fruit.

4 If you remain in me and my word
    lives in you;
  then you will be my disciples.

5 Those who love me are loved by
    my Father;
  we shall be with them and dwell in
    them.

6 Peace I leave with you, my peace I
    give to you;
  peace which the world cannot give
    is my gift.

*Refrain: John 12:24;
verses from Scripture
(2 Tim 2, John 12, 14, 15)
versified by Bernadette Farrell*

## 813 (90)

**We're forgiven, we're all of us free,
we're forgiven, we're all of us free,
we're forgiven, we're all of us free,
and none of our sins are held
    against us, we are free.**

1 It was like a blindness,
  darkness all around, *(three times)*
  When he shone his light, I
  Realised that I could see.

2 It was like a deafness,
  couldn't hear a thing, *(three times)*
  When he spoke his word, I
  Heard he was addressing me.

3 It was like a dumbness,
  my tongue was tied, *(three times)*
  When he touched my mouth, I
  Found that I was talking free.

4 It was like a prison,
  chains around my feet, *(three times)*
  When he took my chains off,
  It was like a jubilee!

5 It was like a coffin,
couldn't move a limb, *(three times)*
When he took my hand, he
Raised me up and said, Be free!

*Hubert Richards*

# 814 (91)

**We shall draw water joyfully,
singing joyfully, singing joyfully,
We shall draw water joyfully
from the wellsprings of salvation.**

1 Truly God is our salvation,
we trust, we shall not fear.
For the Lord is our strength, our
song;
he became our saviour.

2 Give thanks, O give thanks to the
Lord;
give praise to his holy name!
make his mighty deeds known
to all of the nations,
proclaim his greatness.

3 Sing a psalm, sing a psalm to the
Lord
for he has done glorious deeds.
Make known his works to all of
the earth;
people of Zion, sing for joy,
for great in your midst, great in
your midst
is the Holy One of Israel.

*Paul Inwood, from Isaiah 12*

# 815 (92)

1 We walk by faith, and not by
sight:
no gracious words we hear

of him who spoke as none e'er
spoke,
but we believe him near.

2 We may not touch his hands and
side,
nor follow where he trod;
yet in his promise we rejoice,
and cry 'My Lord and God!'

3 Help then, O Lord, our unbelief,
and may our faith abound;
to call on you when you are near,
and seek where you are found:

4 That when our life and faith is
done
in realms of clearer light
we may behold you as you are
in full and endless sight.

5 We walk by faith, and not by
sight:
no gracious words we hear
of him who spoke as none e'er
spoke,
but we believe him near.

*Henry Alford (1810-71) alt.*

# 816 (93)

1 What do you want of me, Lord?
Where do you want me to serve
you?
Where can I sing your praises?
I am your song.
**Jesus, Jesus, you are the Lord.
Jesus, Jesus, you are the way.**

2 I hear you call my name, Lord,
and I am moved within me.
Your Spirit stirs my deepest self.
Sing your songs in me.
**Jesus, Jesus, you are my Lord.
Jesus, Jesus, you are the way.**

3 Above, below and around me,
Before, behind, and all through
me,
your Spirit burns deep within me.
Fire my life with your love.
**Jesus, Jesus, be warmth of my
heart.**
**Jesus, Jesus, you are the way.**

4 You are the light in my darkness.
You are my strength when I'm
weary.
You give me sight when I'm
blinded.
Come, see for me.
**Jesus, Jesus, you are my Light.**
**Jesus, Jesus, you are the way.**

5 I am your song and servant,
singing your praise like Mary.
Surrendered to your Spirit,
'Let it be done to me.'
**Jesus, Jesus, 'Let it be done to
me.'**
**Jesus, Jesus, you are the way.**

*Sr. Donna Marie Cargill OSM*

# 817 (94)

1 What does the Lord require
for praise and offering?
What sacrifice, desire
or tribute bid you bring?
Do justly;
love mercy;
walk humbly with your God.

2 Rulers of earth, give ear!
should you not justice know?
Will God your pleading hear,
while crime and cruelty grow?
Do justly;
love mercy;
walk humbly with your God.

3 Masters of wealth and trade,
all you for whom men toil,
Think not to win God's aid
if lies your commerce soil.
Do justly;
love mercy;
walk humbly with your God.

4 Still down the ages ring
the prophet's stern commands:
to merchant, worker, king,
he brings God's high demands:
Do justly;
love mercy;
walk humbly with your God.

5 How shall our life fulfil
God's law so hard and high?
Let Christ endue our will
with grace to fortify.
Then justly,
love mercy;
walk humbly with your God.

*Albert F. Bayly (1901-84)*
*based on Micah 6:6-8*

# 818 (95)

1 What is this place where we are
meeting?
Only a room, the earth its floor.
Walls and a roof, refuge for
people,
windows for eyes, an open door.
House which becomes a body that
lives
when we are gathered here,
and know that God is near.

2 Word from the past, stars that are
falling,
sparks sown among us long ago.
Names for our God, dreams, signs
and wonders,
voicing the world's relentless flow.

We are but dust who see and who
    hear,
who speak what we have heard:
God's free resplendent word.

Table for one, bread that is
    broken,
Cup to be shared, one bread, one
    wine.
Wonder of God: peace among
    people,
ancient yet new this hidden sign.
Breaking and sharing, how can
    this be,
impossible come true?
From death comes life anew.

*Huub Oosterhuis,*
*tr. Tony Barr (after David Smith)*

not in the power of wind and
    flame,
but of his love and peace the
    token,
seen as a dove, the Spirit came.

3 O Son of Man, our nature sharing,
in whose obedience all are blest,
Saviour, our sins and sorrows
    bearing,
hear us and grant us this request:
Daily to grow, by grace defended,
filled with the Spirit from above;
in Christ baptized, beloved,
    befriended,
children of God in peace and love.

*Timothy Dudley-Smith*

# 819 (96)

1 When John baptized by Jordan's
    river
in faith and hope the people came,
that John and Jordan might de-
    liver
their troubled souls from sin and
    shame.
They came to seek a new begin-
    ning,
the human spirit's ageless quest,
repentance, and an end of sinning,
renouncing every wrong con-
    fessed.

2 There as the Lord, baptized and
    praying,
rose from the stream, the sinless
    one,
a voice was heard from heaven
    saying,
'This is my own beloved Son.'
There as the Father's word was
    spoken,

# 820 (97)

1 When the King shall come again
all his power revealing,
splendour shall announce his
    reign,
life and joy and healing:
earth no longer in decay,
hope no more frustrated;
this is God's redemption day
longingly awaited.

2 In the desert trees take root
fresh from his creation;
plants and flowers and sweetest
    fruit
join the celebration:
rivers spring up from the earth,
barren lands adorning; valleys,
this is your new birth,
mountains, greet the morning!

3 Strengthen feeble hands and
    knees,
fainting hearts, be cheerful!

God who comes for such as these
seeks and saves the fearful:
now the deaf can hear the dumb
sing away their weeping;
blind eyes see the injured come
walking, running, leaping.

4 There God's highway shall be seen
where no roaring lion,
nothing evil or unclean
walks the road to Zion:
ransomed people homeward
    bound
all your praises voicing,
see your Lord with glory crowned,
share in his rejoicing!

*Christopher Idle*

# 821 (98)

**With open hands we come before
  you
offering to you, Lord, gifts from
  your creation.
With loving hearts as one before
  you
grant us, O Lord, your peace and
  your salvation.**

1 Blest are you, Lord, God of
    creation
through your goodness there is
  bread here for us,
fruit of the earth and work of
  human hands;
it will become the bread of life.

2 Blest are you, Lord, God of
    creation
through your goodness there is
  wine here for us,

fruit of the vine and work of
  human hands;
it will become your precious
  blood.

*Aidan Whelan*

# 822 (99)

1 You are the Lord, you are the
    Lord,
you are the Lord of creation,
you are the Lord.
You are master of ocean and sky,
and all earth bow in adoration.

**O Lord, as we gather before you
to adore you and your mercy proclaim,
we give thanks, Lord,
for the love that you show us,
for you know us,
you have called us by name.**

2 You are the light, you are the
    light,
you are light for the nations,
you are the light,
shining brightly throughout every
  land
to end the darkness of sin and suffering.

3 You, who are love and compas-
    sion,
you who are love and compassion,
in your likeness we have all been
  made.
Help us to carry each other's burdens.

4 You are the hope, you are the
    hope,
  you are the hope of your people,
  you are the hope,
  for your word holds the promise
    of peace
  for all who follow the path of jus-
    tice.

*Owen Alstott*

# 823 (100)

You shall go out with joy
and be led forth with peace.
The mountains and the hills will
break forth before you;
there'll be shouts of joy,
and all the trees of the field
will clap, will clap their hands.

And all the trees of the field
will clap their hands,
the trees of the field
will clap their hands.
The trees of the field
will clap their hands
while you go out with joy.

*Repeat* You shall go out . . .

*Stuart Dauermann*

# 824 (101)

1 You are the King of Glory,
  you are the Prince of Peace,
  you are the Lord of heav'n and
    earth,
  you're the sun of righteousness.
  Angels bow down before you,
  worship and adore, for
  you have the words of eternal life;
  you are Jesus Christ, the Lord.

**Hosanna to the Son of David!**
**Hosanna to the King of kings!**
**Glory in the highest heaven,**
**for Jesus the Messiah reigns.**

2 You touched the broken hearted;
  you made the blind to see;
  you made the lame to walk again;
  you set the prisoners free.
  You bring us joy in sadness,
  fill our hearts with hope, for
  you give us joy and peace from
    heaven;
  you are Jesus Christ the Lord.

3 You are the Lord who conquers;
  yours is the victory;
  triumphing over Satan's power
  You rose to life again.
  Now, Lord, you sit in heaven
  reigning with the Father,
  all knees shall bow in praise and
    worship;
  you are Jesus Christ the Lord.

*V.1 Mavis Ford*
*Vv 2-3 by Julie Sharp*

## 825 (102)

**You are the Vine, we are the branches,
together we are one;
without your word love has no meaning
so let your will be done.**

1 The fruit of the vine
will become the true wine;
through joy and sorrow
our love will grow to be a sign;
be a sign of the Kingdom
giving hope to light our way,
with love that forms us
as the potter moulds the clay.

2 Together you stand,
divided you fall,
but those who listen
receive my word and hear my call.
Make your home here within me
and you'll find I'll be with you,
with you forever
making life forever new.

*Chris O'Hara*

## 826 (103)

**You have put on Christ,
in him you have been baptised,
alleluia, alleluia, alleluia!**

1 We who were dead are now reborn;
we who were buried now are raised.
We who were dwelling in the dark now see light.

2 For though in Adam all have sinned,
in Jesus Christ are all made clean;
the grace abounding of his death
sets us free.

3 One Lord we serve who died for us;
one faith we hold, in life to come;
one God and Father of us all we proclaim.

4 And this we know, that nothing ill,
no prince nor power, nor death nor sin,
can separate us from God's love in Christ.

*Refrain from the Rite of Baptism
Verses from Scripture
(Romans 5, 6, 8; Ephesians 4)
adapted by Stephen Dean*

## 827 (103)
# THE CREED

We believe in God the Father,
maker of the universe,
and in Christ His Son our saviour,
come to us by virgin birth.
We believe He died to save us,
bore our sins, was crucified.
Then from death He rose victorious,
ascended to the Father's side.

**Jesus, Lord of all, Lord of all,**
*(four times)*
**Name above all names.**
*(three times).*

We believe He sends His Spirit,
on His church with gifts of power.
God His word of truth affirming,
sends us to the nations now.
He will come again in glory,

Judge the living and the dead,
every knee shall bow before Him,
then must every tongue confess.

*Graham Kendrick*

# S 1

1. God gives his people strength
   if we believe in his way,
   he's swift to repay all those
   who bear the burden of the day.
   God gives his people strength.

2. God gives his people hope.
   If we but trust in his word,
   our prayers are always heard.
   He warmly welcomes
       anyone who's erred.
   God gives his people hope.

3. God gives his people love.
   If we but open wide our heart,
   he's sure to do his part;
   he's always the first to make a start.
   God gives his people love.

4. God gives his people peace.
   When sorrow fills us to the brim,
   and courage grow dim,
   he lays to rest
       our restlessness in him.
   God gives his people peace.

*Medical Mission Sisters*

# S 2

1. I have counted the cost
       of the years that are gone,
   all the battles I lost
       and the few that I won.
   And the plans that would dawn
       that I somewhere mislaid,
   and the hopes that were born
       and the dreams that decayed.
   Still in spite of the loss
       and the labour in vain,
   still in spite of it all.
       I'll start over again,
   still in spite of it all
       I'll start over again.

2. Lord, I thought that I knew
       all the questions you'd ask,
   what you'd want me to do
       ev'ry truth, ev'ry task;
   and your word seemed so near

and your light seemed so strong
and the road seemed so clear
    that you called me along.
Still in spite of it all
    I will walk in your way,
still in spite of it all,
    I will walk in your way.

3. I had mastered it all,
       all my answers were true,
   but when I heard your call
       all your questions were new;
   all the ways that you came,
       the disguises you wore,
   you were just not the same,
       not the same anymore.
   Still in spite of the loss
       and in spite of the pain,
   still in spite of it all
       I will find you again,
   still in spite of it all
       I will find you again.

*Kevin Nichols*

# S 3

1. Now the green blade riseth
       from the buried grain,
   wheat that in the dark earth
       many days has lain;
   love lives again,
       that with the dead has been:
   love is come again
       like wheat that springeth green.

2. In the grave they laid him,
       Love whom men had slain,
   thinking that never
       he would wake again,
   laid in the earth
       like grain that sleeps unseen:
   love is come again
       like wheat that springeth green.

3. Forth he came at Easter,
       like the risen grain,
   he that for three days
       in the grave had lain,
   quick from the dead
       my risen Lord is seen:
   love is come again
       like wheat that springeth green.

4. When our hearts are wintry,
       grieving or in pain,
   thy touch can call us
       back to life again,
   fields of our heart
       that dead and bare have been:
   love is come again
       like wheat that springeth green.

*J. M. C. Crum*

# s 4

*St. David*

1. O Great Saint David,
       still we hear thee call us,
   unto a life that knows
       no fear of death;
   Yea, down the ages,
       will thy words enthral us,
   strong happy words:
       'Be joyful, keep the faith'.

*Chorus:*
*On Cambria's sons stretch out*
    *thy hands in blessing;*
*For our dear land*
    *thy help we now implore.*
*Lead us to God,*
    *with humble hearts confessing*
*Jesus, Lord and King*
    *for evermore.*

2. Christ was the centre rock
       of all thy teaching,
   God's holy will —
       the splendour of its theme.
   His grace informed,
       his love inflamed thy preaching
   Christ's sway on earth,
       the substance of thy dream.

*Chorus: On Cambria's sons, etc.*

3. In early childhood,
       choosing Jesus only,
   Thy fervour showed his yoke
       was light and sweet
   and thus for thee,
       life's journey was not lonely —
   the path made plain
       by prints of wounded feet.

*Chorus: On Cambria's sons, etc.*

4. O glorious saint,
       we wander in the dark;
   With thee we seek
       our trusted guide in Rome.
   Help him to steer
       on earth Saint Peter's barque,
   that we may safely reach
       our heavenly home.

*Chorus: On Cambria's sons, etc.*

*Francis E. Mostyn (1860-1939)*

# s 5

1. Saint Andrew,
       called to follow Christ,
   to learn to fish for men;
   sought out his brother Peter first
   and brought him to the Lord.

2. Then with five thousand to be fed
   in desert wild and drear;
   'twas Andrew found a boy with bread
   and brought him to the Lord.

3. And when the Greeks
       through Philip sought
   that Jesus they might see;
   'twas Andrew first whom
       Philip brought
   to bring them to the Lord.

4. So may we, this St Andrew's-tide,
   share Andrew's burning zeal;
   and fish for men both far and wide,
   to bring them to the Lord.

*Frank Gibson*

# s 6

1. Hail, holy Joseph, hail!
   husband of Mary, hail!
   Chaste as the lily flower
   in Eden's peaceful vale.

2. Hail, holy Joseph, hail!
   Father of Christ esteemed,
   Father be thou to those
   thy foster Son redeemed.

3. Hail, holy Joseph, hail!
   Prince of the house of God,
   may his blest graces be
   by thy pure hands bestowed.

4. Hail, holy Joseph, hail!
   comrade of angels, hail:
   cheer thou the hearts that faint,
   and guide the steps that fail.

5. Hail, holy Joseph, hail!
   God's choice wert thou alone;
   to thee the Word made flesh
   was subject as a Son.

6. Mother of Jesus, bless,
   and bless, ye saints on high,
   all meek and simple souls
   that to Saint Joseph cry.

*Frederick William Faber (1814-1863)*

# s 7

Lord make me an instrument
of thy peace.

1. Where there is hatred,
   let me sow love,
   Where there is injury, pardon.

2. Where there is doubt,
   let me bring faith.
   Where there's despair, hope.

3. Where there is darkness,
   let me bring light.
   Where there is sadness, joy.

4. Grant I may not seek
   to be consoled as to console;
   not seek to be understood
   as to understand;
   to be loved as to love.

5. For it is in giving
   that we receive,
   in pardoning
   that we are pardoned;
   and it is in giving
   that we are born to eternal life.

*Words (Based on St Francis of Assisi)*

# s 8

1. Spirit of God
      in the clear running water,
   blowing to greatness
      the trees on the hill.
   Spirit of God
      in the finger of morning,
   fill the earth, bring it to birth
      and blow where you will.
   Blow, blow, blow till I be but breath
      of the Spirit blowing in me.

2. Down in the meadow
      the willows are moaning,
   sheep in the pasture-land
      cannot lie still.
   Spirit of God
      creation is groaning,
   fill the earth, bring it to birth
      and blow where you will.
   Blow, blow, blow till I be but breath
      of the Spirit blowing in me.

3. I saw the scar
      of a year that lay dying,
   heard the lament
      of a lone whip-poorwill.
   Spirit of God
      see that cloud crying,
   fill the earth, bring it to birth
      and blow where you will.
   Blow, blow, blow till I be but breath
      of the Spirit blowing in me.

4. Spirit of God,
      every man's heart is lonely,
   watching and waiting
      and hungry until,
   Spirit of God,
      man longs that you only,
   fulfill the earth, bring it to birth
      and blow where you will.
   Blow, blow, blow till I be but breath
      of the Spirit blowing in me.

*Medical Mission Sisters*

# The Divine Office

*The full texts will be found in the books containing the Divine Office. A selection is given here which will allow a parish or group to celebrate a form of morning, evening or night prayer according to their needs.*

## Invitatory
To begin the first office of the day

*All make the sign of the cross on their lips.*

Leader: O Lord, op-en our lips. All: And we shall praise your name.

*Psalm 94 (95) is sung (no 679, with optional refrain as follows:)*

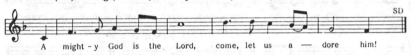

A might-y God is the Lord, come, let us a — dore him!

*Another setting of this psalm: no 435*

*Or as follows:*

1 To God with gladness sing,
   your Rock and Saviour bless,
   Within his temple bring
   Your songs of thankfulness!
   O God of might,
   To you we sing
   enthroned as King
   on heaven's height!

2 He cradles in his hand
   The heights and depths of earth;
   he made the sea and land,
   he brought the land to birth!
   O God most high,
   we are your sheep
   on us you keep
   your Shepherd's eye!

3 Your heav'nly Father praise,
   Acclaim his only Son,
   Your voice in homage raise
   to him who makes all one!
   O Dove of peace,
   on us descend
   that strife may end
   and joy increase!

(66 66 88)                          *James Quinn SJ*

*Alternative Invitatories: Psalm 23(24) or 99(100)*

# Morning Prayer

**Introduction** (omitted if Invitatory has been sung)

O God come to our aid. O Lord, make haste to help us.

Glo — ry be to the Fa—ther, the Son and the Ho — ly Spi — rit,

as it was in the be — gin — ning, is now and e — ver

*Except in Lent*

shall be world without end, A — men, Al — le — lu — ia.

**Hymn** *From the Morning section or ad libitum*

**Psalmody**

*See Complete List of Psalms at the end of this section. Suitable psalms are nos 42, 50, 62; a Canticle (Daniel, no 796) and a Praise psalm (150) or as here:*

Tone 1    LB

Gelineau Tone

## Ps 148

Práise the Lórd from the héavens,
práise him in the héights.
práise him, all his ángels,
práise him, all his hósts.

Práise him, sún and móon,
práise him, shining stárs.
práise him, highest héavens
and the wáters abóve the héavens.

Let them práise the náme of the Lórd.
He commánded: they were máde.
He fíxed them for éver,
gave a láw which shall nót pass awáy.

Práise the Lórd from the éarth,
séa creatures and all óceans,
fire and háil, snow and míst,
stormy winds that obéy his wórd;

346

áll móuntains and hílls,
all frúit trees and cédars,
béasts, wíld and táme,
réptiles and bírds on the wíng;

áll earth's kíngs and péoples,
earth's prínces and rúlers;
yóung men and máidens,
old men togéther with chíldren.

Let them práise the náme of the Lórd
for he alóne is exálted.
The spléndour of his náme
réaches beyond héaven and éarth.

He exálts the stréngth of his péople.
He is the práise of all his sáints,
of the sóns of Ísrael,
of the péople to whóm he comes clóse.

Give glóry to the Fáther almíghty,
To his Són, Jesus Chríst, the Lórd,
to the Spírit who dwélls in our héarts,
both nów and for éver, Ámén.

**Reading** (optional)

**Response to the Word of God**

Refrain

We praise you, Lord; we hear your word, be here a — mong us this day. O-pen our ears, o-pen our hearts, and may your word be our way.

VERSE (Cantor)

| | | | |
|---|---|---|---|
| 1. Advent: | Let us see, O Lord, your mercy; | and give us your | sa - ving help. **R.** |
| 1. Christmas: | The Word was made flesh, | and | lived among us. **R.** |
| 1. Lent: | A pure heart create for me, O Lord, | put a steadfast spi - rit with-in me. **R.** |
| 1. Easter: | This day was made by the Lord, | we rejoice and are glad. **R.** |
| 1. General: | Your words are spirit, Lord, and they are life; | you have the message of e-ter - nal life. **R.** |
| 2. | Glory be to the Father, and to the Son; | and to the Ho - ly Spirit. **R.** |

*Other suitable songs and hymns are:*

| | | | |
|---|---|---|---|
| Adoramus te Domine | 696 | Bless the Lord | 728 |
| Dona nobis pacem | 701 | Confitemini Domino | 735 |
| Glory be to God the Father | 702 | O Christe Domine Jesu | 777 |
| Misericordias Domini | 709 | Psallite Domino | 790 |

The Divine Office—Evening Prayer

**Gospel Canticle** The Benedictus (695)

**Intercessions**
*A response such as the following is made:*

Have mer-cy on us, Lord, and hear our prayer.

*Alternative response:* O Lord hear my prayer (710)

**The Lord's Prayer** *is said or sung.*

**Concluding Prayer** *by the leader.*

**Blessing and Dismissal**

*A priest or deacon uses the usual form of blessing; a layperson says:*
The Lord bless us and keep us from all evil, and bring us to everlasting life. Amen.

---

# Evening Prayer

**Introduction** *as at Morning Prayer*

**Hymn** *From the Evening section or ad libitum*

---

*If Evening Prayer begins with a Service of Light (Lucernarium), the following or a similar greeting may be used:*

**Leader:** Jesus Christ is the light of the world!
**All:**     **A light the darkness cannot overpower!**

**Hymn**

1 O gracious Light, Lord Jesus Christ,
in you the Father's glory shone.
Immortal, holy, blest is he,
and blest are you, his only Son.

2 Now sunset comes, but light shines forth
the lamps are lit to pierce the night.
Praise Father, Son and Spirit: God
who dwells in the eternal light.

3 Worthy are you of endless praise,
O Son of God, Life-giving Lord;
wherefore you are through all the earth
and in the highest heaven adored.

(88 88)

*2nd C., tr. F. Bland Tucker*

348

## Evening Thanksgiving

**Leader:** Let us give thanks to God the Father, always <u>and</u> for everything
**All:**     **In the name of our Lord J<u>e</u>sus Christ!**

## Incense Psalm

*Incense may be used as a symbol of prayer. While this is going on Ps 140(141) is sung with a refrain:*

O Lord, let my prayer rise be - fore you like in - cense, the
raising of my hands like an e — vening sa - cri — fice.

## Psalmody

*See Complete List of Psalms at the end of this section. The Psalms for Sunday Evening Prayer are given here.*

## Ps 109(110)
Weeks 1–4

1. The Lord's revelation to my **Master:**
   'Sit **on** my right:
   your foes I will put be**neath** your feet.'

2. The Lord will wield from **Sion** your scep**tre** of power:
   rule in the midst of **all** your foes.

3. A prince from the day of your **birth**
   on the **holy** mountains;
   from the womb before the dawn **I** begot you.

4. The Lord has sworn an oath he will not **change.**
   'You are a **priest** for ever,
   a priest like Melchi**zedek** of old.'

5. The master standing at **your** right hand
   will shatter kings in the day **of** his wrath.

6. He shall drink from the stream **by** the wayside
   and therefore he shall lift **up** his head.

7. Glory be to the Father, and **to** the Son
   and to the **Holy** Spirit.

8. As it was in the beginning, is now, and
   ever shall be,
   world without **end,** Amen.

349

## Ps 113a(114) Week 1

SD

1. When Israel came forth **from** Egypt,
   Jacob's sons from an **alien** people,
   Judah became the **Lord's** temple,
   Israel became his kingdom.

2. The sea fled at **the** sight:
   the Jordan turned back **on** its course,
   the mountains leapt **like** rams
   and the hills like **yearl**ing sheep.

3. Why was it sea, that **you** fled,
   that you turned back, Jordan, **on** your course?
   Mountains, that you leapt **like** rams,
   hills, like **yearl**ing sheep?

4. Tremble, O earth, before **the** Lord,
   in the presence of the **God** of Jacob,
   who turns the rock into **a** pool
   and flint into a **spring** of water.

5. Glory be to the Father, and to **the** Son
   and to the **Holy** Spirit,
   as it was in the beginning, is now and ever
     shall be,
   world without **end**. Amen.

## Ps 113b(115) Week 2

*Ian Forrester*

1. Not to us, Lord, **not** to us,
   but to your name **give** the glory
   for the sake of your love **and** your truth.
   lest the heathen say: 'Where **is** their God?'

2. But our God is **in** the heavens;
   he does what**ever** he wills.
   Their idols are silver **and** gold,
   the work of **human** hands.

3. They have mouths but they **cannot** speak;
   they have eyes but they **cannot** see;
   they have ears but they **cannot** hear;
   they have nostrils but they **cannot** smell.

4. With their hands they cannot feel;
   with their feet they **cannot** walk.
   No sound comes **from** their throats.
   Their makers will come **to** be like them,
   and so will **all** who trust in them.

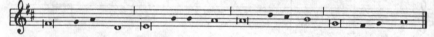

*Steven Foster*

5. Sons of Israel, trust **in** the Lord;
   he is their help **and** their shield.
   Sons of Aaron, trust **in** the Lord;
   he is their help **and** their shield.

6. You who fear him, trust **in** the Lord;
   he is their help **and** their shield.
   He remembers us, and **he** will bless us;
   he will bless the sons of Israel.
   He will bless the **sons** of Aaron.

7. The Lord will bless **those** who fear him,
   the little no less **than** the great:
   to you may the Lord **grant** increase,
   to you and **all** your children.

8. May you be blessed **by** the Lord
   the maker of heaven and earth.
   The heavens belong **to** the Lord
   but the earth has **given** to men.

9. The dead shall not **praise** the Lord,
   nor those who go down **into** the silence.
   But we who live **bless** the Lord
   now and for **ever**. Amen.

10. Glory be to the Father, and **to** the Son
    and to the **Holy** Spirit,
    as it was in the beginning, is now and ever
      shall be
    world without **end**. Amen.

350

## Ps 110(111) Week 3

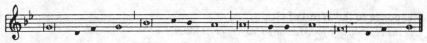

*Ian Forrester*

*Graham Elliott*

1. I will thank the Lord with **all** my heart
   in the meetings of the just and **their** assembly.
   Great are the works **of** the Lord;
   to be pondered by **all** who love them.

2. Majestic and glori**ous** his work,
   his justice stands **firm** for ever.
   He makes us remem**ber** his wonders.
   The Lord is compas**sion** and love.

3. He gives food to **those** who fear him;
   keeps his covenant **ever** in mind.
   He has shown his might **to** his people
   by giving them the lands **of** the nations.

4. His works are jus**tice** and truth:
   his precepts are all **of** them sure,
   standing firm for ev**er** and ever:
   they are made in upright**ness** and truth.

5. He has sent deliverance to his peo**ple**
   and established his cove**nant** for ever.
   Holy his name, **to** be feared.
   To fear the Lord is the first stage of wis**dom;**
   alll who do so prove **them**selves wise.
   His praise shall **last** for ever!

6. Glory be to the Father, and **to** the Son,
   and to the **Holy** Spirit,
   as it was in the begin**ning,** is now and
       ever shall be,
   world without **end.** Amen.

## Ps 111(112) Week 4

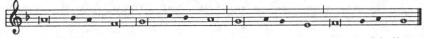

*John Harper*

*John Harper*

1. Happy the man who **fears** the Lord,
   who takes delight in all **his** commands.
   His sons will be power**ful** on earth;
   the children of the up**right** are blessed.

2. Riches and wealth are **in** his house;
   his justice stands **firm** for ever.
   He is a light in the darkness **for** the upright:
   he is generous, **merciful** and just.

3. The good man takes **pity** and lends,
   he conducts his af**fairs** with honour.
   The just man will **never** waver:
   he will be remem**bered** for ever.

4. He has no fear of **evil** news;
   with a firm heart he trusts **in** the Lord.
   With a steadfast heart he **will** not fear;
   he will see the downfall **of** his foes.

5. Open-handed, he gives to the poor;
   his justice stands **firm** for ever.
   His head will be **raised** in glory.
   The wicked man sees and is angry,
   grinds his teeth and **fades** away;
   the desire of the wicked **leads** to doom.

6. Glory be to the Father, and **to** the Son
   and to the **Holy** Spirit,
   as it was in the beginning, is now and **ever**
       shall be
   world without **end.** Amen.

**Reading** (optional)

**Response to the Word of God**
*See the Responsory for Morning Prayer; or as follows*

**Texts of the Short Responsories for Sunday Evening Prayer:**

Weeks 1 & 3

Bless – ed are you in the vault of heaven.

You are ex – alt – ed and glo-ri-fied a – bove all else for e – ver.

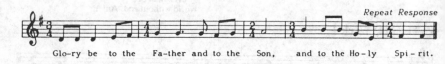

Glo-ry be to the Fa-ther and to the Son, and to the Ho – ly Spi – rit.

Weeks 2 & 4

Great is our Lord: great is his might.

His wis – dom can ne – ver be mea – sured.

Glo – ry be to the Fa-ther and to the Son, and to the Ho – ly Spi-rit.

**Gospel Canticle** The Magnificat (414, 479, 694, 749)

**Intercessions**

*A response such as the following is made:*

Lord in your mer - cy hear our prayer.

*OR see the Intercessions for Morning Prayer.*
*Alternative suggestion:* O Lord hear my prayer (710)

**The Lord's Prayer** *is said or sung.*

**Concluding Prayer** *by the leader.*

**Blessing and Dismissal**

*A priest or deacon uses the usual form of blessing: a layperson says:*
The Lord bless us and keep us from all evil, and bring us to everlasting life. **Amen.**

---

# Night Prayer

## Introduction as at Morning Prayer

*Here an examination of conscience is commended. In a common celebration this may be included in a penitential act using the formulas given in the Missal.*

**Hymn** *From the Evening/Night section (esp. no 564) or:*

1 We praise you, Father, for your gifts
  of dusk and nightful over earth.
  Foreshadowing the mystery
  of death that leads to endless day.

2 Within your hands we rest secure;
  in quiet sleep our strength renew;
  Yet give your people hearts that wake
  in love to you, unsleeping Lord.

3 Your glory may we ever seek
  in rest, as in activity,
  until its fulness is revealed.
  O source of life, O Trinity.

*The Benedictines of West Malling*

## Psalmody

*See Complete List of Psalms at the end of this section, especially Ps 90(91).*
*The Psalms for Sunday Night Prayer are given here.*

### Psalm 4

When I cáll, ánswer me, O Gód of jústice;
from ánguish you reléased me, have mércy and héar me.

O mén, how lóng will your héarts be clósed,
will you lóve what is fútile and séek what is fálse ?

It is the Lórd who grants fávours to thóse whom he lóves;
the Lórd hears me whenéver I cáll him.

Fear him; do not sín; pónder on your béd and be stíll;
Make jústice your sácrifice and trúst in the Lórd.

'Whát can bring us háppiness ?' mány sáy;
Let the líght of your fáce shíne on us, O Lórd.

You have pút into my héart a gréater jóy
than théy have from abúndance of córn and new wíne.

I will líe down in péace and sléep comes at ónce
for yóu alone, Lórd, make me dwéll in sáfety.

Glory bé to the Fáther, the Són and Holy Spírit
both nów and for éver, wórld without énd.

### Psalm 133 (134)

O come, bless the Lord,
all yóu who sérve the Lórd,
who stand in the house of the Lord,
in the córts of the hóuse of our Gód.

Lift up your hands to the holy place
and bléss the Lórd through the níght.
May the Lord bless you from Síon,
he who máde both heáven and éarth.

Give glory to the Father Almíghty,
to his Són, Jesus Chríst, our Lórd,
to the Spírit who dwélls in our hearts
both nów and for éver, Amén.

## Scripture Reading  *Deuteronomy 6:4–7*

Hear, O Israel: the Lord our God is one Lord; and you shall love the Lord your God with all your heart, and with all your soul, and with all your might. And these words which I command you this day shall be upon your heart; and you shall teach them diligently to your children, and shall talk of them when you sit in your house, and when you walk by the way, and when you lie down, and when you rise.

## Response to the Word of God
*(Bracketed words are omitted outside Eastertime)*

R. In - to your hands, O Lord, I commend my Spi-rit. (Al-le-lu - ia, al-le-lu — ia). R.

You have re-deemed us Lord, God of Truth. R. Glo-ry be to the Fa-ther, and to the

Son, and to the Ho-ly Spi-rit. R.

## Gospel Canticle  The Nunc Dimittis (695) with the antiphon:

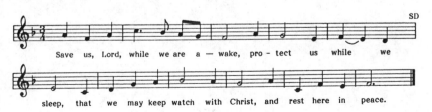

Save us, Lord, while we are a — wake, pro - tect us while we

sleep, that we may keep watch with Christ, and rest here in peace.

**Concluding Prayer** *by the leader.*

**Blessing**    The Lord grant us a quiet night and a perfect end. **Amen.**

**Anthem to Our Lady**
Salve Regina 718    Regina Caeli 717 (Eastertide)
*Or the* Hail Holy Queen *may be said.*

356

# Psalm versions elsewhere in the book:

## CANTICLES AND HYMNS BASED ON SCRIPTURE

# ACKNOWLEDGEMENTS (WORDS ONLY)

The following are, as far as can be ascertained, the copyright holders or their administrators. While every effort has been made to make this list as accurate as possible, it may be that some errors or omissions have occurred, for which we apologise. These will be corrected in future editions.

Where a publisher's address appears frequently it is not repeated after the first time. A list of addresses is given at the end of the section.

S1 © Medical Mission Sisters, 92 Sherman St, Hartford Ct 06105 USA

S2 Kevin Nichols

S3 From the Oxford Book of Carols, by permission of the Oxford University Press, 37 Dover Street, London W1X 4AH

S5 McCrimmon Publishing Co Ltd

S7 McCrimmon Publishing Co Ltd

S8 Vanguard Music Corporation, 1959 Broadway, New York, N.Y. 10019

2 World Library Publications Inc, 3815 North Willow Road, Schiller Park, Illinois 60176

3 Joseph Weinberger Ltd 12-14 Mortimer Street London W1N 8EL

4 Roberton Publications (for J.Curwen & Sons Ltd)

5 McCrimmon Publishing Co Ltd

6 McCrimmon Publishing Co Ltd

11 Franciscan Communications Center, 1229 S Sante Street, Los Angeles, California 90015 USA

12 McCrimmon Publishing Co Ltd

14 Willard F.Jabusch, Mundelein Seminary, Mundelein, Ill. 60060

16 Anthony Sharpe

23 McCrimmon Publishing Co Ltd

25 Roger Ruston OP

31 Search Press Ltd, Wellwood, N.Farm Road, Tunbridge Wells TN2 3DR

32 Anne Conway

35 The Literary Estate of Eleanor Hull, and Chatto & Windus Ltd. From the Poem Book of the Gael

41 © 1969 James Quinn. Reproduced by permission of Geoffrey Chapman (a division of Cassell Ltd) Artillery House, Artillery Row, London SW1P 1RT

42 Search Press Ltd

43 McCrimmon Publishing Co Ltd

45 © 1974 Thankyou Music, PO Box 75, Eastbourne BN23 6NW

46 © 1969 James Quinn. Reproduced by permission of Geoffrey Chapman

47 McCrimmon Publishing Co Ltd

51 Kevin Mayhew Ltd, R attlesden, Bury St Edmunds, Suffolk

53 © 1969 James Quinn. Reproduced by permission of Geoffrey Chapman

54 McCrimmon Publishing Co Ltd

59 © 1969 James Quinn. Reproduced by permission of Geoffrey Chapman

62 SPCK, Holy Trinity Church, Marylebone Rd, London NW1 4DU

63 Franciscan Communications Center

64 As no.63

70 Christopher Alston

72 © 1967 Stainer & Bell Ltd, 82 High Road, London N2 9PW

74 B.Feldman & Co, 138-40 Charing Cross Rd, London WC2H 0LD

76 Franciscan Communications Center

78 © 1969 James Quinn. Reproduced by permission of Geoffrey Chapman

81 McCrimmon Publishing Co Ltd

82 Sister M Teresine OSF

83 McCrimmon Publishing Co Ltd

85 McCrimmon Publishing Co Ltd

86 Franciscan Communications Center

87 McCrimmon Publishing Co Ltd

90 The Trustees of Clifford Howell SJ

114 Mount St London W1Y 6AH

94 Harold Riley

97, From Enlarged Songs of Praise, by permission of Oxford University Press, Ely House, London W1X 4AH

99 Vanguard Music USA

102 McCrimmon Publishing Co Ltd

107 Search Press Ltd

111 Franciscan Communications Center

114 McCrimmon Publishing Co Ltd

116 McCrimmon Publishing Co Ltd

118 Kevin Mayhew Ltd

119 From The English Hymnal, by permission of Oxford University Press

120 The Trustees of Clifford Howell SJ

122 © 1972 Lexicon Music, administered by Word (UK) Ltd, Northbridge Road, Berkhampsted, Herts HP4 1EH

125 McCrimmon Publishing Co Ltd

126 English language rights, Kevin Mayhew Ltd

127 McCrimmon Publishing Co Ltd

128 Kevin Mayhew Ltd

129 Kevin Mayhew Ltd

130 © 1969 James Quinn. Reproduced by permission of Geoffrey Chapman

131 Stainer & Bell Ltd

135 McCrimmon Publishing Co Ltd

136 Mr D. Dunkerley

138 McCrimmon Publishing Co Ltd

139 McCrimmon Publishing Co Ltd

140 McCrimmon Publishing Co Ltd

141 © Shalom Community, 1504 Polk, Wichita Falls, Texas 76309 USA. All rights reserved

145 John Glynn

146 McCrimmon Publishing Co Ltd

148 McCrimmon Publishing Co Ltd

155 McCrimmon Publishing Co Ltd

160 Search Press Ltd

170 Franciscan Communications Center

172 Richard Connolly

173 McCrimmon Publishing Co Ltd

174 From the Oxford Book of Carols, by permission of Oxford University Press

# ACKNOWLEDGMENTS

175 McCrimmon Publishing Co Ltd
177 Sr M Teresine, OSF
179 Joseph Weinberger Ltd
181 From Enlarged Songs of Praise, by permission of Oxford University Press
182 Franciscan Communications Center
185 McCrimmon Publishing Co Ltd
186 © 1969 James Quinn. Reproduced by permission of Geoffrey Chapman
188 Search Press Ltd
189 Franciscan Communications Center
190 McCrimmon Publishing Co Ltd
191 © Willard F.Jabusch
193 Kevin Mayhew Ltd
194 McCrimmon Publishing Co Ltd
196 David Higham Associates Ltd, 5-8 Lower John St, London W1R 4HA. Words from The Children's Bells, published by OUP
197 McCrimmon Publishing Co Ltd
205 Vv.2-5, Kevin Mayhew Ltd
207 Search Press Ltd
208 McCrimmon Publishing Co Ltd
209 McCrimmon Publishing Co Ltd
210 McCrimmon Publishing Co Ltd
217 McCrimmon Publishing Co Ltd
218 © 1969 James Quinn. Reproduced by permission of Geoffrey Chapman
221 From The English Hymnal by permission of Oxford University Press
223 The Trustees of Clifford Howell SJ
224 as 223
225 © Shalom Community, 1504 Polk, Wichita Falls, Texas 76309 USA. All rights reserved. Used with permission
228 From The English Hymnal by permission of Oxford University Press
237 McCrimmon Publishing Co Ltd
245 © 1969 James Quinn. Reproduced by permission of Geoffrey Chapman
226 Joseph Weinberger Ltd
227 Gospel Light Publications, Shirley House, 27 Camden Road, London NW1 9LN, on behalf of Manna Music
231 McCrimmon Publishing Co Ltd
234 Dom Gregory Murray OSB
240 McCrimmon Publishing Co Ltd
242 © Willard F.Jabusch
252 McCrimmon Publishing Co Ltd
255 McCrimmon Publishing Co Ltd
256 McCrimmon Publishing Co Ltd
257 Kevin Mayhew Ltd
258 McCrimmon Publishing Co Ltd
261 McCrimmon Publishing Co Ltd
263 McCrimmon Publishing Co Ltd
265 Mgr David McRoberts
267 © Roger Ruston OP
268 McCrimmon Publishing Co Ltd
269 © 1967 Sacred Songs, a division of Word Inc
273 Kevin Mayhew Ltd
275 © The Trustees of Clifford Howell SJ
276 Kevin Mayhew Ltd
278 McCrimmon Publishing Co Ltd
280 Vanguard Music USA
281 Roland F.Palmer SSJE
282 Franciscan Communications Center

284 As no.282
287 F.E.L. Publications
289 © 1935, 1963 Moody Press, Moody Bible Institute of Chicago 820 North La Salle St, Chicago Ill. 60610
290 Search Press Ltd
292 © Belwyn Mills Music, 250 Purley Way, Croydon CR9 4QD
296 Franciscan Communications Center
297 © World Library Publications Inc. Reprinted with permission
298 Bosworth & Co, 14/18 Haddon St, London W1R 8DP
299 Vanguard Music USA
304 McCrimmon Publishing Co Ltd
307 McCrimmon Publishing Co Ltd
310 © Willard F.Jabusch
313 Franciscan Communications Center
314 McCrimmon Publishing Co Ltd
317 McCrimmon Publishing Co Ltd
320 Mike Anderson
322 McCrimmon Publishing Co Ltd
324 McCrimmon Publishing Co Ltd
325 © 1969 James Quinn. Reproduced by permission of Geoffrey Chapman
327 As no.325
328 A.R.Mowbray & Co
332 Search Press Ltd
336 McCrimmon Publishing Co Ltd
337 A.R.Mowbray & Co
340 McCrimmon Publishing Co Ltd
342 F.E.L. Publications
343 McCrimmon Publishing Co Ltd
344 © Willard F.Jabusch
345 As no.344
348 Tro Essex Music, 85 Gower St London WC1E 6HJ. © 1960, 1963 Ludlow Music Inc. Assigned to Tro Essex Music
350 McCrimmon Publishing Co Ltd
351 © 1977 Alba House Communications, Canfield Ohio 44406
352 © Willard F.Jabusch
353 Stainer & Bell Ltd
356 McCrimmon Publishing Co Ltd
357 McCrimmon Publishing Co Ltd
358 Search Press Ltd
361 McCrimmon Publishing Co Ltd
362 McCrimmon Publishing Co Ltd
367 McCrimmon Publishing Co Ltd
368 McCrimmon Publishing Co Ltd
369 McCrimmon Publishing Co Ltd
370 McCrimmon Publishing Co Ltd
371 McCrimmon Publishing Co Ltd
376 The Missionary Society of St Paul the Apostle in the State of New York, 1865 Broadway, New York USA
377 The Benedictine Foundation of the State of Vermont, Inc, Weston Priory, Weston, Vermont 05161, USA. Used with permission
378 International Committee on English in the Liturgy, Inc, 1275 K Street, Suite 1202, Washington DC 20005-4097. ©1981. From Resource Collection of Hymns and Service Music for the Liturgy. All rights reserved. Used with permission
379 © Honor Mary Thwaites. Used with permission
381 Faber Music Ltd, 3 Queen Square, London WC1N 3AU. Reprinted from The New Catholic Hymnal. Used with permission

# ACKNOWLEDGMENTS

382 © 1980 James Quinn. Reproduced by permission of Geoffrey Chapman

383 © 1977 North American Liturgy Resources, 10802 N.23rd Ave, Phoenix, Arizona 85029

384 © 1974 Shalom Community, 1504 Polk, Wichita Falls, Texas 76309 USA. All rights reserved. Used with permission

385 © The Archdiocese of Durban, 408 Innes Road Durban 4001

388 Novello & Company Ltd, Borough Green, Sevenoaks, Kent TN15 8DT

390 © 1965 World Library Publications Inc. Reprinted with permission

392 Bonaventure Hinwood

393 Bonaventure Hinwood

394 © 1971, 1975 Celebration Services (International) Ltd, Cathedral of the Isles, Millport, Isle of Cumbrae, KA28 0HE

395 The Word of God Music, PO Box 8617, Ann Arbor MI 48107 USA

397 United Reformed Church, 86 Tavistock Place, London WC1H 9RT

366 McCrimmon Publishing Co Ltd

399 Stainer & Bell Ltd

400 Anne Conway

401 © 1978 Kevin Mayhew Ltd

402 Sheed and Ward Ltd, 2 Creechurch Lane, London EC3

403 © English language rights: Kevin Mayhew Ltd

405 Mrs Mildred Peacey

406 Michael Hewlett

408 McCrimmon Publishing Co Ltd

409 © 1977 Thankyou Music

410 Aniceto Nazareth, St Pius College, Bombay 63

411 © 1976 Dan Schutte SJ and North American Liturgy Resources

413 © 1975 Hope Publishing Co, Carol Stream, Illinois 60188 USA

414 McCrimmon Publishing Co Ltd

415 McCrimmon Publishing Co Ltd

416 Famous Music, by permission of Chapel Music Ltd, London W1Y 3FA

417 © 1979 Celebration Services (International) Ltd

418 Joseph Walsh OSCO, Mount Melleray Abbey, Co.Waterford, Eire

419 French original SEFIM. English version Stainer & Bell Ltd

420 James G.Johnson

422 McCrimmon Publishing Co Ltd

423 © 1977 Augsburg Publishing House, 426 South Fifth Street, Box 1209, Minneapolis MN 55440 USA. From Lead Us, Lord, ed. Howard S. Olson

424 Pamela Stotter

426 N. & K.Donnelly

428 Stainer & Bell Ltd

430 © English language rights: Kevin Mayhew Ltd

431 © 1965 World Library Publications Inc. Reprinted with permission

433 © 1976 Joint Board of Christian Education of Australia and New Zealand, 5th Floor, 117 Collins St, Melbourne, Victoria, Australia 300

434 © 1975 John Glynn

435 Stephen Dean

436 McCrimmon Publishing Co Ltd

438 McCrimmon Publishing Co Ltd

440 Pamela Stotter

442 © 1980 James Quinn. Reproduced by permission of Geoffrey Chapman

443 © 1974 Hope Publishing Co, Carol Stream, Illinois 60188 USA

444 © 1987 Kevin Mayhew Ltd

445 © 1973 North American Liturgy Resources

446 Fred Kaan

447 Aniceto Nazareth, St Pius College, Bombay 63

448 McCrimmon Publishing Co Ltd

450 © 1975 Thankyou Music

451 Christian Conference of Asia, 480 Lorong 2, Toa Payoh, Singapore 1231, on behalf of D.P.Niles

452 Chevalier Press, PO Box 13, Kensington NSW 2033, Australia. Reproduced from Eagles' Wings by Fr Frank Andersen MSC

453 Stewart Cross

455 Oxford University Press

456 © 1975 Celebration Services (International) Ltd

457 © 1971, 1974 Celebration Services (International) Ltd

458 © 1969 Singspiration Inc., 1415 Lake Drive SE, Grand Rapids, Michigan 49506 USA

459 © The Archdiocese of Durban, 408 Innes Road, Durban 4001

460 © 1978 Kevin Mayhew Ltd

461 Stainer & Bell Ltd

462 Stainer & Bell Ltd

463 © 1970 Enrico Garzilli, 33 Vermont St, Cranston, Rhode Island 02920 USA

465 UK Rights, McCrimmon Publishing Co Ltd

466 © Willard F. Jabusch

467 McCrimmon Publishing Co Ltd

468 Stainer & Bell Ltd

469 © 1978 Kevin Mayhew Ltd

470 © 1965 World Library Publications Inc. Reprinted with permission

471 Original German © Buckhardhaus Verlag, Gelnhausen. English version © McCrimmon Publishing Co Ltd

473 © 1976 Dan Schutte SJ and North American Liturgy Resources

474 French original SEFIM. English version Oxford University Press

475 © The Archdiocese of Durban, 408 Innes Road, Durban 4001

477 © 1972 Lexicon Music, administered by Word (UK) Ltd, Northbridge Road, Berkhampsted, Herts HP4 1EH

478 © 1978 Kevin Mayhew Ltd

479 English Language rights, Kevin Mayhew Ltd

481 McCrimmon Publishing Co Ltd

482 French original SEFIM. English tr. © Pamela Stotter

483 © The Archdiocese of Durban, 408 Innes Road, Durban 4001

485 Bonaventure Hinwood

486 Hymns Ancient & Modern Ltd, St Mary's Plain, Norwich NR3 3BG

487 © Franciscan Communications Center

489 Helena Scott

490 © 1975 Carey Landry and North American Liturgy Resources

# ACKNOWLEDGMENTS

491 The Missionary Society of St Paul the Apostle in the State of New York, 1865 Broadway, New York USA

492 © Willard F. Jabusch

494 Psalm verses from THE PSALMS: A NEW TRANSLATION published by Wm Collins Sons & Co Ltd. Reproduced by permission of A.P. Watt Ltd on behalf of The Grail, England

495 © Willard F. Jabusch

496 Dove Communications Pty Ltd, Suite 1, 60-64 Railway Road, Blackburn, Victoria 3130, Australia

497 © 1975 Hope Publishing Co, Carol Stream, Illinois 60188 USA

499 © 1969 Hope Publishing Co

500 © 1974/78 Thankyou Music

501 © 1971 GIA Publications Inc

502 © 1975 John Glynn

503 The Word of God Music, PO Box 8617, Ann Arbor MI 48107 USA

504 The Benedictine Foundation of the State of Vermont, Inc

505 Jabulani Music, 4784 Riverside Drive, Keizer OR 97303

506 Eric A. Thorn, 17 Rowan Walk, Crawley Down, W.Sussex

507 McCrimmon Publishing Co Ltd

508 © 1981 Dan Schutte SJ and North American Liturgy Resources

509 © 1975 John Glynn

510 © 1978 Kevin Mayhew Ltd

511 © 1975 Carey Landry and North American Liturgy Resources

512 © 1971, 1974 Celebration Services (International) Ltd

513 McCrimmon Publishing Co Ltd

514 Aniceto Nazareth, St Pius College, Bombay 63

515 © 1975 John Foley SJ and North American Liturgy Resources

516 © The Archdiocese of Durban

517 McCrimmon Publishing Co Ltd

518 The Benedictine Foundation of the State of Vermont, Inc

519 Nick Hodson

520 John C. Ylvisaker

521 Stephen Dean

522 McCrimmon Publishing Co Ltd

523 Methodist Church Division of Education and Youth, 2 Chester House, Pages Lane, London N10 1PR

524 © 1976 Joint Board of Christian Education of Australia and New Zealand, 5th Floor, 117 Collins St, Melbourne, Victoria, Australia 300

525 © 1978 Kevin Mayhew Ltd

526 © 1965 World Library Publications Inc. Reprinted with permission

527 © 1981/2 Kevin Mayhew Ltd

528 © 1977 North American Liturgy Resources

529 McCrimmon Publishing Co Ltd

530 © Willard F. Jabusch

531 Jabulani Music, 4784 Riverside Drive N, Keizer OR 97303

532 Fred Kaan

533 Mrs William Booth-Clibborn

534 J. Gordon Nichols

535 © 1975 Hope Publishing Co, Carol Stream, Illinois 60188 USA

536 The Missionary Society of St Paul the Apostle in the State of New York, 1865 Broadway, New York USA

537 © Kevin Mayhew Ltd

538 McCrimmon Publishing Co Ltd

539 McCrimmon Publishing Co Ltd

540 © Celebration Services (International) Ltd

541 McCrimmon Publishing Co Ltd

542 © 1975 Hope Publishing Co, Carol Stream, Illinois 60188 USA

544 Anne Conway

545 Joseph Weinberger Ltd

547 Mrs J. Tyrell

548 © The Archdiocese of Durban

550 Ediciones Paulinas, Madrid. English tr.© Fr Edmund O'Shea

552 © English language rights: Kevin Mayhew Ltd

553 © 1976 by Damean Music. Published exclusively by NALR, 10802 N.23rd Avenue, Phoenix, Arizona 85029. Used with permission

554 Fred Kaan

555 © 1975 John Glynn

556 McCrimmon Publishing Co Ltd

557 Jabulani Music, 4784 Riverside Drive N, Keizer OR 97303

558 © 1965 World Library Publications Inc. Reprinted with permission

559 © 1975 Carey Landry and North American Liturgy Resources

560 McCrimmon Publishing Co Ltd

561 John C. Ylvisaker

562 McCrimmon Publishing Co Ltd

563 © Willard F. Jabusch

564 Novello & Co

565 © 1975 Celebration Services (International) Ltd

566 Chrysogonus Waddell and Mount St Joseph's Abbey, Roscreen, Co. Tipperary, Ireland

568 © Kevin Mayhew Ltd

569 © The Archdiocese of Durban

570 Ampleforth Abbey Trustees

571 © 1967, 1970 The American Catholic Press, 1223 Rossell Oak Park, Ill.60302 USA

572 McCrimmon Publishing Co Ltd

574 © 1978 Kevin Mayhew Ltd

576 McCrimmon Publishing Co Ltd

577 The text of "Our Father, we have wandered" from the *Resource Collection of Hymns and Service Music for the Liturgy*, © 1981 International Committee on English in the Liturgy, Inc, 1275 K Street, Suite 1202, Washington DC 20005-4097. All rights reserved

578 Jabulani Music, 4784 Riverside Drive, Keizer OR 97303

579 McCrimmon Publishing Co Ltd

580 Stainer & Bell Ltd

581 McCrimmon Publishing Co Ltd

583 © 1973 Carey Landry and North American Liturgy Resources

584 McCrimmon Publishing Co Ltd

586 McCrimmon Publishing Co Ltd

587 Tony Barr, 4784 Riverside Drive, Keizer OR 97303

588 Anne Seymour

589 McCrimmon Publishing Co Ltd

590 © 1975 John Glynn

591 McCrimmon Publishing Co Ltd

# ACKNOWLEDGMENTS

593 © 1972 Maranatha! Music, PO Box 1396, Costa Mesa, California 92626

594 © The Archdiocese of Durban

595 McCrimmon Publishing Co Ltd

596 © 1965 World Library Publications Inc. Reprinted with permission

597 © World Library Publications Inc. Reprinted with permission

598 McCrimmon Publishing Co Ltd

599 © 1976 North American Liturgy Resources

600 Anne Conway

601 McCrimmon Publishing Co Ltd

602 McCrimmon Publishing Co Ltd

603 © 1970 John Foley SJ and North American Liturgy Resources

604 © 1975 Bob Dufford SJ and North American Liturgy Resources

605 © 1978 Patrick Lee, reproduced by permission of Magnificat Music

606 Bonaventure Hinwood

607 Fred Kaan

609 Timothy Dudley-Smith

610 © 1975 Carey Landry and North American Liturgy Resources

612 McCrimmon Publishing Co Ltd

614 The Word of God Music, PO Box 8617, Ann Arbor MI 48107 USA

615 McCrimmon Publishing Co Ltd

616 © 1980 James Quinn. Reproduced by permission of Geoffrey Chapman

617 © 1969 North American Liturgy Resources

618 © 1978 Kevin Mayhew Ltd

619 © 1965 World Library Publications Inc. Reprinted with permission

620 Vv. 2-5, McCrimmon Publishing Co Ltd

621 © 1965 World Library Publications Inc. Reprinted with permission

622 World Student Federation, Geneva

623 Vv.1,2 © 1972 Lexicon Music, administered by Word (UK) Ltd, Northbridge Road, Berkhampsted, Herts HP4 1EH. Vv.3-5 © 1982 Kevin Mayhew Ltd

624 Anne Conway

626 © 1970 Augsburg Publishing House, 426 South Fifth Street, Box 1209, Minneapolis MN 55440 USA. From Contemporary Worship 2: The Holy Communion

627 © 1976 Medical Mission Sisters, 92 Sherman St, Hartford Ct 06105 USA

628 © 1974 Ephpheta House, 3330 Adams Road, Auburn Heights, Michigan 48057 USA

630 © 1975 Dan Schutte SJ and North American Liturgy Resources

632 McCrimmon Publishing Co Ltd

633 William Armitage

634 © 1975 John Glynn

635 © 1976 Robert F.O'Connor SJ and North American Liturgy Resources

636 French original SEFIM. English tr. © Fred Kaan

638 Christopher Walker

640 McCrimmon Publishing Co Ltd

641 John C.Ylvisaker

642 © 1975 Celebration Services (International) Ltd

643 © Willard F.Jabusch

644 G. Schirmer Inc

645 Donal Murray

646 © 1969 James Quinn. Reproduced by permission of Geoffrey Chapman

647 The Benedictine Foundation of the State of Vermont, Inc

648 Dawntreader Music/Thankyou Music, PO Box 75 Eastbourne BN23 6NW

650 © 1971, 1980 The Medical Mission Sisters, 92 Sherman St, Hartford, Ct 06105 USA

651 The Benedictines of Stanbrook, Stanbrook Abbey, Callow End, Worcester WR2 4TD

653 French original SEFIM. English tr. © 1978 Margaret Daly

654 McCrimmon Publishing Co Ltd

656 Jabulani Music, 4784 Riverside Drive, Keizer OR 97303

657 Alan Gaunt and John Marsh

659 © 1971 Dan Schutte SJ and North American Liturgy Resources

660 © 1976 Hope Publishing Co, Carol Stream, Illinois 60188 USA

661 McCrimmon Publishing Co Ltd

662 English language rights assigned to Kevin Mayhew Ltd

663 © 1975 Bob Dufford SJ and North American Liturgy Resources

664 © 1973, 1975 Celebration Services (International) Ltd

665- Psalm verses from THE PSALMS: A NEW TRANS-
691 LATION published by Wm Collins Sons & Co Ltd. Reproduced by permission of A.P.Watt Ltd on behalf of The Grail, England

692 World Library Publications Inc

693- Reproduced by permission of A.P. Watt Ltd on be-
695 half of The Grail, England

696 © Les Presses de Taizé. By permission of Collins Liturgical Publications, 8 Grafton St, London W1X 3LA

699 Stephen Dean

700 Jabulani Music

705 McCrimmon Publishing Co Ltd

708 McCrimmon Publishing Co Ltd

709 © Les Presses de Taizé. By permission of Collins Liturgical Publications

710 As no.709

711 As no.709

712 Linda Stassen/New Song Ministries, PO Box 11662, Costa Mesa, California 92626 USA

713 Verlag Merseburger Berlin GmbH, Buro Kassel, 35 Kassel, Motzstrasse 13, West Germany

714 Jabulani Music, 4784 Riverside Drive, Keizer OR 97303

724 © 1983 GIA Publications Inc. Reprinted with permission

725 © 1983 GIA Publications Inc. Reprinted with permission

726 © 1984 GIA Publications Inc. Reprinted with permission

727 © Brian Black/Jubilate Hymns

728 © Les Presses de Taizé. By permission of Collins Liturgical Publications

729 © Christopher Idle/Jubilate Hymns

730 © Michael Baughen/Jubilate Hymns

731 © Michael Baughen/Jubilate Hymns

# ACKNOWLEDGMENTS

732 English words, McCrimmon Publishing Co Ltd

733 © 1982 Bernadette Farrell. By permission of Magnificat Music

735 © Les Presses de Taizé. By permission of Collins Liturgical Publications

736 © The United Reformed Church, 86 Tavistock Place, London WC1H 9RT

737 © 1982 GIA Publications Inc. Reprinted with permission

738 Anthony Sharpe

739 © James Walsh OSB. Reproduced by permission of Magnificat Music

740 By permission of Oxford University Press

742 © 1982 GIA Publications, Inc. Reprinted with permission

743 By permission of Oxford University Press

744 © 1966, 1987 James Quinn. Reproduced by permission of Geoffrey Chapman, a division of Cassell Publishers Ltd, Artillery House, Artillery Row, London SW1P 1RT

745 Faber Music, 3 Queen Square, London WC1N 3AV. From *New Catholic Hymnal*

746 Timothy Dudley-Smith

747 Stainer & Bell Ltd

748 French original, SEFIM. English tr. Oxford University Press

749 © 1983 Paul Inwood

750 Jabulani Music

751 The text of "Hear us, Almighty Lord" from the *Resource Collection of Hymns and Service Music for the Liturgy*, © 1981 International Committee on English in the Liturgy, Inc, 1275 K Street, Suite 1202, Washington DC 20005-4097. All rights reserved

752 © GIA Publications Inc. Reprinted with permission

753 Michael Perry/Jubilate Hymns

755 Psalm verses from THE PSALMS: A NEW TRANSLATION published by Wm Collins Sons & Co Ltd. Reproduced by permission of A.P. Watt Ltd on behalf of The Grail, England

756 Jabulani Music

757 IN THE ABUNDANCE by Owen Alstott: © 1976, 1981 OCP Publications, 5536 NE Hassalo, Portland OR 97213. All rights reserved. Used with permission.

758 © 1981, 1986 C & M Productions

759 © Les Presses de Taizé. English translation by Paul Inwood

760 © 1984, 1985 Chris O'Hara and McCrimmon Publishing Co Ltd

761 Anthony Sharpe

762 © 1979 Springtide/Word Music (UK)

764 Christopher Walker

765 © 1973, 1979 Raven Music Company, 4107 Woodland Park Ave N., Seattle WA 98103

766 © 1977, 1980 Thankyou Music

767 © 1985 GIA Publications Inc. Reprinted with permission

768 © 1987 Graham Kendrick. Administered by Thankyou Music

768 Anthony Sharpe

769 © 1976 Rocksmith Music. Administered by Leosong Copyright Service Ltd for UK and Eire, 4a Newman Passage, London W1

770 Anthony Sharpe

771 Anthony Sharpe

772 Hope Publishing Co, Carol Stream, Illinois 60188 USA

773 Hubert J. Richards

774 © GIA Publications, Inc. Reprinted with permission

775 Timothy Dudley-Smith

776 Stainer & Bell Ltd

777 © Les Presses de Taizé. By permission of Collins Liturgical Publications

778 © GIA Publications Inc. Reprinted with permission

779 HOW LOVELY by Randall DeBruyn: © 1982 Randall DeBruyn. All rights reserved. Published by OCP Publications, 5536 NE Hassalo, Portland. R 97213.

780 © 1965, 1966 World Library Publications Inc. Reprinted with permission

781 Psalm verses from THE PSALMS: A NEW TRANSLATION published by Wm Collins Sons & Co Ltd. Reproduced by permission of A.P. Watt Ltd on behalf of The Grail, England. Text of the Response © 1985 Paul Inwood

782 IN PERFECT CHARITY by Randall DeBruyn: © 1982. Randall DeBruyn. All rights reserved. Published by OCP Publications, 5536 NE Hassalo, Portland OR 97213. All rights reserved. From Leonardo Defillippis' "St Francis: Troubadour of God's Peace." Used with permission

783 © 1984, 1985 Chris O'Hara and McCrimmon Publishing Co Ltd

785 © 1981 Thankyou Music

787 Dutch original © L. de Vocht, tr. © C.J. Marivoet

788 © 1984 Bernadette Farrell, by permission of Magnificat Music

789 Stephen Dean

790 © Les Presses de Taizé. By permission of Collins Liturgical Publications

791 Timothy Dudley-Smith

792 Timothy Dudley-Smith

793 © 1969 James Quinn. Reproduced by permission of Geoffrey Chapman

794 © 1981 Ernest Sands, by permission of Magnificat Music

795 Mike Anderson

796 © Les Presses de Taizé. By permission of Collins Liturgical Publications

797 © Diocesan Liturgy Centre of Melbourne Commission for Liturgy, 406 Albert Square, East Melbourne, Victoria 3002

798 Mrs Morfydd E.Rees

799 © GIA Publications Inc. Reprinted with permission

800 McCrimmon Publishing Co Ltd

801 © 1984, 1985 Chris O'Hara and McCrimmon Publishing Co Ltd

802 BEHOLD THE LAMB by Martin Willett; © 1984 OCP Publications, 5536 NE Hassalo, Portland OR 97213. All rights reserved. Used with permission.

804 © Irene C.Mueller

805 © Les Presses de Taizé. By permission of Collins Liturgical Publications

806 Jabulani Music

807 Oxford University Press

808 © Michael Perry/Jubilate Hymns

809 The Rev. E. Burns

810 © Willard F. Jabusch

811 © GIA Publications Inc. Reprinted with permission

# ACKNOWLEDGMENTS

812 © 1983 Bernadette Farrell. Reproduced by permission of Magnificat Music.

813 Hubert J. Richards

814 © Paul Inwood

815 © GIA Publications Inc. Reprinted with permission

816 SERVANT SONG by Sr.Donna Marie McGargill OSM; organ accompaniment by Craig S.Kingsbury: © 1984 OCP Publications, 5536 NE Hassalo, Portland OR 97213. All rights reserved. Used with permission.

817 Oxford University Press

818 © 1988 Jabulani Music, 4784 Riverside Drive, Keizer OR 97303

819 Timothy Dudley-Smith

820 Christopher Idle/Jubilate Hymns

821 Aidan Whelan

822 YOU ARE THE LORD: text by Owen Alstott; © 1984 OCP Publications, 5536 NE Hassalo, Portland OR 97213. All rights reserved. Used with permission

823 Lillenas Publishing Co, Box 527, Kansas City Missouri 64141. All rights reserved. Used with permission.

824 © Stephen Dean

824 v.1 © Copyright 1978 Springtide/Word Music (UK), (A division of Word (UK) Ltd), 9 Holdom Avenue, Bletchley, Milton Keynes, MK1 1QU Vv2-3 © Julie Sharp

825 © Chrs O'Hara and McGimmon Publishing Co. Ltd

826 © Stephen Dean

827 © 1986 Thankyou Music

Divine Office: Psalms from THE PSALMS: A NEW TRANSLATION published by Wm Collins Sons & Co Ltd. Reproduced by permission of A.P. Watt Ltd on behalf of The Grail, England.

Ps 94 (Invitatory) © 1969 James Quinn SJ. Reproduced by permission of Geoffrey Chapman.

Texts of the Introduction to Morning Prayer, and the Short Responsories at Evening and Night Prayer © Bishops' Conference of England and Wales.

Hymn *O gracious light*
© Church Pension Fund, 800 Second Avenue, New York NY10017

Hymn *We praise you father*
© The Benedictine Abbey of West Malling.

Other texts © 1988 McCrimmon Publishing Co Ltd and Stephen Dean. Music marked SD © 1984, 1988 Stephen Dean. Other music © 1988 McCrimmon Publishing Co Ltd.

# ADDRESSES OF PUBLISHERS

The Benedictine Foundation of the State of Vermont, Inc, Weston Priory, Weston, Vermont 05161, USA.

Celebration Services (International) Ltd, Cathedral of the Isles, Millport, Isle of Cumbrae, KA28 0HE

Geoffrey Chapman (a division of Cassell Ltd) Artillery House, Artillery Row, Westminster, London SW1P 1RT

Collins Liturgical Publications, 8 Grafton Street, London W1X 3LA

Franciscan Communications Center, 1229 S Sante Street, Los Angeles, California 90015 USA.

GIA Publications Inc, 7404 S.Mason Avenue, Chicago Illinois 60638

Jubilate Hymns, 61 Chessel Avenue, Southampton SO2 4DY

Kevin Mayhew Ltd, The Paddock, Rattlesden, Bury St Edmunds, Suffolk

Magnificat Music, St Thomas More Centre, The Burroughs, Hendon, London NW4 4TY

North American Liturgy Resources, 10802 N.23rd Ave, Phoenix, Arizona 85029

OCP Publications, 5536 NE Hassalo, Portland OR 97213

Oxford University Press, Ely House, 37 Dover St London W1X 4AH

Search Press Ltd, Wellwood, North Farm Road, Tunbridge Wells, Kent TN2 3DR

SEFIM, 13 avenue Savornin, 92240 L'Hay les Roses, France

Stainer & Bell Ltd, 82 High Road, London N2 9PW

Thankyou Music, PO Box 75, Eastbourne BN23 6NW

Vanguard Music Corporation, 1959 Broadway, New York, N.Y. 10019

Joseph Weinberger Ltd, 12-14 Mortimer Street, London W1N 8EL

World Library Publications Inc, 3815 North Willow Road, Schiller Park, Ill 60176.

# Index of Uses

# INDEX OF USES: The Mass, Sacraments

## RECESSIONAL

## 1b. SACRAMENTS AND RITES

**BAPTISM:** see Christian Initiation

**BENEDICTION:** see Worship of the Eucharist

**CHRISTIAN INITIATION:**

**N.B.** The following categories overlap

### Catechumenate

see also God's love and care; Our love of God; Praise; Thanksgiving; Trust

### Celebration of Baptism

see also the preceding category; and Confirmation, Church, Communion (Mass Section)

# INDEX OF USES: The Mass, Sacraments

# INDEX OF USES: The Mass, Sacraments

# INDEX OF USES: The Sacraments/Times & Seasons

# INDEX OF USES: Times & Seasons

# INDEX OF USES: Times & Seasons

# INDEX OF USES: Times & Seasons

# INDEX OF USES: Times & Seasons/Topical

## 3. TOPICAL INDEX

### COMMITMENT, DISCIPLESHIP

# INDEX OF USES: Topical

# INDEX OF USES: Topical

# INDEX OF USES: Topical

# INDEX OF USES: Topical

# INDEX OF FIRST LINES

# INDEX OF FIRST LINES

# INDEX OF FIRST LINES

# INDEX OF FIRST LINES

# INDEX OF FIRST LINES

384

# INDEX OF FIRST LINES